# THIS BOOK
# BELONGS TO

_____

_____

PLATE I
"The morning dawned upon us without
a prospect of hope."

# The Swiss Family Robinson

Johann David Wyss

Illustrated by

T.H. Robinson

**BARNES & NOBLE**

NEW YORK

Cover art: Andrea Dezsö
Cover design: Jo Obarowski
Book design: Patrice Kaplan

Barnes & Noble, Inc.
122 Fifth Avenue
New York, NY 10011

ISBN: 978-1-4351-3345-7

Printed and bound in China

3   5   7   9   10   8   6   4   2

# Contents

## PART II

#  List of Plates

# PART I

## ✦ I ✦

## A SHIPWRECK, AND PREPARATIONS FOR DELIVERANCE

LREADY THE TEMPEST HAD CONTINUED SIX TERRIBLE DAYS; and far from subsiding on the seventh, its fury seemed to increase: the morning of the seventh dawned upon us without bestowing the smallest prospect of hope for we had wandered so materially from the right track, and were so forcibly driven toward the south-east, that not a creature on board knew where we were. The ship's company were exhausted by constant labour and watching, and the courage which had hitherto sustained them, now began to fail. The masts, shivered to pieces, had been cast into the sea; several leaks appeared, and the ship began to fill. The sailors forbore from swearing, and were now employed in prayers, or in making the absurdest vows as the condition of their release from danger. Each recommended his soul to God, but at the same moment thought of contriving the best means for preserving life. My children, said I to my four boys who clung to me in terrible alarm, God can save us, for nothing is impossible to him; we must however hold ourselves resigned, and instead of murmuring at his decree, rely that what he sees fit to do is best, and that should he call us from this earthly scene, we shall be near him in heaven, and united through eternity. Death may be well supported when it does not separate those who love.

My excellent wife wiped the tears which were falling on her cheeks, and from this moment became more tranquil; she encouraged the youngest children, who were leaning on her knees; while I, who owed them an example of firmness, was scarcely able to resist the grief that assailed my heart at the thought of what would most likely be the fate of beings so tenderly beloved. We all fell on our knees, and supplicated the God of mercy to protect us; and the emotion and the fervour of the innocent creatures are a convincing proof, that even in childhood, devotion may be felt and understood, and that tranquillity and consolation, its natural effects, may at that season be no less certainly experienced.

Fritz, my eldest son, implored in a loud voice that God would deign to save his dear parents and his brothers, generously unmindful of himself: the boys rose from their posture with a state of mind so improved, that they seemed forgetful of the impending danger. I myself began to feel my confidence in Providence increase as I beheld the affecting group. Heaven will surely have pity on them, thought I, and will save their parents to guard their tender years!

At this moment a cry of Land, land, was heard through the roaring of the waves, and instantly the vessel struck against a rock with so violent a motion as to drive every one from his place; a tremendous cracking succeeded, as if the ship was going to pieces; the sea rushed in, in all directions; we perceived that the vessel had grounded and could not long hold together. The captain in a mournful voice called out that all was lost, and bade the men lose not a moment in putting out the boats. The sounds fell on my heart like a thrust from a dagger: We are lost! I exclaimed; and the children broke out into piercing cries. I then recollected myself, and endeavoured to be more composed; and addressing them again, I exhorted them to courage, by observing that the water had not yet reached us, that the ship was near land, and that Providence would assist the brave. Keep where you are, added I, while I go and examine what is best to be done.

I left my family and went on the deck. A wave instantly threw me down and wetted me to the skin; another followed, and then another. I sustained myself as steadily as I could; and when I could look around, a scene of terrific and complete disaster met my eyes: the ship was shattered in all directions, and on one side there was a complete breach. The ship's company crowded into the boats till they could contain not one man more, and the last who entered were now cutting the ropes to move off. I called to them with entreaties and prayers to stop and receive us also, but in vain; for the roaring of the sea prevented my being heard, and the waves, which rose to the height of mountains, would have made it impossible for a boat to return. All hope therefore from this source was extinguished, for while I spoke, the boats and all they contained were driving out of sight. My best consolation now was to observe that while I spoke, the slanting position the ship had taken would afford us present protection from the water: and that the stern, under which was the cabin that inclosed all that was dear to me on earth, had been driven to a considerable height between two rocks, where it appeared immoveably fixed. At the same time in the distance southward, I descried through clouds and rain, several nooks of land, which, however rude and savage in appearance, were the object of every hope I could form in this distressing moment.

Sunk and desolate from the loss of all chance for human aid, it was yet my duty to make every effort to appear serene before my family. Courage, dear ones, cried I, on entering their cabin, all is not yet lost. I will not conceal from you that the ship is aground: but we are at least in greater safety than we should be if she were beating upon the rocks: our cabin is above water; and should the sea be more calm tomorrow, we may yet find means to reach the land in safety.

What I had just said, appeased the fears of all; for they had the habit of confiding in my assurances. They now therefore began to feel the advantage of the ship's remaining still; for its motion had cruelly annoyed them by jostling them one against another, or whatever was nearest. My wife, however, more accustomed than the children to read my inmost thoughts, perceived the anxiety which devoured me. I made her a sign which conveyed an idea of the hopelessness of our situation, and I had the consolation to see that she was resolved to support the trial with resignation. Let us take some nourishment, said she: our courage will strengthen with our bodies; we shall perhaps need this comfort to support a long and melancholy night.

Soon after the evening set in: the tempest and the waves continued their fury; the planks and beams of the vessel separated in many parts with a horrible crash. We thought of the boats, and feared that all the persons they contained must have sunk under the foaming surge.

Papa, cried my youngest boy, six years old, will not God assist us soon?

4   Johann David Wyss

Hold your tongue, replied his eldest brother. Do you not know that it is our duty not to prescribe to God, but to wait for his assistance with patience and humility?

Well spoken, my boy, said I; but you should not have reproved your brother so sharply. The eldest instantly ran and kissed the innocent little creature.

In the mean while, their mother had prepared our meal, and the four boys partook of it with an appetite to which their parents were strangers. They afterwards went to bed, and in a short time, in spite of the tempest, they were snoring soundly. Fritz, the eldest, sat up with us. I have been examining, said he after a long silence, how it may be possible to save ourselves. If we had only some instruments for swimming, some bladders or cork jackets for my mother and my brothers, you and I, father, would soon contrive to swim to land.

That is a good thought, said I: we will see if we can bring it to bear this very night, for fear of the worst.

Fritz and I immediately looked about for some small empty tubs or casks, or tin canisters; heavy enough to keep one of our children in a state of equilibrium on the surface of the water; these we fastened two and two together with handkerchiefs or towels, leaving about a foot distance between them; attaching this sort of swimming-jacket we fastened under the arms of each child, my wife, at the same time, preparing one for herself. We all provided ourselves with knives, some string, some turfs, and other necessaries which could be put into the pocket, proceeding upon the hope, that if the ship should go to pieces in the night, we should either be able to swim to land or be driven thither by the waves.

Fritz, who had been up the whole of the preceding night, and was fatigued with his new and laborious occupation, now lay down near his brothers, and was soon asleep; but their mother and I, too full of anxiety to close our eyes, kept watch, listening to every sound that seemed to threaten a further change in our situation. We passed this terrible night in prayer, in agonizing apprehensions, and in forming various resolutions as to what we should next attempt. We hailed with joy the first gleam of light which shot through a small opening of the window. The raging of the winds had begun to abate, the sky was become serene, and with hope swelling in my bosom, I beheld the sun already tinging the horizon: thus revived, I hastily summoned my wife and the boys to the deck, that they might partake of the scene. The children asked with much surprise why we were there alone, and what had become of the ship's company? I answered that they were gone away in boats. Next followed, why did they not take us with them? How are we to do without their assistance? How should we know where we are?

Dearest children, said I, a Being more powerful than man has helped us to the present moment, and will, no doubt, continue to help us, if we do not abandon ourselves to a fruitless complaining and despair. Observe, our companions, in whom we had so much confidence, have deserted us without mercy, and that Divine Providence has given us protection! But, my dear ones, we must now trust to our own exertions. Let us be willing to help ourselves, and we shall obtain support from Heaven. Let us never forget this useful maxim, and let each labour according to his strength. Now let us see what in our situation it is best to set about next.

Fritz advised that we should all throw ourselves into the sea, while it was calm, and swim to land. Ah! that may be well enough for you, said Ernest, for you can swim; but we others should soon be drowned. Would it not be better to make a float of rafts, and get to land altogether upon it?

Vastly well, answered I, if we had the means for contriving such a float, and if, after all, it were not a dangerous sort of conveyance. Come along, my boys, let each go a different way about the ship, and see what he can do to be useful, and what he can find to enable us to get away.

They now all sprang from me with eager looks to do what I had desired. I, on my part, lost no time in examining what we had to depend upon in regard to provisions and fresh water, the first principles of life; my wife and the youngest boy visited all the animals, whom they found in a pitiable condition, and nearly perishing with hunger and thirst. Fritz repaired to the ammunition chamber, Ernest to the carpenter's cabin, and Jack to the apartment of the captain but scarcely had he opened the door, when two large dogs sprung joyfully upon him, and saluted him with such rude affection, that, finding himself nearly thrown down, he roared for assistance as if they had been killing him. Hunger, however, had rendered the animals so gentle, that they licked his hands and face, uttering all the time a low sort of groan, and continuing their caresses till he was almost suffocated. Poor Jack exerted all his strength in aiming blows at them to drive them away: at last he began to sympathize in their joyful movements, and put himself upon another footing; got upon his legs; and gently taking the largest dog by the ears, sprang upon his back, and with great gravity presented himself thus mounted before me as I came out of the ship's hold. I could not refrain from laughing, and I praised his courage: but I added a little exhortation to be cautious, and not go too far with animals of this species, who in a state of hunger might be dangerous.

By and by my little company were again assembled round me, and each boasted of what he had to contribute. Fritz had two fowling pieces, some powder and small shot contained in horn flasks, and some bullets in bags.

Ernest produced his hat filled with nails, and held in his hands a hatchet and a hammer; in addition, a pair of pincers, a pair of large scissars, and an auger, peeped out at his pocket-hole.

Even the little Francis carried under his arm a box of no very small size, from which he eagerly produced what he called some little sharp-pointed hooks. His brothers smiled scornfully. Vastly well, gentlemen, said I; but let me tell you that the youngest has brought the most valuable prize: and this is often the case in the world; the person who least courts the smiles of Fortune, and in the innocence of his heart is scarcely conscious of her existence, is often he to whom she most readily presents herself. These little sharp-pointed hooks, as Francis calls them, are fishing hooks, and will probably be of more use in preserving our lives than all we may find besides in the ship. In justice, however, I must confess that what Fritz and Ernest have contributed, will also afford us essential service.

I, for my part, said my wife, have brought nothing; but I have some tidings to communicate which I hope will secure my welcome: what I have to tell, is, that I have found on board the ship, a cow and an ass, two goats, six sheep, and a sow big with young, all of which I have just supplied with food and water, and that I reckon on being able to preserve their lives.

All this is admirable, said I to my little labourers, and there is only master Jack, who, instead of thinking of something that might be useful, has done us the favour to present us two personages who no doubt will be principally distinguished by being willing to eat more than we shall have to give them.

Ah! replied Jack; but I know that if we can once get to land, you will see that they will assist us in hunting and shooting.

True enough, said I; but be so good as to tell us how we are to get to land, and whether you have contrived the means.

I am sure it cannot be very difficult, said Jack with an arch motion of his head. Look here at these large tubs. Why cannot each of us get into one of them, and float to the land? I remember I succeeded very well in this manner on the water when I was visiting my godfather at S***.

Every hint is good for something, cried I, and I begin to think that what Jack has suggested is worth a trial; the counsels of even a child may be worth consideration, and should be accepted with gratitude. Quick! then, Jack, give me the saw, the auger, and some nails; we will see what is to be done. I recollected having seen some empty casks in the ship's hold; we went down, and found them floating in the water which had got into the vessel; it cost us but little trouble to hoist them up and place them on the lower deck, which was at this time scarcely above water. We saw with delight that they were all made of excellent wood, well guarded by iron hoops, and in every respect in sound condition; they were exactly suited for my object; and with the assistance of my sons I instantly began to saw them in two. In a certain time I had produced eight tubs of equal size and of the proper height. We now allowed ourselves some refreshment from the wine and biscuit with which some of these very casks were still filled. I contemplated with perfect satisfaction my eight little tubs ranged in a line. I was surprised to see that my wife was still dejected; she sighed deeply as she looked at them: Never, never, cried she, can I venture to get into one of these.

Do not decide so hastily, my dear, said I: my plan is not yet complete, and you will see presently that it is more worthy of our confidence than this shattered vessel, which cannot move from its place.

I then sought for a long plank capable of being a little curved, and contrived to fasten my eight tubs to it, leaving a space at each end of the plank, reaching beyond the tubs, and presenting an outline like the keel of a vessel; we next nailed all the tubs to the plank, and then the tubs to each other as they stood side by side, to make them the firmer, and afterwards two other planks of the same length as the first, on each side of the tubs. When all this was finished, we found we had produced a kind of narrow boat divided into eight compartments, which I had no doubt would be able to perform a short course in calm water.

But, unfortunately, our marvellous machine proved so heavy, that with the strength of all united, we were not able to move it an inch from its place. I bade Fritz fetch me a crow, who soon returned with it: in the meanwhile I sawed a thick round pole into several pieces, to make some rollers. I now with the crow easily raised the foremost part of my machine, while Fritz placed one of the rollers under it.

How astonishing, said Ernest, that this engine, which is smaller than any of us, can do more than our united strength was able to effect! I wish I could know how it is constructed.

I explained to him as well as I could, the power of Archimedes's lever, with which he said he could move the world if you would give him a point from which his mechanism might act, and promised to explain the nature of the operation of the crow when we should be safe on land.

One of the points of my system of education was to awaken the curiosity of my sons by interesting observations, to leave time for the activity of their imagination, and then to correct any error they might fall into. I contented myself now, however, with this general remark, That God sufficiently compensated the natural weakness of man by the gifts of reason, invention, and the adroitness of the hands; and that human meditation and reflection had composed a science called mechanics, the object of which was to teach us how to make our own natural strength act to an incredible distance and with extraordinary force, by the intervention of instruments.

Jack here remarked that the action of the crow was very slow.

Better slow than never, Jack, replied I. Experience has ever taught, and mechanical observations have established as a principle, that what is gained in speed is lost in strength; the purpose of the crow is not to enable us to raise any thing rapidly, but to raise what is exceedingly heavy; and the heavier the thing we would move, the slower is the mechanical operation. But are you aware, what we have at our command, to compensate this slowness?

Yes, it is turning the handle quicker.

Your guess is wrong; that would be no compensation: the true remedy, my boy, is to call in the assistance of patience and reason; with the aid of these two fairies I am in hopes to set my machine afloat. As I said this, I tied a long cord to its stern, and the other end of it to one of the timbers of the ship which appeared to be still firm, so that the cord being left loose would serve to guide and restrain it when launched. We now put a second and a third roller under, and applying the crow, to our great joy our construction descended into the water with such a velocity, that if the rope had not been well fastened it would have gone far out to sea. But now a new misfortune presented itself: the machine leaned so much on one side that my boys all exclaimed they could not venture to get into it. I was for some moments in the most painful perplexity; but it suddenly occurred to me that ballast only was wanting to set it straight. I threw every thing I could find that was weighty and of small size into the tubs: by degrees the machine recovered, and was at length quite straight and firm in the water, and seeming to invite us to take refuge in its protection. All now would have thrown themselves at once into it, and the boys began to push each other, and dispute which should get in first. I however drew them back, plainly perceiving that at best the voyage would be hazardous, and that the least motion of even one of these boisterous children might upset it and cause us to be all drowned. In seeking for a remedy for this inconvenience, I recollected that savage nations make use of a paddle for preventing their canoes from upsetting. With this thought I once more set to work to make one of these, that the completion of a contrivance which promised safety to so many cherished beings might not be wanting.

I took two poles of equal length, upon which the sails of the vessel had been stretched, and having descended into the machine, fixed one of them at the head and the other at the stern of my floating machine in such a manner as to enable us to turn them at pleasure to right or left, as should best answer the purpose of guiding and putting it out to sea. I stuck the end of each pole, or paddle, into the bung-hole of an empty brandy keg, which served

JOHANN DAVID WYSS

to keep the paddles steady, and to prevent any interruption in the management of the machine.

There remained nothing more for me to do, but to find out in what way I could clear out from the incumbrance of the wreck and get completely to sea. I got into the first tub, and steered the head of the machine, so as to make it enter the cleft in the ship's side, where it could remain quiet. I then remounted the vessel, and sometimes with the saw and sometimes with the hatchet, I cleared away to right and left every thing that could obstruct our passage: and that being effected, we next secured some oars for the voyage we resolved on attempting.

We had spent the day in laborious exertions; it was already late; and as it would not have been possible to reach the land that evening, we were obliged, though much against our inclination, to pass a second night in the wrecked vessel, which at every instant threatened to fall to pieces. We next refreshed ourselves by a regular meal, for during the day's work, we had scarcely allowed ourselves to take a bit of bread or a glass of wine. Being in a more tranquil and unapprehensive state of mind than the preceding day, we all abandoned ourselves to sleep; not however till I had used the precaution of tying the swimming apparatus round my three youngest boys and my wife, as a means of safety, if the storm should again come on and should put the finishing stroke to the destruction of the vessel. I also advised my wife to dress herself in the clothes of one of the sailors, which was so much more convenient for swimming, or any other exertions she might be compelled to engage in. She consented, but not without reluctance, and left us to look for one that might best suit her size. In a quarter of an hour she returned, dressed in the clothes of a young man who had served as volunteer on board the ship, and which she had found in his chest. She approached us with a natural timidity: but soon found means to reconcile her to the change, by representing the many advantages it gave her. At length she joined in the merriment her dress occasioned, and one and all crept into our separate hammocks, where a delicious repose prepared us for the renewal of our labours.

# A LANDING, AND CONSEQUENT OCCUPATIONS

B Y BREAK OF DAY WE WERE ALL AWAKE AND ALERT, FOR HOPE as well as grief, is unfriendly to lengthened slumbers. When we had finished our morning prayer, I said, we now, my best beloved, with the assistance of heaven, must enter upon the work of our deliverance. The first thing to be done, is to give to each poor animal on board, before we leave them, a hearty meal; we will then put food enough before them for several days; we cannot take them with us; but we will hope it may be possible, if our voyage succeeds, to return and fetch them. Are you now all ready? Bring together whatever we mean to take, whatever is absolutely necessary for our wants. It is my wish that our first cargo should consist of a barrel of gunpowder, three fowling pieces, and three carbines, with as much small shot and lead and as many bullets as our boat will bear; two pair of pocket pistols and one of large ones, not forgetting a mould to cast balls in: each of the boys and their mother also, should have a bag to carry game in; you will find plenty of these in the cabins of the officers. We added a chest containing cakes of portable soup, another full of hard biscuits, an iron pot, a fishing rod, a chest of nails and another of different utensils, such as hammers, saws, pincers, hatchets, augers, etc. and lastly some sail cloth to make a tent. In short, the boys brought so many things, that we were obliged to reject some of them, though I had already exchanged the worthless ballast for articles of use for our subsistence.

When all was ready, we stepped bravely each into a tub. At the moment of our departure we heard all the cocks and hens begin to crow, as if they were conscious that we had deserted them, yet willing to bid us a sorrowful adieu. This suggested to me the idea of taking the geese, ducks, fowls, and pigeons with us; observing to my wife that if we could not find means to feed them, at least they would feed us.

We accordingly executed this plan. We put ten hens and an old and a young cock into one of the tubs, and covered it with planks; we set the rest of the poultry at liberty, in the hope that instinct would direct them towards the land, the geese and the ducks by water, and the pigeons by the air.

We were waiting for my wife, who had the care of this last part of our embarkation, when she joined us loaded with a large bag, which she threw into the tub which already contained her youngest son. I imagined that she intended it for him to sit upon, and also to confine him so as to prevent his being tossed from side to side. I therefore asked no questions concerning it. The order of our departure was as follows:

In the first tub at the boat's head, my wife, the most tender and exemplary of her sex, placed herself.

In the second, our little Francis, a lovely boy six years old, full of the happiest dispositions, but whose character was not yet pronounced.

JOHANN DAVID WYSS

In the third, Fritz, our eldest boy, between fourteen and fifteen years of age, a handsome curl-pated youth full of intelligence and vivacity.

In the fourth was the barrel of gunpowder, with the cocks and hens and the sail-cloth.

In the fifth, the provisions for the support of life.

In the sixth, my son Jack, a light-hearted, enterprising, audacious, generous lad, about ten years old.

In the seventh, my son Ernest, a boy of twelve years old, of a rational reflecting temper, well informed, but somewhat disposed to indolence and the pleasures of the senses.

In the eighth, a father, to whose paternal care the task of guiding the machine for the safety of his beloved family was intrusted. Each of us had useful implements within reach; the hand of each held an oar, and near each was a swimming apparatus in readiness for what might happen. The tide was already at half its height when we left the ship, and I had counted on this circumstance as favourable to our want of strength. We held the two paddles longways, and thus we passed without accident through the cleft of the vessel into the sea. The boys devoured with their eyes the blue land they saw at a distance (for to us it appeared to be of this colour). We rowed with all our strength, but long in vain, to reach it: the boat only turned round and round: at length, however, I had the good fortune to steer in such a way that it proceeded in a straight line. The two dogs we left on board, perceiving that we had abandoned them, plunged immediately into the sea and swam to the boat; they were too large for us to think of giving them admittance, and I dreaded lest they should jump in and upset us. Turk was an English dog, and Ponto of the Danish breed. I was in great uneasiness on their account, for I feared it would not be possible for them to swim so far. The dogs however managed the affair with perfect intelligence. When they found themselves fatigued, they rested their fore paws on one of the paddles, which were now turned crossways, and the rest of their bodies followed with very little effort.

Jack was disposed to refuse them this accommodation: but he soon yielded to my argument, that it was cruel and unwise to neglect creatures thrown on our protection, and who indeed might hereafter protect us in their turn by guarding us from harm, and assisting in our pursuit of animals for food. Besides, added I, animals are created beings, and God has given the dog to man to be his friend and faithful companion.

Our voyage proceeded securely, though slowly; but the nearer we approached the land, the more gloomy and unpromising we thought its aspect appeared. The coast was occupied by barren rocks, which seemed to offer nothing but hunger and distress. The sea was calm; the waves, gently agitated, washed the shore, and the sky was serene; in every direction we perceived casks, bales, chests, and other vestiges of shipwrecks, floating round us. In the hope of obtaining some good provisions, I determined on endeavouring to secure two of the casks. I bade Fritz have a rope, a hammer, and some nails ready, and to try to seize them as we passed. He succeeded in laying hold of two of them, and in such a way that we found it easy to draw them after us to the shore. Now that we were close on land, its hideous aspect was considerably softened; the rocks no longer appeared one undivided chain; Fritz with his hawk's eyes already descried some trees, and exclaimed that they were palm trees. Ernest expressed his joy that he should now get much larger and better cocoa-nuts than those of Europe. I, for my part was venting audibly my regret, that I had not thought of bringing with us a telescope that I knew was in the captain's cabin, when Jack drew a small spy-glass from his pocket, and, with a look of triumph that he was able to compensate this neglect, instantly presented it to me.

So, so, then, said I, you meant to keep this spy-glass for yourself, and to let no one else have the benefit of it! This was not fair; pleasures and pain, all should be in common in such a situation as ours. Jack assured me that he had forgot to give it to me sooner, and that he had taken it for the benefit of all. In reality, the glass was of great importance; for with its aid I was able to make the necessary observations, and consequently became more sure of the route I ought to take. I remarked that the shore before us had a desert and savage aspect, but that towards the left, the scene was much more agreeable: but when I attempted to steer in that direction, a current carried me irresistibly towards the coast that was rocky and barren. By and by we perceived a little opening between the rocks, near the mouth of a creek, towards which all our geese and ducks betook themselves; and I, relying on their sagacity, followed in the same course. This opening formed a little bay, the water of which was tranquil, and neither too deep nor too shallow to receive our boat. I entered it, and cautiously put on shore on a spot where the coast was about the same height above the water as our tubs, and where at the same time there was a quantity sufficient to keep us afloat. The shore extended inland in a shelving declivity in the form of an isosceles triangle, the upper angle of which terminated among the rocks, while the margin of the sea formed the basis.

All that had life in the boat jumped eagerly on land. Even little Francis, who had been wedged in his tub like a potted herring, now got up and sprang forward; but, with all his efforts, he could not succeed without his mother's help. The dogs, who had swam on shore, received us as if they were appointed to do the honours of the place, jumping round us with every demonstration of joy: the geese kept up a loud continual cackling, to which the ducks, with their broad yellow beaks, contributed a perpetual thorough bass: the cocks and hens, which we had already set at liberty, chuckled; the boys chattering all at once produced altogether an overpowering confusion of sounds: to this was added the disagreeable scream of some penguins and flamingos, which we now perceived, some flying over our heads, others sitting on the points of the rocks at the entrance of the bay. By and by the notes of the latter had the ascendant, from the superiority of their numbers; and their society became the more unpleasant, from a comparison we could not avoid making, between the sounds they uttered, with the harmony of the feathered musicians of our own country. I had however one advantage in perspective; it was the reflection that, should we hereafter be short of food, these very birds might serve for our subsistence.

The first thing we did on finding ourselves safe on terra firma, was to fall on our knees, and return thanks to the Supreme Being who had preserved our lives, and to recommend ourselves with entire resignation to the care of his paternal kindness.

We next employed our whole attention in unloading the boat. Oh, how rich we thought ourselves in the little we had been able to rescue from the merciless abyss of waters! We looked everywhere for a convenient place to build a tent under the shade of the rocks; and having all consulted and agreed upon a place, we set to work.

We drove one of our poles firmly into a fissure of the rock; this formed the ridge of our tent, and rested upon another pole, which was driven perpendicularly into the ground. A frame for a dwelling was thus made secure. We next threw some sail-cloth over the ridge; and, stretching it to a convenient distance on each side, fastened its extremities to the ground with stakes. By way of precaution, we left the chests of provisions and other heavy matters on the shore, and lastly, I fixed some tenterhooks along the edge of one side of the sail-cloth in front, that we might be able to inclose the entrance during night. I next desired my sons to look about and collect all the grass and moss they could find, and spread it to dry in the sun, as it would then serve us for beds. During this occupation, in which even the little Francis could take a share, I erected at a small distance from the tent, and near a river from which I hoped to be supplied with fresh water, a kind of little kitchen. A few flat stones that I found in the bed of the river, served for a fire-place. I got a quantity of dry branches: with the largest I made a small inclosure round it; and with the little twigs, added to some of our turf, I made a brisk cheering fire. We put some of the soup cakes, with water, into our iron pot, and placed it over the heat; and my wife, with her little Francis for a scullion, took charge of preparing the dinner. Francis, from their colour, had mistaken the soupcakes for glue. Why, papa, said he, what are you going to use glue for? I am going to make some soup of it, said his mother laughing. That is droll enough, answered he; for how shall we get any meat to put into it, here, where there is nothing like a butcher's shop?

Little blockhead, said I, what you have been thinking was glue, is in reality excellent meat, reduced as you see to a jelly by the process of cookery, and which being dried, is in no danger

PLATE 2
"My wife with her little Francis as a scullion."

of becoming stale. In this state it will bear long voyages by sea, where it would be difficult to take sufficient animals for the use of the ship's company, who would otherwise be kept constantly on a less wholesome soup made from salted meat; but ours, I assure you, Francis, will be excellent. The poor child was hungry enough to believe he should partake of it with joy.

In the mean while Fritz had been reloading the guns, with one of which he had wandered along the side of the river. He had proposed to Ernest to accompany him; but Ernest replied that he did not like a rough and stony walk, and that he should go alone to the sea-shore. Jack took the road towards a chain of rocks which jutted out into the sea, with the intention of gathering some of the muscles which grew upon them. My own occupation was now an endeavour to draw the two floating casks on shore, but in which I could not succeed; for our place of landing, though convenient enough for our machine, was too steep for the casks. While I was looking about to find a more favourable spot, I heard loud cries proceeding from a short distance, and recognised the voice of my son Jack. I snatched my hatchet, and ran in an agony of apprehension to his assistance. I soon perceived him up to his knees in water in a shallow, and that a large sea-lobster had fastened its claws in his leg. The poor boy screamed pitiably, and made useless efforts to disengage himself. I jumped instantly into the water; and the enemy was no sooner sensible of my approach, than he let go his hold, and would have scampered out to sea, but that I indulged the fancy of a little malice against him for the alarm he had caused us. I turned quickly upon him, and took him up by the body and carried him off, followed by Jack, who shouted our triumph all the way. He begged me at last to let him hold the animal in his own hand, that he might himself present so fine a booty to his mother. Accordingly, having observed how I held it to avoid the gripe, he laid his own hand upon it in exactly the same manner; but scarcely had he grasped it, than he received a violent blow on the face from the lobster's tail, which made him loose his hold, and the animal fell to the ground. Jack again began to bawl out, while I could not refrain from laughing heartily. In his rage he took up a stone and killed the lobster with a single blow. I was a little vexed at this conclusion to the scene. This is what we call killing an enemy when he is unable to defend himself, Jack, said I;—it is wrong to revenge an injury while we are in a state of anger: the lobster, it is true had given you a bite; but then you on your part, would have eaten the lobster. So I think the game was equal. Another time I advise you to be both more prudent and more merciful. But pray, papa, let me carry it to my mother, said Jack, fearless now of further warfare; and accordingly he carried it to the kitchen, triumphantly exclaiming, Mamma, mamma, a sea-lobster!—Ernest, a sea-lobster! Where is Fritz? Where is Fritz? Take care, Francis, he will bite you. In a moment we were all round him to examine the wonderful creature, and all proclaimed their astonishment at his enormous size; while they observed that its form was precisely that of the common lobster so much in use in Europe.

Yes, yes, said Jack, holding up one of his claws; you may well wonder at his size: this was the frightful claw which seized my leg, and I believe that if I had not had on my thick sea pantaloons, he would have bit it through and through; but I have taught him what it is to attack *me*: I have paid him well.

Oh, ho! Mr. Boaster, cried I, you give a pretty account of the matter. Now mine would be, that if I had not been near, the lobster would have shown you another sort of game; for the slap he gave you in the face compelled you, I think, to let go your hold. And it is well it should be thus; for he fought with the arms with which nature had supplied him, but you must have recourse to a great stone for your defence. Believe me, Jack, you have no great reason to boast of the adventure.

Ernest, ever eager about his meals, bawled out that the lobster had better be put into the soup, which would give it an excellent flavour; but this his mother opposed, observing, that we must be more economical of our provisions than that, for the lobster of itself would furnish a dinner for the whole family. I now left them, and walked again to the scene of this adventure, and examined the shallow. I then made another attempt upon my two casks, and at length succeeded in getting them into it, and in fixing them there securely on their bottoms.

On my return, I complimented Jack on his being the first to have procured us an animal that might serve for our subsistence, and I promised him for his own share, the famous claw which had already furnished us with so lively a discussion.

Ah! but *I* have seen something too that is good to eat, said Ernest; and I should have got it if it had not been in the water, so that I must have wetted my feet—;

Oh, that is a famous story, cried Jack; I can tell you what he saw—some nasty muscles: why, I would not eat one of them for the world.—Think of my lobster!

That is not true, Jack; for it was oysters, and not muscles, that I saw: I am sure of it, for they stuck against the foot of the rock, and I know they must be oysters.

Fortunate enough, my dainty gentleman, cried I, addressing

myself to Ernest; and since you are so well acquainted with the place where these shell-fish can be found, you will be so obliging as to dismiss your fears about wetting your feet, and to return and procure us some. In such a situation as ours, every member of the family must be actively employed for the common good, and above all none must be afraid of wetting his feet. Take example by Fritz and your father: they bear a greater evil, the scorching heat of the sun, without complaining.

I will do my best with all my heart, answered Ernest; and at the same time I will bring home some salt, of which I have seen immense quantities in the holes of the rocks, where I suppose it is dried by the sun. I tasted some of it, and it was excellent. Is it not left there by the sea?

No doubt it is, Mr. Reasoner, for where else do you think it could come from? You would have done more wisely if you had brought us a bag of it, instead of spending your time in such profound reflections upon an operation so simple and obvious; and if you do not wish to dine upon a soup without flavour, you had better run and fetch us a little immediately.

He set off, and soon returned: what he brought had the appearance of sea salt, but was so mixed with earth and sand, that I was on the point of throwing it away. My wife however prevented me; and by dissolving, and afterwards filtering some of it through a piece of muslin, we found it admirably fit for use.

Why could we not have used some seawater, asked Jack, instead of having all this trouble?

Sea water, answered I, is even more bitter than it is salt; and it has besides a disagreeable sickly taste. While I was speaking, my wife tasted the soup with a little stick with which she had been stirring it, and pronounced that it was all the better for the salt, and now quite ready. But, said she, Fritz is not come in. And then, how shall we manage to eat our soup without spoons or dishes? Why did we not remember to bring some from the ship?

Why did we not think of them?—Because, my dear, one cannot think of every thing at once. We shall be lucky if we do not discover that we have forgotten even more important things. But indeed, said she, this is a matter which cannot easily be set to rights. How will it be possible for each of us to raise this large boiling pot to his lips?

A moment's further reflection convinced me my wife was right. We all cast our eyes upon the pot with a sort of silent and stupid perplexity, and we looked a little like the fox in the fable, when the stork desires him to help himself from a vessel with a long neck. Silence was at length broken, by all bursting into a hearty laugh at our want of every kind of utensil, and at the thought of our own folly, in not recollecting that spoons and forks were things of absolute necessity.

Ernest observed, that if we could but get some cocoa-nuts, we might divide and empty them, and use the pieces of the shells for spoons.

Yes, yes, that is true enough, replied I; *if we could but get,*— but we have them not; our *ifs* will do but little good; and if wishing were to any purpose, I had as lief wish at once for a dozen silver spoons; but alas! of what use is wishing?

But at least, said the boy, we can use some oyster-shells for spoons.

Why, this is well, Ernest, replied I, and is what I call a useful thought. Run then quickly, and get us some of them. But, gentlemen, I must give you notice, that no one of you must give himself airs because his spoon is without a handle, or if he should chance to grease his fingers in the soup.

Jack ran the first, and was up to his knees in the water before Ernest could reach the place. Jack tore off the fish with eagerness, and threw them to the slothful Ernest, who put them into his pocket handkerchief, having first secured in his pocket, one shell he had met with of a large size. The boys came back together with their booty.

Fritz not having yet returned, his mother was beginning to be uneasy, when we heard him shouting to us from a small distance, to which we answered by similar sounds. In a few minutes he was among us; his two hands behind him, and with a sort of would-be melancholy air, which none of us could well understand. What have you brought? asked his brothers; let us see your booty, and you shall see ours. Ah! said he, I have unfortunately nothing, for I have seen nothing. What! nothing at all? said I. Nothing at all, answered he. But now, on fixing my eye upon him, I perceived a smile of proud success through his assumed dissatisfaction. At the same instant Jack, having stolen behind him, exclaimed: A sucking pig! A sucking pig! Fritz, finding his trick discovered, now proudly displayed his prize, which I immediately perceived, from the description I had read in different books of travels, was an agouti, an animal common in that country, and not a sucking pig, as the boys had supposed. The agouti, says M. de Courtills in his *Voyage to St. Domingo*, is of the size of a hare, and runs with the same swiftness; but its form is more like the pig, and he makes the same grunting noise. He is not a voracious animal, but is nice in the choice of his food. When his appetite is satiated, he buries what remains, and keeps it for another time. He is naturally of a gentle temper; but if provoked, his hair becomes erect, he bites, and strikes the ground with his hind feet like the rabbit, which he also resembles in digging himself a burrow under ground: but this burrow has but one entrance; he conceals himself in it during the hottest part of the day, taking care to provide himself with a store of patates and bananas. He is usually taken by coursing, and sometimes by dogs, or with nets. When it is found difficult to seize him, the sportsman has only to whistle. As soon as the agouti hears the sound, he is instantly still, remains resting on his hind feet, and suffers himself to be taken. His flesh is white, like that of the rabbit; but it is dry, has no fat, and never entirely loses a certain wild flavour, which is extremely disagreeable to Europeans. He is held in great esteem by the natives, particularly when the animal has been feeding near the sea on plants impregnated with salt. They are therefore caught in great numbers, and for this reason the species is much diminished. Where did you find him? How did you get at him? Did he make you run a great way? asked all at once the young brothers. Tell me, tell us all. . . . etc. I, for my part, assumed a somewhat serious tone. I should have preferred, said I, that you had in reality brought us nothing, rather than to have heard you assert a falsehood. Never allow yourself, even in jest, my dear boy, to assert what you know to be an untruth. By such trifles as these, a habit of lying, the most disgusting and frightful of vices, may be induced. Now then that I have given you this caution, let us look at the animal. Where did you find it?

Fritz related, that he had passed over to the other side of the river. Ah! continued he, it is quite another thing from this place; the shore is low, and you can have no notion of the quantity of

PLATE 3
"Fritz related that he had passed over to
the other side of the river."

casks, chests, and planks, and different sorts of things washed there by the sea. Ought we not to go and try to obtain some of these treasures? We ought also, answered I, to make our little voyage to the vessel, and fetch away our animals; at least you will all agree that of the cow we are pretty much in want. If our biscuit were soaked in milk, it would not be so hard, said our glutton Ernest. I must tell you too, continued Fritz, that over on the other side there is as much grass for pasturage as we can desire, and besides, a pretty wood, in the shade of which we could repose. Why then should we remain on this barren desert side? Patience, patience, replied I, there is a time for every thing, friend Fritz; we shall not be without something to undertake tomorrow, and even after tomorrow. But, above all, I am eager to know if you discovered in your excursion any traces of our ship companions. Not the smallest trace of man, dead or alive, on land or water; but I have seen some other animals that more resembled pigs than the one I have brought you, but with feet more like those of the hare: the animal I am speaking of leaps from place to place on the grass, now sitting on his hind legs, rubbing his face with his front feet, and then seeking for roots and gnawing them like the squirrel. If I had not been afraid of his escaping me, I should have tried to catch him with my hands, for he appeared almost tame.

Ernest, with the look and manner of a deep observer, now turned the agouti backwards and forwards to examine him on all sides. After a long silence, he said with importance, I cannot be sure that this animal, as you all believe, is a sucking pig; his hair and his snout, it is true, pretty much resemble those of a pig: but pray observe his teeth; he has but four incisores in front similar to the genus Voracious animals: in general he has a greater resemblance to the rabbit than to the hare. I have seen an engraving of him in our book of natural history; if I am not mistaken he is named the *agouti*.

Ah! ha! said Fritz, here is a learned professor, profound in the subject of natural history!

And who this once is not mistaken? cried I. Spare your raillery, Fritz, for it is really an agouti. I do not myself know any thing of the animal: but by his description in books or engravings, with which the appearance of this animal perfectly corresponds; he is a native of America, lives under ground on the roots of trees, and is, as travellers report, excellent food. But of this we will judge for ourselves.

While we were speaking, Jack was trying with all his might to open one of the oysters with his knife; but he could not succeed. I laughed heartily at his disappointment, and put a few of them on the fire, where they soon opened of themselves. Now then, boys, you may have as fine and choice a regale as if you were in a palace. I swallowed one myself; but I have never been fond of oysters; and the boys, observing the wry face I made, all looked at me with surprise. I thought every body was fond of oysters, papa, said one of them. I do not mean to dispute the taste of others, replied I; but, for myself, nothing but a craving hunger could force me to make a meal of them; but you can yourselves try the experiment, and perhaps you will like them. This sort of shellfish is so little agreeable to the eye of those unaccustomed to see them, that not one of the boys had any inclination to touch them. Shortly, however, Jack, in the character of the most courageous, swallowed one hastily, shutting and squeezing up his eyes as if it were a medicine, and the others followed his example; but one and all declared that the oyster was a fish not at all to their taste, and each hastened to dip his shell into the pot to get out a little soup; but, as I had foreseen, each drew out a scalded finger, and it was who could scream the loudest. Ernest was the only one who had been too cautious to expose himself to this misfortune; he quietly took his muscle-shell, as large and deep as a small saucer, from his pocket, and carefully dipping it into the pot, drew it out filled with as much soup as was his fair share; and casting a look of exultation on his brothers, he set it down to wait till it should be cold enough to eat.

You have taken excellent care of yourself, I perceive, said I. But now answer me, dear boy, is the advantage worth the pains you take to be better off than your companions? Yet this is the constant failing of your character. As your best friend, I feel it to be my duty to balk you of the expected success. I therefore adjudge your dish of delicious soup to our faithful followers, Turk and Ponto. For ourselves, we will all fare alike, you as well as the rest; we will simply dip our oyster-shells into the pot till hunger is appeased; but the picked dish for the dogs, Ernest, and all the rest *alike!*

This gentle reproach sunk, I perceived, into his heart; he placed the shell, filled with soup, upon the ground, and in the twinkling of an eye the dogs had licked up every drop. We on our parts were almost as sharp set as they, and every eye was fixed on the pot, watching when the steam would subside a little, that we might begin dipping; when on looking round we saw Turk and Ponto standing over the agouti, gnawing and tearing him fiercely with their teeth and paws. The boys all screamed together; Fritz seized his gun, and struck them with it; called them the unkindest names, threw stones at them, and was so furious, that, if I had not interfered, it is probable he would have killed them. He had already bent his gun with the blows he had aimed at them, and his voice was raised so high as to be re-echoed from the rocks.

When he had grown a little cool, I seriously remonstrated with him on his violence of temper. I represented to him what distress he had occasioned his mother and myself for the event of a rage so alarming; that his gun, which might have been so useful, was now entirely spoiled; and that the poor animals, upon whose assistance we should probably so much depend, he had, no doubt, greatly injured. Anger, continued I, is always a bad counsellor, and may even lead the way to crimes; you are not ignorant of the history of Cain, who, in a moment of violent anger, killed his brother. Say no more, my dearest father, interrupted Fritz in a tone of horror.—Happy am I to recollect on this occasion, resumed I, that they were animals, and not human creatures, you treated thus. But an angry person never reasons; he scarcely knows whom he attacks. The most convincing proof of this, is, that you just now fell upon two dumb animals incapable of judgement, and who most likely thought that your agouti was placed there, as the soup had been before, for them to eat. Confess too, that it was vanity which excited the furious temper you exhibited. If another than yourself had killed the agouti, you would have been more patient under the accident. Fritz agreed that I was right, and, half drowned in tears, entreated my forgiveness.

Soon after we had taken our meal, the sun began to sink into the west. Our little flock of fowls assembled round us, pecking here and there what morsels of our biscuit had fallen on the ground. Just at this moment my wife produced the bag she had so mysteriously huddled into the tub. Its mouth was now opened—it contained the various sorts of grain for feeding poultry—barley, peas, oats, etc., and also different kinds of seeds and roots of vegetables for the table. In the fullness of her kind heart she scattered several handfuls at once upon the ground, which the innocent creatures began eagerly to seize. I complimented her on the benefits her foresight had secured for us; but I recommended a more sparing use of so valuable an acquisition, observing that the grain, if kept for sowing, would produce a harvest, and that we could fetch from the ship spoiled biscuit enough to feed the fowls. Our pigeons sought a roosting place among the rocks; the hens, with the two cocks at their head, ranged themselves in a line along the ridge of the tent; and the geese and ducks betook themselves in a body, cackling and quacking as they proceeded, to a marshy bit of ground near the sea, where some thick bushes afforded them shelter.

A little later, we ourselves began to follow the example of our winged companions by beginning our preparations for repose. First, we charged our guns and pistols, and laid them carefully in the tent: next, we assembled all together and joined in offering up our thanks to the Almighty for the succour afforded us, and supplicating his watchful care for our preservation. With the last ray of the sun we entered our tent, and laid ourselves down close to each other on the grass and moss we had collected in the morning.

The children observed, with surprise, that darkness came upon us all at once; that night succeeded to day without an intermediate twilight.—This, replied I, makes me suspect that we are not far from the equator, or at least between the tropics, where this is of ordinary occurrence; for the twilight is occasioned by the rays of the sun being broken in the atmosphere; the more obliquely they fall, the more their feeble light is extended and prolonged; while, on the other hand, the more perpendicular the rays, the less their declination: consequently the change from day to night is much more sudden when the sun is under the horizon.

I looked once more out of the tent to see if all was quiet around us, and then carefully inclosed the sail-cloth across the entrance. The old cock, awakened by the rising of the moon, chaunted our vespers, and then I lay down to sleep. In proportion as we had been during the day oppressed with heat, we were now in the night inconvenienced by the cold, so that we were obliged to cling close to each other for warmth. A sweet sleep began to close the eyes of my beloved family; I was secretly endeavouring to keep awake till I was sure my wife's solicitude had yielded to the same happy state, and then I closed my own. Thanks to the fatigue we had undergone, our first night in the desert island was very tolerably comfortable.

## ✲ III ✲

# VOYAGE OF DISCOVERY

I WAS AWAKED AT THE FIRST DAWN OF DAY BY THE CROWING OF the cocks. I awoke my wife, and we consulted together as to our occupation for the day. We both agreed, that the thing of the most importance was to seek for such traces as might be found of our late ship companions, and at the same time to examine the nature of the soil on the other side of the river before we came to a determination about a fixed place of abode. My wife easily perceived that such an excursion could not be undertaken by all the members of the family; and full of confidence in the protection of Heaven, she courageously consented to my proposal of leaving her with the three youngest boys, and proceeding myself with Fritz on a journey of discovery. I entreated her not to lose a moment in giving us our breakfast. She gave us notice that the share of each would be but small, there being no more soup prepared. What then, I asked, is to become of Jack's lobster? That he can best tell you himself, answered his mother. But now pray step and awake the boys, while I make a fire and put on some water.

The children were soon roused; even our slothful Ernest submitted to the hard fate of rising so early in the morning. When I asked Jack for his lobster, he ran and fetched it from a cleft in the rock in which he had carefully concealed it. I was determined, said he, that the dogs should not treat my lobster as they did the agouti, for I knew them for a sort of gentlemen to whom nothing comes amiss. I am glad to see, son Jack, said I, that that giddy head upon your shoulders can be prevailed upon to reflect. Happy is he who knows how to profit by the misfortunes of others, says the proverb. But will you not kindly give Fritz the great claw which bit your leg (though I promised it to you) to carry with him for his dinner in our journey?

What journey? asked all the boys at once. Ah! we will go too: a journey,—a journey—repeated they, clapping their hands and jumping round me like little kids. For this time, said I, it is impossible for all of you to go; we know not yet what we are to set about, nor whither we are going. Your eldest brother and myself shall be better able to defend ourselves in any danger, without you; besides, that with so many persons we could proceed but slowly. You will then all three remain with your mother in this place, which appears to be one of perfect safety, and you shall keep Ponto to be your guard, while we will take Turk with us. With such a protector, and a gun well loaded, who shall dare treat us with disrespect? Fritz, make haste and tie up Ponto, that he may not follow us; and have your eye on Turk, that he may be at hand to accompany us, and see the guns are ready.

At the word guns the colour rose in the cheeks of my poor boy. His gun was so curved as to be of no use; he took it up and tried in vain to straighten it; I let him alone for a short time; but at length I gave him leave to take another, perceiving with pleasure that the vexation had produced a proper feeling in his mind. A moment after, he attempted to lay hold of Ponto to tie him up; but the dog recollecting the blows he had so lately received, began to snarl and would not go near him. Turk behaved the same, and I found it necessary to call with my own voice to induce them to approach us. Fritz then in tears entreated for some biscuit of his mother, declaring that he would willingly go without his breakfast to make his peace with the dogs; he accordingly carried them some biscuit, stroked and caressed them, and in every motion seemed to ask their pardon. As of all animals, without excepting man, the dog is least addicted to revenge, and at the same time is the most sensible of kind usage, Ponto instantly relented, and began to lick the hands which fed him; but Turk, who was of a more fierce and independent temper, still held off, and seemed to feel a want of confidence in Fritz's advances. Give him a claw of my lobster, cried Jack, for I mean to give it all to you for your journey.

I cannot think why you should give it all, said Ernest, for you need not be uneasy about their journey. Like Robinson Crusoe, they will be sure enough to find some cocoa-nuts, which they will like much better than your miserable lobster: only think, a fine round nut, Jack, as big as my head, and with at least a tea-cup full of delicious sweet milk in it!

Oh! brother Fritz, pray do bring me some, cried the little Francis.

We now prepared for our departure: we took each a bag for game, and a hatchet; I put a pair of pistols in the leather band round Fritz's waist in addition to the gun, and provided myself with the same articles, not forgetting a stock of biscuit and a flask of fresh river water. My wife now called us to breakfast, when all attacked the lobster; but its flesh proved so hard, that there was a great deal left when our meal was finished, and we packed it for our journey without further regret from any one. The sea-lobster is an animal of considerable size, and its flesh is much more nutritious, but less delicate, than the common lobster.

Fritz urged me to set out before the excessive heat came on. With all my heart, said I, but we have forgotten one thing of importance. What is that? asked Fritz looking round him; I see nothing else to do but to take leave of my mother and my brothers. I know what it is, said Ernest, we have not said our prayers this morning.

That is the very thing, my dear boy, said I. We are too apt to forget God, the parent of all, for the cares of this world; and yet never had we so much need of his support and protection as in our present situation, and particularly at the moment of undertaking a journey to an unknown soil.

Upon this our little pickle Jack began to imitate the sound of church-bells, and to cry Bom! bom! bidi bom, bidiman, bom, To prayers, to prayers, bom, bom.—Thoughtless boy! cried I, with a look of displeasure, will you then never learn that there is a sacredness in devotion that, in a well disposed mind, banishes for the time every thought of levity or amusement? Recollect yourself, and let this be the last time you force from me a reproof on a subject of so grave a nature.

In about an hour we had completed all that was necessary to be done previous to our departure, and were ready to set out. I had loaded the guns we left behind, and I now enjoined my wife to keep by day as near the boat as possible, which in case of danger was the best and most speedy means of escape. My next concern was to shorten the moment of separation, judging by my own heart of the emotion of my dear wife; for it was impossible we could mutually be without the most painful apprehension, as to what new misfortune might occur on either side during the interval. We all melted into tears—; I seized this instant for drawing Fritz away, and in a few moments the sobs and often repeated adieus of those we left behind were drowned in the noise of the waves which we were approaching on our way, and which now turned our thoughts upon ourselves and the immediate object of our journey.

The river we were about to pass, was on each side so steep as to be inaccessible, except by one narrow slip near the mouth, on one side, and from whence we had already drawn our supply of fresh water; but there was no means of effecting a passage across from this place, the opposite shore being an unbroken line of sharp, high, perpendicular rocks. We therefore walked on, following the course of the river till we arrived at a cluster of rocks at which the stream formed a cascade: a few paces beyond, we observed some large fragments of rock which had fallen into the bed of the river; by stepping upon these, and making now and then some hazardous leaps, we at length contrived to reach to the other side. We had proceeded a short way along the rock we ascended in landing, forcing ourselves a passage through overgrown grass mixed with plants, and rendered more capable of resistance by being half dried up by the sun. Perceiving however, that walking on this kind of surface, joined to the heat, would soon exhaust our strength, we looked for a path by which we might descend and proceed along the river, in which direction we hoped to meet with fewer obstacles, and perhaps might discover traces of the boats and our ship companions.

When we had walked about a hundred paces, we heard a loud noise behind us as if we were pursued, and perceived a rustling motion in the grass, which was almost as tall as ourselves. I confess I was a good deal alarmed, thinking that it was probably occasioned by some frightful serpent, a tiger, or other ferocious animal, which might instantly devour us. But I was well satisfied with the courage of Fritz, who, instead of being frightened and running away, stood still and firm to face the danger, the only motion he made being that of seeing that his piece was fit to be discharged, and turning himself to front the spot from whence the noise proceeded. Our alarm however was of short duration; for what was our joy on seeing rush out, not an enemy, but our faithful Turk, whom in the distress of the parting scene we had quite forgotten, and whom no doubt our anxious relatives had sent on to us! I received the poor creature with lively joy, and did not fail to commend both the bravery and discretion of my son, in not yielding to even a rational alarm, and for waiting till he was sure of the object before he resolved to fire: had he done otherwise, he might have destroyed an animal formed to afford us various kinds of aid, and to contribute by the kindness of his temper to the pleasures of our domestic scene. Observe, my dear boy, said I, to what dangers the tumult of the passions exposes us: the anger which overpowered you yesterday, and the terror natural to the occasion we have this moment witnessed, if you had unfortunately given way to it might either of them have produced to us an irretrievable misfortune.

Fritz assured me he was sensible of the truth and importance of my remarks; that he would watch constantly over the defects of his temper: and then he fell to caressing the faithful and interesting animal.

Conversing on such subjects as these, we pursued our way. On our left was the sea, and on our right, the continuation of the ridge of rocks which began at the place of our debarkation about half a league behind us, and ran in a direction nearly parallel with the shore, the summit every where adorned with a fresh verdure and a great variety of trees; and the space between, partly covered with tall grass and partly with small clumps of bushes, which on one side extended to the rocks, and on the other to the sea. We were careful to proceed in a course as near the shore as possible, fixing our eyes rather upon its smooth expanse than upon the land, at every instant in hopes to see something of the boats. We did not however wholly neglect the shore, where we looked about in all directions for the objects of our search: but our endeavours were in vain; no sign appeared of their having been near the spot.

Fritz proposed to fire his gun from time to time, suggesting that, should they be any where concealed near us, they might thus be led to know of our pursuit.

This would be vastly well, answered I, if you could contrive for our friends to hear the report of the gun and not the savages, who are most likely not far distant, and would be induced by the alarm to watch and surprise us. I am thinking, father, interrupted Fritz, that there is no good reason why we should give ourselves so much trouble and uneasiness about persons who abandoned us so cruelly, and thought only of their own safety.

There is not only one good reason, but many, replied I: first, we should not return evil for evil; next, it may be in their power to be of use and assist us; and lastly, that they are most likely at this moment in the greatest want of our exertions. It was their lot to escape with nothing but their persons from the ship, if indeed they are still alive, while we had the good fortune to secure provisions enough for present subsistence, to a share of which they are as fully entitled as ourselves.

But, father, while we are wandering here and losing our time almost without a hope of benefit to them, might we not better employ ourselves in returning to the vessel and saving the lives of the animals on board?

When a variety of duties present themselves for our choice we should always give the preference to that which can confer the most solid advantage. The saving of the life of a man, is a more exalted action than to be employed in contributing to the further comfort of a few quadrupeds, whom we have already supplied with food for several days longer, particularly as the sea is in so calm a state, that we need entertain no apprehension that the ship will be sunk or go entirely to pieces just at present.

My son made no reply to what I said, and we each seemed by mutual silent consent to take a few moments for reflection.

When we had gone about two leagues, we entered a wood situated a little further from the sea: here we threw ourselves on the ground, and under the shade of a tree, by the side of a clear running stream, took out some provisions and refreshed ourselves. We heard on every side around us the chirping, singing, and the motion of unknown birds among the leaves, and which in reality were more attractive by their splendid plumage than by any charm of note. Fritz assured me that between the branches of the bushes he saw some animals resembling apes: this indeed was further confirmed by the restless movements we had observed in Turk, who began to smell about him, and to bark so loud that the wood resounded with the noise. Fritz stole softly about to be sure, and raising his head to spy into the branches above his height, he stumbled on a small round body which lay on the ground: he took it up and brought it to me, observing that he thought it must be the nest of some bird. What makes you of that opinion? said I. It is, I think, much more like a cocoa-nut.

But I have read that there are some kinds of birds who build their nests quite round; and look, father, how the outside is crossed and twined!

That is true, Fritz; but it is wrong from a single view to be so positive. Do you not perceive that what you take for straws crossed and twined by the beak of a bird, is in fact a coat of fibres formed by the hand of nature? Do you not remember to have read that the nut of a cocoa shell is inclosed within a round fibrous covering, which again is surrounded by a skin of a thin and fragile texture? I see that in the one you hold in your hand, this skin has been destroyed by time, and this is the reason why the twisted fibres (or inner covering) are so apparent; but now let us break the shell, and you will see the nut inside.

We soon accomplished this; but the nut, alas, from lying on the ground, had perished, and appeared but little different from a bit of dried skin, and not the least inviting to the palate.

Fritz was much amused at this discovery. How I wish Ernest could have been here! cried he. How he envied me the fine large cocoa-nuts I was to find, and the whole teacup full of sweet delicious milk which was to spring out upon me from the inside! But, father, I myself believed that the cocoa-nut contained a sweet refreshing liquid, a little like the juice of almonds; travellers surely tell untruths!

Travellers certainly do sometimes tell untruths, but on the subject of the cocoa-nut I believe them to be innocent. The cocoa-nut is well known to contain the liquid you describe, just before they are in a state of ripeness. It is the same with our European nuts, with only the difference of quantity; and the circumstance is common to both, that as the nut ripens the milk diminishes, by thickening and becoming the same substance as the nut. If you put a ripe nut a little way under the earth, in a good soil, the kernel will shoot and burst the shell; but if it remain above ground, or in a place that does not suit its nature, the principle of vegetation is extinguished by internal fermentation, and the nut perishes as you have seen.

I am now surprised that this principle is not extinguished in every nut; for the shell is so hard, it seems impossible for a softer substance to break it.

The peach stone is no less hard; the kernel notwithstanding never fails to break it, if it is placed in a well nurtured soil.

Now I begin to understand. The peach stone is divided into two parts like a muscle-shell; it has a kind of seam round it, which separates of itself when the kernel is swelled by moisture;—but the cocoa-nut in my hand is not so divided, and I cannot conceive of its separating.

I grant that the cocoa-nut is differently formed; but you may see by the fragments you have just thrown on the ground, that nature has in another manner stepped in to its assistance. Look near the stalk, and you will discover three round holes, which are not, like the rest of its surface, covered with a hard impenetrable shell, but are stopped by a spongy kind of matter; it is through these that the kernel shoots.

I will gather all the pieces and take them to Ernest, and tell him all these particulars; I wonder what he will say about it, and how he will like the withered nut.

Now the fancy of your father, my dear boy, would be to find you without so keen a relish for a bit of mischief. Joke with Ernest if you will about the withered nut; but I should like to see you heal the disappointment he will feel, by presenting him at last with a sound and perfect nut, provided we should have one to spare.

After looking for some time, we had the good luck to meet with one single nut. We opened it, and finding it sound, we sat down and ate it for our dinner, by which means we were enabled to husband the provisions we had brought. The nut, it is true, was a little oily and rancid; yet, as this was not a time to be nice, we made a hearty meal, and then continued our route. We did not quit the wood, but pushed our way through it, being often obliged to cut a path through the bushes overrun by creeping plants, with our hatchet. At length we reached a plain, which afforded a more extensive prospect and a path less perplexed and intricate.

We next entered a forest to the right, and soon observed in it here and there some trees of a particular species. Fritz, whose sharp eye was continually on a journey of discovery, remarked that some of them were of so very extraordinary an appearance that he could not resist the curiosity he felt to examine them closely. O heavens! father, he next exclaimed, what a singular kind of trees, with wens growing all about their trunks! We both walked up to some of them, and I perceived, with great surprise and satisfaction, that they were of the gourd tree kind, the trunks of which bear fruit. Fritz, who had never heard of such a tree, could not conceive the meaning of what he saw, and asked me if the fruit was a sponge or a wen. We will see, I replied, if we cannot unravel the mystery. Try to get down one of them, and we will examine them minutely.

I have got one, cried Fritz, and it is exactly like a gourd, only the rind is thicker and harder.

It then, like the rind of that fruit, can be used for making various utensils, observed I; plates, dishes, basons, flasks. We will give it the name of the gourd tree.

Fritz jumped for joy. O heavens! cried he in ecstasy, how happy my mother will be! She will no longer have the vexation, when she makes soup, of thinking that we shall all scald our fingers!

What, my boy, do you think is the reason that this tree bears its fruit only on the trunk and on its topmost branches?

I think it must be because the middle branches are too feeble to support such a weight.

You have guessed exactly right.

But are these gourds good to eat?

At worst they are, I believe, harmless; but they have not a very tempting flavour. The negro savages set as much value on the rind of this fruit as on gold, for its use to them is indispensable. These rinds serve them to keep their food and drink in, and sometimes, they even cook their victuals in them.

Oh, father! it must be impossible to cook their victuals in them; for the heat of fire would soon consume such a substance.

I did not say the rind was put upon the fire.

How droll! Pray how are victuals to be cooked without fire?

Nor did I say that victuals could be cooked without a fire; and my meaning was, that there is no need to put the vessel that contains the food upon the fire.

I have not the least idea of what you mean; there seems to be a miracle.

So be it, my son. A little tincture of enchantment is the lot of man. When he finds himself deficient in intelligence, or is too indolent to give himself the trouble to reflect, he is driven by his weakness to ascribe to a miracle, or to witchcraft, what is, most likely, nothing but the most ordinary operation of art or nature.

Well, father, I will then believe in what you tell me of these rinds.

That is, you will cut the matter short, by resolving to swear on the word of another; this is an excellent method for letting your own reason lie fallow. Come, come, no such idleness; let me help you to understand this amazing phenomenon. When it is intended to dress food in one of these rinds, the process is, to cut the fruit into two equal parts, and scoop out the whole of the inside; some water is put into one of the halves, and into the water some fish, a crab, or whatever else is to be dressed; then some stones red hot, beginning with one at a time, are thrown in, which impart sufficient heat to the water to dress the food, without the smallest injury to the pot.

But is not the food spoiled by ashes falling in, or by pieces of the heated stones separating in the water?

Certainly it is not very easy to make fine sauces or ragouts in such a vessel; but a dressing of the meat is actually accomplished, and the negroes and savages, who are principally the persons to make use of what is thus cooked, are not very delicate: but I can imagine a tolerable remedy for even the objection you have found. The food might be inclosed in a vessel small enough to be contained in our capacious half of a gourd, and thus be cooked upon the principle so much used in chemistry, the application of a milder heat than fire. And this method of cooking has also another advantage, that the thing contained cannot adhere to the sides or bottom of the vessel.

We next proceeded to the manufacture of our plates and dishes. I taught my son how to divide the gourd with a bit of string, which would cut more equally than a knife; I tied the string round the middle of the gourd as tight as possible, striking it pretty hard with the handle of my knife, and I drew tighter and tighter till the gourd fell apart, forming two regular shaped bowls or vessels; while Fritz, who had used a knife for the same operation, had entirely spoiled his gourd by the irregular pressure of his instrument. I recommended his making some spoons with the spoiled rind, as it was good for no other purpose. I, on my part, had soon completed two dishes of convenient size, and some smaller ones to serve as plates.

Fritz was in the utmost astonishment at my success. I cannot imagine, father, said he, how this way of cutting the gourd could occur to you!

I have read the description of such a process, replied I, in books of travels; and also, that such of the savages as have no knives, and who make a sort of twine from the bark of trees, are accustomed to use it for this kind of purpose. So you see what benefit may be derived from reading, and from afterwards reflecting on what we read.

And the flasks, father; in what manner are they made?

For this branch of their ingenuity they make preparation a long time beforehand. If a negro wishes to have a flask or bottle with a neck, he ties a very young gourd round in the proper place with a piece of string, of linen, bark of a tree, or any thing he can get hold of; he draws this bandage so tight, that the part at liberty soon forms itself to a round shape, while the part which is confined, contracts, and remains ever after narrow. By this method it is that they obtain flasks or bottles of a perfect form.

Are then the bottle-shaped gourds I have seen in Europe trained by a similar preparation?

No, they are not; they are of another species, and what you have seen is their natural shape.

Our conversation and our labour thus went on together. Fritz had completed some plates, and was not a little proud of the achievement. Ah, how delighted my mother will be to eat upon them! cried he. But how shall we convey them to her? They will not, I fear, bear travelling well.

We must leave them here on the sand for the sun to dry them thoroughly; this will be accomplished by the time of our return this way, and we can then carry them with us; but care must be taken to fill them with sand, that they may not shrink or warp in so ardent a heat. My boy did not dislike this task; for he had no great fancy to the idea of carrying such a load on our journey of further discovery. Our sumptuous service of porcelain was accordingly spread upon the shore, and abandoned to its fate.

We amused ourselves as we walked along in endeavouring to fashion some spoons from the fragments of the gourd-rinds. I had the fancy to try my skill upon a piece of cocoa-nut; but I must needs confess that what we produced had not the least resemblance to those I had seen in the Museum at London, and which were shown there as the work of some of the islanders of the Southern Seas. A European without instruments must always find himself excelled in such attempts by the superior adroitness and patience of savages; in this instance too, of ourselves, we had the assistance of knives, while the savages have only flat stones with a sharp edge to work with.

My attempt has been scarcely more successful than your own, I cried; and, to eat soup with either your spoon or mine we ought to have mouths extending from ear to ear.

True enough, father, answered Fritz; but it is not my fault. In making mine, I took the curve of my bit of rind for a guide; if I had made it smaller, it would have been too flat, and it is still more difficult to eat with a shovel than with an oyster-shell. But I am thinking that they may serve till I have learned to improve upon my first attempt, and I am quite sure of the pleasure they will afford my mother. I imagine it pleases God sometimes to visit his creatures with distress, that they may learn to be satisfied with a little.

That is an excellent remark, my boy, said I, and gives me more pleasure than a hundred crowns would do. Fritz burst into a fit of laughter. You do not rate my remark very high when you say this, father, cried he, for of what use would a hundred crowns be to you at present? If you had said a good soup or a hundred cocoa-nuts, I should be much prouder for having made it.

But as it is, my son, you have a right to be proud. I am well pleased to find you are beginning to estimate things according to their real value and usefulness, instead of considering them as good or bad, like children, upon feeble views. Money is only a means of exchange in human society; but here on this solitary coast, nature is more generous than man, and asks no payment for the benefits she bestows.

While these different conversations and our labours had been going on, we had not neglected the great object of our pursuit—

the making every practicable search for our ship companions. But all, alas, was in vain.

After a walk of about four leagues in all, we arrived at a spot where a slip of land reached far out into the sea, on which we observed a hill or rising piece of ground of considerable height. On a moment's reflection we determined to ascend to its summit, which could not fail to give us a clear view of all adjacent parts; this would save us the fatigue of further rambles. We accordingly accomplished the design.

We did not reach the top of the hill without many courageous efforts and a plentiful perspiration: but when there, it presented a magnificent scene of wild and solitary beauty, comprehending a vast extent of land and water. It was, however, in vain that we made use of our spying glass; no trace of man appeared.

A highly embellished nature presented herself; and though deprived of human succour, we were in the highest degree sensible of her thousand charms. The shore, rounded by a bay of some extent, the bank of which ended in a promontory on the further side; the agreeable blue tint of its surface; the sea, gently agitated with waves, in which the rays of the sun were reflected; the woods of variegated hues and verdure, formed altogether a picture of such new and exquisite delight that, if the recollection of our unfortunate companions, already perhaps ingulfed in this very ocean, had not intervened to damp our spirits, we should have yielded to the ecstasy the scene was calculated to inspire. In reality, from this moment we began to lose the consolatory hope we had hitherto entertained, and a certain sadness stole involuntarily into our hearts. We, however, became but the more sensible of the goodness of the Divine Being in the special protection afforded us, in permitting us to find a

PLATE 4
"No trace of man appeared."

home where there seemed to be no cause for fear of danger from without, where we had not experienced even the want of food, and where there seemed to be a prospect of future safety for us all. We had encountered no venomous or ferocious animals; and, as far as our sight could yet reach, we were not threatened by the approach of savages. I remarked to Fritz that we seemed destined to a solitary life, and that it was a rich country which appeared to be allotted us for a habitation; at least our habitation it must be, unless some vessel should happen to put on shore on the same coast, and be in a condition to take us back to our native land. And God's will be done! added I, for he knows what is best for us.

Having left our native country, fixed in the intention of inhabiting some more propitious soil, it was natural to expect that we must at first encounter difficult adventures. Let us, therefore, consider our present situation as no disappointment in any essential respect. We can pursue our scheme for agriculture. We shall learn to invent arts. Our only want is numbers.

As for me, answered Fritz, I care but little about being so few of us. If I have the happiness of seeing you and my mother well and satisfied, I shall not give myself much uneasiness about those wicked unkind ship companions of ours.

Do not say that, my boy; they were not all bad people; and the greater part of them would have become better men here, because they would not have been exposed to the attacks of seduction. Social intercourse, common interests, united exertions, mutual services and counsels, together with the reflections which would have grown in such a state as this, are agents capable of powerfully contributing to the well-being of the individual, and to a happy and successful industry.

We, however, of ourselves, observed Fritz, form a larger society than was the lot of Adam before he had children; and, as we grow older, we will perform all the necessary labour, while you and my mother enjoy a serene repose.

Your assurances are as kind as I can desire, and they encourage me to struggle with what hardships may present themselves. Who can foresee in what manner it may be the will of Heaven to dispose of us? In times of old, God said to one of his chosen: "I will cause a great nation to descend from thy loins."

And why may not we too become patriarchs, if it please God to continue our lives?

Why not? you ask—and I have not now time to answer. But come along, my young patriarch, and let us find a shady spot, that we may not be consumed with the intensity of the sun's heat before the patriarchal condition can be conferred upon us. Look yonder at that inviting wood: let us hasten thither to take a little rest, then eat our dinner, and return to our dear expecting family.

We descended from the hill, and having regained the shore, made our way to the wood of palms, which I had just pointed out to Fritz; but not without considerable difficulty, for our path lay through a quantity of reeds, entwined with other plants, which greatly obstructed our march. We advanced slowly and cautiously, fearing at every step we might receive a mortal bite from some serpent that might be concealed among them. We made Turk go before us, to give us timely notice of any thing dangerous. I also cut myself a stalk of the reeds of uncommon length and thickness, the better to defend myself against an enemy that might attack me from the ground. It was not without astonishment that I perceived a glutinous kind of sap proceed from the divided end of the stalk. Prompted by curiosity, I tasted the sap, and found it sweet and of an agreeable flavour, so that not a doubt remained in my mind that we were passing through a fine plantation of sugar-canes. I again applied the cane to my lips, and sucked it for some moments, and soon after felt myself singularly refreshed and strengthened from its use. I determined not to tell Fritz immediately of the fortunate discovery I had made, preferring that he should find the pleasure out for himself. As he was at some distance on before, I called out to him to cut a reed for his defence. This he instantly did, and, without any remark, used it simply for a stick, striking lustily with it on all sides to clear a passage. This motion occasioned the sap to run out abundantly upon his hand, and he stopped to examine so strange a circumstance. He lifted it up, and still a larger quantity escaped. He now tasted what was on his fingers. Oh! then for the exclamations. Father, father, I have found some sugar!—some syrup! I have a sugar-cane in my hand! Run quickly, father! We were soon together, jointly partaking of the pleasure we had in store for his dear mother and the younger brothers. In the mean time Fritz eagerly devoured the single cane he had cut, till his relish for it was appeased. I thought this a profitable moment to say a word or two about excesses; of the wisdom of husbanding even for lawful pleasures, and of the advantages of moderation in our most rational enjoyments.

But I was so thirsty, and the sap was so delicious!

Your excuse is like that of the drunkard, who tells you he drinks immoderately because he is thirsty, and because wine has a pleasant flavour; while, however good the excuse, it does not protect the person from being deprived of his reason.

Well, father, I will observe. But I will take home a good provision of sugar-canes, however. I shall only just taste of them once or twice as I walk along. But it will be so delightful to regale my mother and my little brothers with them!

I have not the least objection; but do not take too heavy a load, for recollect you have other things to carry, and we have yet far to go.

Counsel was given in vain. He persisted in cutting at least a dozen of the largest canes, tore off their leaves, tied them together, and, putting them under his arm, dragged them as well as he was able through thick and thin to the end of the plantation. We arrived without accident at the wood of palms, which we entered in search of a place of shade, where we might stretch our limbs on the ground, and finish our repast. We were scarcely settled, when, suddenly a great number of large monkeys, terrified by the sight of us and the barking of Turk, stole so nimbly, and yet so quietly, up the trees, that we scarcely perceived them till they had reached the topmost parts. From this height they fixed their eyes upon us, grinding their teeth, making most horrible grimaces, and saluting us with frightful screams of hostile import. I observed that the trees were palms, bearing cocoa-nuts, and I instantly conceived the hope of obtaining some of this fruit in an unripe and milky state, through the monkeys. Fritz, on his part, prepared to shoot at them instantly. He threw his burdens on the ground, and it was with difficulty I could prevent him from firing, by pulling his arm in another direction. What are you going to do, said I, in this youthful ardour of yours? What use or what pleasure can it be to you to destroy one of these monkeys?

Ah, father, why did you not let me kill him? Monkeys are such malicious, mischievous animals! Look how they raise their backs in derision of us!

And is it possible that this can excite your vengeance, my most reasonable Mr. Fritz? To say the truth, I am not myself a patron of the race of monkeys, who, as you say, are naturally prone to be malicious. But as long as an animal does us no injury, or that his death can in no shape be useful in preserving our own lives, we have no right to destroy it, and still less to torment it for our amusement, or from an insensate desire of revenge.

We could as easily roast a monkey as any kind of game.

Many thanks for the hint! A fine repast you would have provided us! Thanks to our stars, too, we are each too heavily loaded to have carried the dead body to our kitchen, and I shrewdly suspect that it would not have found the way thither of its own accord. Does not your large bundle of sugar-canes convince you that I speak the truth? But the living monkeys we may perhaps find means to make contribute to our service. See what I am going to do;—but step aside, for fear of your head. If I succeed, the monkeys will furnish us with plenty of our much desired cocoa-nuts.

I now began to throw some stones at the monkeys; and though I could not make them reach to half of the height at which they had taken refuge, they showed every mark of excessive anger. With their accustomed habit of imitation, they furiously tore off, nut by nut, all that grew upon the branches near them, to hurl them down upon us, so that it was with difficulty we avoided the blows; and in a short time a large quantity of cocoa-nuts lay on the ground round us. Fritz laughed heartily at the excellent success of our stratagem; and as the shower of cocoa-nuts began to subside, we set about collecting them. We chose a place where we could repose at our ease, to regale ourselves on this rich harvest. We opened the shells with a hatchet, but not without having first enjoyed the sucking of some of the milk through the three small holes, round which we found it easy to insert a knife, and let the milk escape. The milk of the cocoa-nut has not in reality a very pleasant flavour; but it is excellent for quenching violent thirst. What we liked best, was a kind of solid cream which adheres to the shell, and which we scraped off with our spoons. We mixed with it a little of the sap of our sugar-canes, and it made a delicious repast; while Turk obtained for his share, what remained of the sea-lobster, which we now regarded with disdain, and to which we added a small quantity of biscuit. All this, however, was insufficient to satisfy the hunger of so large an animal, and he sought about for bits of the sugar-canes and of the cocoa-nuts.

Our meal being finished, we prepared to leave the place. I tied together such of the cocoa-nuts as had retained the stalks, and threw them across my shoulder. Fritz resumed his bundle of sugar-canes. We divided the rest of the things between us, and continued our way towards home.

# IV

# RETURN FROM THE VOYAGE OF
# DISCOVERY—A NOCTURNAL ALARM

M Y POOR BOY NOW BEGAN TO COMPLAIN HEAVILY OF FATIGUE; the bundle of sugar-canes galled his shoulders, and he was obliged to move it from place to place. At last, he stopped to take breath. No, cried he, I never could have thought that a few sugar-canes could be so heavy. How sincerely I pity the poor negroes who carry them in even larger quantities, and to a greater distance! I should however be so glad, if my mother and my brothers could but partake of our booty! A little patience and a little courage, dear Fritz, replied I, will enable you to accomplish this wish; recollect Esop's breadbasket, which at first was so overwhelming a burden, but which at last became so light. We can cause it to be the same with your sugar-canes, if we consent to diminish them by sucking a certain number of them on the road; as a precedent, you may dispose of one to me, and I will use it at one moment as a walking-stick, and at another as a sugarplum. Take you one, also, the rest we will bind together and put at your back, hanging them upon the barrel of your gun, by which means you will carry them with ease. In such a situation as ours we must learn to call forth all our intelligence; reflection and the faculty of invention must be made to compensate our want of means.

While we were conversing and proceeding on our way, Fritz perceived that from time to time I sucked the end of my sugar-cane, and he would needs do the same. It was in vain, however that he tried; scarcely a drop of the sap reached his eager lips. What then is the reason, said he, that though the cane is full of juice, I cannot get out a drop?

The reason is, answered I, that you make use neither of reflection nor of your imagination.

Ah! I recollect now, is it not a question about air? Unless there were a particular opening in the cane, I may suck in vain, no juice will come.

You have well explained the difficulty: but how will you manage to set it right?

Father, lend me your cane an instant.

No, no, that will not do; what I wish is, that you should yourself invent the remedy.

Let me see; I imagine that I have only to make a little opening just above the first knot, and then the air can enter.

Exactly right. But tell me what you think would be the operation of this opening near the first knot; and in what manner can it make the juice get into your mouth?

The pith of the cane being completely interrupted by each knot in its growth, the opening that I might make below, could have no effect upon the part above; in sucking the juice, I draw in my breath, and thus exhaust the air in my mouth; the external air presses at the same time through the hole I have made, and fills this void: the juice of the cane forms an obstacle to this effort, and is accordingly driven into my mouth. But how shall I manage when I have sucked this part dry, to get at the part above?

Oh, ho! Mr. Philosopher, what should prevent you, who have been reasoning so well about the force and fluidity of the air, from immediately conceiving so simple a process as that of cutting away the part of the cane you have already sucked dry, and making a second perforation in the part above, so that . . .

Oh, I have it, I have it, I understand;— but if we should become too expert in the art of drawing out the juice, I fear but few of the canes will reach our good friends in the tent.

I also am not without my apprehensions, that of our acquisition we shall carry them only a few sticks for fire-wood; for I must bring another circumstance to your recollection: the juice of the sugar-cane is apt to turn sour soon after cutting, and the more certainly in such heat as we now experience; we may suck them therefore without compunction, and without regret at the diminution of their numbers.

Well then, if we can do no better with the sugar-canes, at least I will take them a good provision of the milk of cocoa-nuts, which I have here in a tin bottle; we shall sit round on the grass and drink it so deliciously!

In this too, my generous boy, I fear, you will also be disappointed. You talk of milk; but the milk of the cocoa-nut, no less than the juice of the sugar-cane, when exposed to the air and heat, turns soon to vinegar. I would almost wager that it is already sour; for the tin bottle which contains it is particularly liable to become hot in the sun.

O heavens, how provoking! I must taste it this very minute. The tin bottle was lowered from his shoulder in the twinkling of an eye, and he began to pull the cork with all his strength; as soon as it was loose, the liquid flew upwards in a brisk stream, and with a loud noise and frothing like champain.

Bravo, Mr. Fritz! you have manufactured there a wine of some mettle. I must now caution you not to let it make you tipsy.

Oh, taste it, father, pray taste it, it is quite delicious; not the least like vinegar; it is rather like excellent new wine; its taste is sweet, and it is so sparkling! do take a little, father. Is it not good? If all the milk remains in this state, the treat will be better even than I thought.

I wish it may prove so: but I have my fears; its present state is what is called the first degree of fermentation; the same thing happens to honey dissolved in water, of which hydromel is made. When this first fermentation is past, and the liquid is clear, it is become a sort of wine, or other fermented liquor, the quality of which depends on the materials used. By the application of heat, there next results a second and more gradual fermentation, which turns the fluid into vinegar. But this may be prevented by extraordinary care, and by keeping the vessel that contains it in a cool place. Lastly, a third fermentation takes place in the vinegar itself, which entirely changes its character, and deprives it of its taste, its strength, and its transparency. In the intense temperature of this climate, this triple fermentation comes on very rapidly, so that it is not improbable that, on entering our tent, you might find your liquids turned to vinegar, or even to a thick liquid of ill odour: we may therefore venture to refresh ourselves with a portion of our booty, that it may not all be spoiled. Come then, I drink your health, and that of our dear family. I find the liquor at present both refreshing and agreeable; but I am pretty sure that, if we would arrive sober, we must not venture on frequent libations.

Our regale imparted to our exhausted frames an increase of strength and cheerfulness; we pursued our way with brisk-ness, to the place where we had left our gourd utensils upon the sands; we found them perfectly dry, as hard as bone, and not the least mis-shapen. We now therefore could put them into our game bags conveniently enough; and this done, we continued our way. Scarcely had we passed through the little wood in which we breakfasted, when Turk sprang furiously away to seize upon a troop of monkeys, who were skipping about and amusing them-selves without observing our approach towards the place of their merriment. They were thus taken by surprise; and before we could get to the spot, our ferocious Turk had already seized one of them: it was a female monkey who held a young one in her arms, which she was caressing almost to suffocation, and which incumbrance in reality deprived her of the power of escaping. The poor creature was killed, and afterwards devoured; the young one hid himself in the grass, and looked on grinding his teeth all the time that this horrible achievement was performing. Fritz flew like lightning to force the ferocious Turk from his prey. He lost his hat, threw down his tin bottle, canes, and other burdens, but all in vain; he arrived too late to prevent the murder of the interesting mother.

The next scene that presented itself was of a different nature, and comical enough; it afforded me considerable amusement. The young monkey, on perceiving Fritz, sprang nimbly on his shoulders, and fastened his feet securely in the stiff curls of his hair; nor could the squalls of Fritz, nor all the shaking he gave him, make him let go his hold. I ran to them, laughing heartily, for I saw that the animal was too young to be capable of doing him any injury, while the expression of the panic in the features of the boy, made the most diverting contrast with the grimaces of the monkey, whom I in vain endeavoured to disengage. There is no remedy, Fritz, said I, but to submit quietly and carry him; he will furnish an addition to our stock of provisions, though less alluring, I must needs confess, than that we could wish to take to your mother. The conduct of the little animal displays a very surprising intelligence; he has lost his mother, and he adopts you for his father; perhaps he discovered in you something of the air of a father of a family.

Or rather the little rogue found out that he had to do with a chicken-hearted fellow, who shrinks with aversion from the idea of ill-treating an animal which has thrown itself on his protection. But I assure you, father, he is giving me some terrible twitches, and I shall be obliged to you to try once more to get him off.

With a little gentleness and management I found means to succeed. I took the creature in my arms as one would an infant, and I confess I could not help pitying and caressing him. He was not larger than a kitten, and quite unable to help himself: its mother appeared to us to be at least as tall as Fritz.

What shall I do with thee, poor orphan? cried I, and how in our state of necessity shall I be able to maintain thee? We have already more mouths to fill, than food to put into them, and our workmen are too young to afford us much hope from their exertions.

Father, cried Fritz, do let me have this little animal in my own keeping. I will take the greatest care of him; I will give him all my share of the milk of the cocoa-nuts till we get our cows and goats;

and who knows? his monkey instinct may one day assist us in discovering some different kinds of wholesome fruits.

I have not the least objection, answered I. You have conducted yourself throughout this tragi-comic adventure like a lad of courage and sensibility, and I am well satisfied with every circumstance of your behaviour. It is therefore but just that the little protégé should be given up to your management and discretion; much will depend on your manner of educating him; by and by we shall see whether he will be fittest to aid us with his intelligence, or to injure us by his malice; in this last case we shall have nothing to do but to get rid of him.

While Fritz and I were conversing on the subject of his adoption of the young monkey, Turk was employed in taking his fill of the remains of its unfortunate mother. Fritz would have driven him away from so cannibal-like a repast: but besides the difficulty of restraining him, we had to consider, that we might ourselves be in danger from the pressing hunger of so powerful an animal; all the food we had before given him in the day seemed to be nothing for his voracious and unbounded appetite.

We now again thought of resuming our journey, and accordingly left the ferocious Turk to pursue his sanguinary dispositions; the little orphan jumped again on the shoulder of his protector, while I on my part relieved my boy of the bundle of canes. Scarcely had we proceeded a quarter of a league when Turk overtook us full gallop. Fritz and I received him without the usual marks of kindness, and reproached him with the cruel action he had committed, as if he could feel and understand us; but he showed no sign of giving himself any concern about the matter, following quietly behind Fritz with an air of cool and perfect satisfaction.

The young monkey appeared uneasy from seeing him so near, and passed round and fixed himself on his protector's bosom, who did not long bear with so great an inconvenience without having recourse to his invention for a remedy. He tied some string round Turk's body in such a way, as to admit of the monkey's being fastened on his back with it, and then in a tone really pathetic addressed the dog as follows: Now, Mr. Turk, since it was you who had the cruelty to destroy the mother, it is for you to take every care of her child. At first the dog was restive and resisted; but by degrees, partly by menaces and partly by caresses, we succeeded in gaining his good will, and he quietly consented to carry the little burden; and the young monkey, who also had made some difficulties, at length found himself perfectly accommodated. Fritz put another string round Turk's neck, by which he might lead him, a precaution he used to prevent him from going out of sight. I must needs confess, we had not the sin of too great haste to answer for, so that I had sufficient leisure for amusing myself with the idea, that we should arrive at our home with something of the appearance of keepers of rare animals for show. I enjoyed in foresight the jubilations of our young ones when they should see the figure we made. Ah! cried Fritz, I promise you, brother Jack will draw from the occasion materials enough for future malicious jokes. Do you then, my son, said I, take as an example your admirable mother, who never fails to make allowance for the buoyant spirits so natural for youth. Your reflections on their faults, which, thanks be to heaven, are such as to do injury to none give me no pleasure; I am aware of their existence without the aid of your observations, and I beg you will leave to me the task of correcting them.

May I however observe, father, that I wish we could cure Turk of his passion for attacking living animals, and tearing them to pieces? It was, I assure you, a most frightful spectacle; the more so, that monkeys so much resemble our own species that I could scarcely convince myself he was not killing a man.

There was reason enough to be disgusted with the sight, though it were only an animal you saw so treated; but, for all this, it would in our situation be dangerous to teach our dogs not to attack and kill, if they can, what unknown animals they meet with. You will see that Turk will soon regard your little monkey as a member of our family; already he is content to carry him on his back. But I assure you we must not discourage him in his fancy for attacking wild beasts. Heaven bestowed the dog on man for his safe-guard and defence, and the horse the same: they may be considered as our allies against the different tribes of pernicious animals. How conspicuous is the goodness of the Almighty in the natural dispositions he has bestowed on these useful creatures, who at all times discover so much affection for man, and so easily submit to the slavery of serving him! A man on horseback, and accompanied by a troop of well conditioned dogs, has no occasion to fear any species of wild beasts, not even the lion, nor the hyena; he may even baffle the voracious rapidity of the tiger.

I see clearly how fortunate we are in the possession of two such creatures, who feel the strongest attachment to our persons and are ever ready to protect us from danger; but what a pity it was that the horses we had on board should have died during our voyage, and have left us with only an ass!

Let us take care how we treat even our ass with disdain. I wish we had him safe on land. Fortunately he is a powerful creature of his species, and not of the common kind. We may train him to do us the same services as are performed by the horse; and it is not improbable that he will even improve under our care, and from the excellent pasture he will find in this climate.

In such conversation as this, on subjects equally interesting to both, we forgot the length of our journey, and soon found ourselves on the bank of the river and near our family before we were aware. Ponto on the other side announced our approach by a violent barking, and Turk replied so heartily, that his motions disturbed the tranquillity of his little burden, who, in his fright, jumped the length of his string from his back to Fritz's shoulder, which he could not afterwards be prevailed upon to leave. Turk, who began to be well acquainted with the country, ran off to meet his companion and announce our arrival; and shortly after, our much-loved family appeared in sight on the opposite shore, exhibiting every demonstration of unbounded joy at our safe return. They advanced along by the course of the river, till they on one side, and we on the other, had reached the place where we had crossed it in the morning. We re-passed again in safety, and threw ourselves into each other's arms. Scarcely had the young ones joined their brother, than they again began their joyful exclamations: A monkey, a live monkey! Papa, mamma, a live monkey! Oh, how delightful! how happy shall we be! How did you catch him? What a droll face he has! He is very ugly, said little Francis, half afraid to touch him. He is much prettier than you, retorted Jack; only see, he is laughing; I wish I could see him eat. Ah! if we had but some cocoa-nut! said Ernest; could you not find any? Are they nice? Have you brought me any milk of almonds? asked Francis. Have you met with any unfortunate adventure?

asked my wife. In this manner, questions and exclamations succeeded to each other without interval, and with such rapidity as not to leave us time to answer them.

At length when it became a little tranquil I answered them thus: Most happy am I to return to you again, my best beloved, and God be praised! without having encountered any new misfortune. We have even the pleasure of presenting you with many valuable acquisitions; but in the object nearest my heart, the discovering what has become of our ship-companions, or of any individual of them, we have entirely failed.

Since it pleases God that it should be so, said my wife, let us endeavour to be content, and let us be grateful to him for having saved us from their unhappy fate, and for having once more brought us all together: I have laboured this day under an unusual uneasiness about your safety, and imagined a thousand evils that might beset you. The day appeared an age. But now I see you once more safe and well, I trust I shall again return to my tranquillity. But put down your burdens; we will all help you; for though we have not, I assure you, spent the day in idleness, we are less fatigued than you. Quick then, my boys, and help to take the loads from your father and your brother. Now then, sit down and tell us your adventures.

Jack received my gun, Ernest the cocoa-nuts, Francis the gourd-rinds, and my wife my game bag. Fritz distributed the sugar-canes, and put his monkey on the back of Turk, to the great amusement of the children, at the same time begging Ernest to relieve him of his gun. But Ernest, ever careful of his own accommodation, assured him, that the large heavy bowls with which he was loaded, were the most he had strength to carry. His mother, a little too indulgent to his lazy humour, relieved him of them: and thus we proceeded all together to our tent.

Fritz whispered to me, that if Ernest had known what the large heavy bowls were, he would not so readily have parted with them. Then turning to his brother, Why, Ernest, cried he, do you know that these bowls are cocoa-nuts, your dear much-desired cocoa-nuts, and each containing the sweet nice milk you have so much wished to taste?

Are they indeed? are they really and truly cocoa-nuts, brother? Oh! mamma, return them to me quickly; I will carry them if you please, and I can carry the gun too without finding it heavy,

No, no, Ernest, answered his mother, I do not intend to be teased with any more of your heavy sighs and moanings about being fatigued; for I am certain you would begin again before we had gone a hundred paces. Ernest would willingly have asked his mother to give him the cocoa-nuts and take the gun herself, but this he dared not do:—I have only, said he, to get rid of these sticks, and carry the gun in my hand.

I would advise you not to give up the sticks either, said Fritz drily; I know you will be sorry if you do; and for this good reason—the sticks are sugar-canes!

Sugar-canes! cried he. Sugar-canes! exclaimed they all; and, surrounding Fritz, made him give them full instructions on the sublime art of sucking sugar-canes.

My wife also, who had always entertained a high respect for the article of sugar in her household management, was quite astonished, and earnestly entreated we would inform her of all particulars. I instantly complied with her request, giving her every explanation respecting our journey, and our new acquisitions, which I alternately exhibited for her inspection. No one of them afforded her more pleasure than the plates and dishes, because to persons of decent habits they were articles of indispensable necessity. We now adjourned to our little kitchen, and with great delight observed the preparations going forward in it for an excellent repast. On one side of the fire we saw a turnspit, which my wife had contrived by driving two forked pieces of wood into the ground, and placing a long even stick, sharpened at one end across them. By this invention she was enabled to roast different kinds of fish, or other food, with the help of little Francis, who was intrusted with the care of turning it round from time to time. On the occasion of our return she had prepared us the treat of a goose, the fat of which ran down into some oyster shells placed there to serve the purpose of a dripping-pan. And besides a dish of fish, which the little ones had caught, the iron pot was upon the fire, provided with a good soup, the agreeable odour of which increased our appetite. By the side of these most exhilarating preparations, stood one of the casks which we had recovered from the waves, the head of which my wife had knocked out, so that it exposed to our view a cargo of the finest sort of Dutch cheeses contained in round tins. All this display was made to excite the appetite of the two travellers, who had fared but scantily during the day; and I must needs observe, that the whole was very little like such a dinner as one should expect to see on a desert island.

You indeed but barely did yourselves justice, my dear ones, in saying that you had not been idle during our absence, cried I. I see before me what must have cost you considerable labour. I am however a little sorry that you have killed one of our geese so soon we must employ the utmost economy in the use of our poultry, which may be of service in a time of need.

Do not make yourself uneasy on this subject, said my wife; for what you see is not one of our geese, but a kind of wild bird, and is the booty of your son Ernest, who calls him by a singular name, and assures me that it is good to eat.

Yes, father, I believe that the bird which I have caught is a kind of penguin, or we might distinguish him by the surname of *Stupid*. He showed himself to be a bird so destitute, of even the least degree of intelligence, that I killed him with a single blow with my stick.

What is the form of his feet, and of his beak? asked I.

His feet were formed for swimming; in other words, he was what is called web-footed; the beak was long, small, and a little curved downwards: I have preserved his head and neck, that you might examine it yourself; it reminds me exactly of the penguin, described as so stupid a bird in my book of natural history.

You now then perceive, my son, of what use it is to read, and to extend our knowledge, particularly on subjects of natural history and the productions of nature in general; by this study and knowledge, we are enabled to recognise at the moment, the objects which chance throws in our way, whether we have seen them before or not. Tell me now what birds there are with feet formed like those which you have just described and which are so formed to enable the creature to strike the water and prevent himself from sinking.

There are the man of war bird, cormorants, and pelicans, father.

By what mark do you distinguish the kind to which you just now said the *penguin* or *Stupid* belonged?

JOHANN DAVID WYSS

Upon my word, interrupted his mother, just give the answer myself: and it will consist of a petition, that you will take some other time for your catechism on birds: when once you have begun on any particular subject, one never sees the end of it. Now to my mind there is a time for every thing; Ernest killed the bird, and was able to tell his kind; we on our parts shall eat him; what more therefore is necessary? Do you not see that the poor child is thinking all the while of his cocoa-nuts? Let me intercede on his behalf, and prevail upon you to let him have the pleasure of examining and tasting them.

Ah! thank you, my good mother; I shall be very glad if papa will consent.

*Father.*—Well, well, you have my full permission. But first you will be obliged to learn from Fritz the best manner of opening them, so as to preserve the milk: and one word more; I recommend to you not to forget the young monkey, who has no longer his mother's milk for food.

*Jack.*—I cannot prevail upon him to taste a bit; I have offered him every thing we have.

*Father.*—It cannot well be otherwise, for he has not yet learned how to eat; you must feed him with the milk of cocoa-nuts till we can procure something more suitable.

*Jack.*—I will give the poor little creature my share with all my heart.

*Ernest.*—I have however the greatest desire to taste this milk myself, just to know what it is like.

And so have I, said the little Francis.

However, gentlemen, the monkey must live, said Jack a little maliciously.

And we and our children must live too, answered their mother. Come then, the supper is ready, and the cocoa-nuts shall be for the dessert.

We seated ourselves on the ground; my wife had placed each article of the repast in one of our newly manufactured dishes, the neat appearance of which exceeded all our expectations. My sons had not patience to wait, but had broken the cocoa-nuts, and already convinced themselves of their delicious flavour; and then they fell to making spoons with the fragments of the shells. The little monkey, thanks to the kind temper of Jack, had been served the first, and each amused himself with making him suck the corner of his pocket-handkerchief dipped in the milk of the cocoa-nut. He appeared delighted with the treatment he received, and we remarked with satisfaction, that we should most likely be able to preserve him.

The boys were preparing to break some more of the nuts with the hatchet, after having drawn out the milk through the three little holes which I have already observed are found near the stalk of the cocoa-nut, and which are guarded by a soft substance which may easily be pierced. I pronounced the word *halt*, and bade them bring me a saw; the thought had struck me, that by dividing the nuts carefully with this instrument, the two halves when emptied, would remain with the form of tea-cups or basons already made to our hands. Jack, who was on every occasion the most active, brought me the saw. I performed my undertaking in the best manner I could, and in a short time each of us was provided with a convenient receptacle for food. Accordingly my wife put the share of soup which belonged to each, into those basons or vessels. The excellent creature appeared delighted that we should no longer be under the necessity, as before, of scalding our fingers by dipping into the pot; and I firmly believe, that never did the most magnificent service of china occasion half the pleasure to its possessor, as our utensils, manufactured by our own hands from gourds and cocoa-nuts, excited in the kind heart of my wife. Fritz asked me if he might not invite our company to taste his fine champain, which he said would not fail to make us all the merrier. I have not the least objection, answered I, but remember to taste it yourself, before you serve it to your guests.

He ran to draw out the stopple and to taste it. . . . How unfortunate! said he, it is already turned to vinegar.

What is it? vinegar, did you say? exclaimed my wife. How lucky! it will make the most delicious sauce for our bird, mixed with the fat which has fallen from it in roasting, and will be as good a relish as a salad. No sooner said than done. This vinegar produced from cocoa-nut proved a most agreeable corrective of the wild and fishy flavour of the penguin, and without which I am afraid we should have found it not very palatable. The same sauce considerably improved our dish of fish also. Each boasted most of what he himself had been the means of procuring; it was Jack and Francis who had caught the fish in one of the shallows, while Ernest was employed with very little trouble to himself in securing his penguin *the stupid*. My poor wife had herself performed the most difficult task of all, that of rolling the cask of Dutch cheeses into the kitchen, and then knocking out its head. But if it was she who had most exerted herself, it was she also who received the highest commendations; for one and all agreed, that nothing we had tasted since, we left the ship, was half so agreeable to our appetites as this cheese which she served for our dessert.

By the time we had finished our meal, the sun was retiring from our view; and recollecting how quickly the night would fall upon us, we were in the greatest haste to regain our place of rest. My wife had considerately procured for us a tenfold quantity of dry grass, which she had spread in the tent, so that we anticipated with joy the prospect which was now afforded, of stretching our limbs on a substance somewhat approaching to the quality of mattresses, while, the night before, our bodies seemed to touch the ground. Our whole flock of fowls placed themselves as they had done the preceding evening; we said our prayers, and, with an improved serenity of mind, lay down in the tent, taking the young monkey with us, who was become the little favourite of all. Fritz and Jack contended for a short time which should enjoy the honour of his company for the night; and it was at last decided that he should be laid between them; after which, each would have a hand in covering him carefully, that he might not catch cold. We now all lay down upon the grass, in the order of the night before, myself remaining last to fasten the sail-cloth in front of the tent; when, heartily fatigued by the exertions of the day, I as well as the rest soon fell into a profound and refreshing sleep.

But I had not long enjoyed this pleasing state, when I was awakened by the motion of the fowls on the ridge of the tent, and by a violent barking of our vigilant safeguards, the dogs. I rushed out instantly; my wife and Fritz, who had also been alarmed by the noise, followed me: we each took a gun and sallied forth to their assistance. Shall you, my dearest, have the courage to fire, if it should be necessary? said I to my wife.

Most certainly, said she, if, as you say, it should be necessary. I can depend upon myself for daring to do whatever can be the means of preservation to our dear children. At the same time it would perhaps be better that I should leave to you the task of firing, while I can undertake to load your guns, and to hand them to you as fast as you may want them.

Best of all, said I; so let us not lose a moment in examining what enemy it is we have to deal with. Our dogs continued barking with the same violence, and at intervals even howled. We had not proceeded many steps from the tent, when to our great astonishment, we perceived by the light of the moon a terrible combat. At least a dozen of jackalls had surrounded our brave dogs, who defended themselves with an almost unexampled courage. Already the fierce champions had laid three or four of their adversaries on the ground, while those which remained, began a timid kind of moaning, as if imploring pity and forbearance. Meanwhile they did not the less endeavour to entangle and surprise the dogs, thus thrown off their guard, and so secure themselves the advantage. But our watchful combatants were not so easily to be deceived; they took good care not to let the enemy approach them too nearly.

I, for my part, apprehended something much worse than jackalls. We shall soon manage to set these gentlemen at rest, said I. Let us fire both together, my boy; but let us take care how we aim, for fear of killing the dogs; your mother shall give us the word of command; mind how you fire, that you may not miss, and I shall do the same. We fired, and two of the intruders fell instantly dead upon the sands. The others made their escape; but we perceived it was with great difficulty, in consequence, no doubt, of being wounded. Turk and Ponto afterwards pursued them, and put the finishing stroke to what we had begun; and thus the battle ended: but the dogs, true Caribees by nature, made a hearty meal on the flesh of their fallen enemies. Their doing this was a proof of the keen hunger they experienced; for dogs do not readily feed on foxes, and the jackall is a more fierce and mischievous species of the fox, than the animal known by that name in Europe. My wife, seeing that all was now quiet, entreated us to lie down again and finish our night's sleep; but Fritz asked my permission to let him first drag the jackall he had killed, towards the tent, that he might be able to exhibit him the next morning to his brothers. Having obtained my consent, he ran to fetch him, and, with great difficulty, succeeded in his plan, the animal being of the size of a large dog. I however observed to Fritz, that, if Turk and Ponto were still hungry, we ought to give them this last jackall in addition, as a recompense for their courageous behaviour.

We had now done with this affair. The body of the jackall was left on the rock, by the side of the tent, in which were the little sleepers, who had not once awaked during the whole of the scene which had been passing. Having therefore nothing further to prevent us, we lay down by their side till day began to break, and till the cocks, with their shrill morning salutation, awoke us both. The children being still asleep, afforded us an excellent opportunity to consult together respecting the plan we should pursue for the ensuing day.

# V

# RETURN TO THE WRECK

I BROKE A SILENCE OF SOME MOMENTS, WITH OBSERVING TO MY wife, that I could not conquer my alarm at the view of so many cares and such a variety of exertions to be made! In the first place, a journey to the vessel. This is of absolute necessity; at least, if we would not be deprived of the cattle and various other useful things, all of which from moment to moment we ran the risk of losing, by the first approach of a heavy sea. On the other hand, there are so many things to think of, so much exertion to be made, for the comfort of all in this desert spot! What ought we to resolve upon? For example,—is it not, above all, necessary to contrive a better sort of habitation, and also the means of procuring a more secure retreat from wild beasts, also a separate place of accommodation for our provisions? I own I am at a loss what to begin upon first.

All will fall into the right order by degrees, observed my wife; patience and regularity in our plans will go as far as actual labour. I cannot, I confess, help shuddering at the thought of this voyage to the vessel; but if you judge it to be of absolute necessity, it appears to me that it cannot be undertaken too soon. In the mean while, nothing that is immediately under my own care shall stand still, I promise you. Let us not be over anxious about the morrow; sufficient unto the day is the evil thereof. These were the words of the great and true friend of mankind, and let us use so wise a counsel for our own benefit.

I will follow your advice, said I, and without further loss of time. You shall stay here with the three youngest boys; and Fritz, being so much stronger and more intelligent than the others, shall accompany me in the undertaking.

At this moment I started from my bed, crying out loudly and briskly: Get up, children, get up; it is almost light, and we have some important projects for today; it would be a shame to suffer the sun to find us still sleeping, we who are to be the founders of a new colony!

At these words Fritz sprang nimbly out of the tent, while his little brothers began to gape and rub their eyes, to get rid of their sleepiness. Fritz ran to visit his jackall, which during the night had become cold and perfectly stiff. He fixed him upon his legs, and placed him like a sentinel at the entrance of the tent, joyously anticipating the wonder and exclamations of his little brothers at so singular and unexpected an appearance. But no sooner had the dogs caught a sight of him, than they began a horrible barking, and set themselves in motion to fall upon him instantly, thinking he was alive. Fritz had enough to do to restrain them, and succeeded only by dint of coaxing and perseverance.

In the mean time, their barking had awaked the younger boys, and they ran out of the tent, curious to know what could be the occasion. Jack was the first who appeared, with the young monkey on his shoulders; but when the little creature perceived the jackall, he sprang away in terror, and hid himself at the furthest extremity of the grass which composed our bed, and covered himself with it so completely, that scarcely could the tip of his nose be seen.

The children were much surprised at the sight of a yellow-coloured animal standing without motion at the entrance of the tent. Oh heavens! exclaimed Francis, and stepping back a few paces for fear; it is a wolf! No, no, said Jack going near the jackall and taking one of his paws; it is a yellow dog, and he is dead; he does not move at all. It is neither a dog nor a wolf, interrupted Ernest in a consequential tone; do you not see that it is a *golden* fox? Best of all, most learned professor! now exclaimed Fritz. So you can tell an agouti, when you see him, but you cannot tell a jackall; for jackall is the creature you see before you, and I killed him myself in the night!

*Ernest.*—In the night, you say, Fritz! In your sleep, I suppose. . . .

*Fritz.*—No, Mr. Ernest; not in my sleep, as you so good-naturedly suppose, but broad awake and on the watch to protect you from wild beasts! But I cannot wonder at this mistake in one who does not know the difference between a jackall and a *golden* fox!

*Ernest.*—You would not have known it either, if papa had not told you. . . .

Come, come, my lads, I will have no disputes, interrupted I. Fritz, you are to blame in ridiculing your brother for the mistake he made. Ernest, you are also to blame for indulging that little peevishness of yours. But as to the animal, you all are right and all are wrong; for he partakes at once of the nature of the dog, the wolf, and the fox; and for his skin, it is really of a *golden* tint! The boys in an instant became friends; and then followed questions, answers, and wonder in abundance.

And now, my boys, let me remind you, that he who begins the day without first addressing the Almighty, ought to expect neither success nor safety in his undertakings. Let us therefore acquit ourselves of this duty before we engage in any other occupation. Having finished our prayers, the next thing thought of was breakfast; for the appetites of young boys open with their eyes. Today their mother had nothing to give them for their morning meal but some biscuit, which was so hard and dry, that it was with difficulty we could swallow it. Fritz asked for a piece of cheese to eat with it, and Ernest cast some searching looks on the second cask we had drawn out of the sea, and which was standing in our kitchen, to discover whether, as we supposed, it also contained Dutch cheeses. In a minute or two he came up to us, joy sparkling in his eyes. Father, said he, if we had but a little butter spread upon our biscuit, do you not think it would improve it?

That indeed *it* would; but—*if,*—*if;* these never-ending *ifs* are but a poor dependence. For my part, I had rather eat a bit of cheese with my biscuit at once, than think of *ifs,* which bring us so meagre a harvest.

*Ernest.*—Perhaps though, the *ifs* may be found to be worth something, if we were to knock out the head of this cask.

*Father.*—What cask, my boy? and what are you talking of?

*Ernest.*—I am talking of this cask, which is filled with excellent salt butter. I made a little opening in it with a knife; and see, I got out enough of it to spread nicely upon this piece of biscuit.

That glutton instinct of yours for once is of some general use, answered I; and justice requires that I should also commend, with moderation, the excellence of your nose. But now let us profit by the event. Who will have some butter on their biscuits? The boys surrounded the cask in a moment, while I was in some perplexity as to the safest and most speedy method of getting out its contents. Fritz proposed taking off the topmost hoop, by which means one of the ends could be got out. But this I objected to, observing, that we should be careful not to loosen the staves, as the great heat of the sun would not fail to melt the butter, which would run out, and thus be wasted. The idea occurred to me, that I would make a hole in the bottom of the cask, sufficiently large to take out a small quantity of butter at a time; and I immediately set about manufacturing a little wooden shovel, to use it for the purpose. All this succeeded vastly well, and we sat down to breakfast, some biscuits and a cocoa-nut shell full of salt butter being placed upon the ground, round which we all assembled, and none of us failing from time to time to wish for a fairy's wand, to enable us to add a little milk from the cow, or from some cocoa-nuts, to quench our thirst. We however toasted our biscuit, and while it was hot, applied the butter, and contrived, without the fairy's wand, to make a hearty breakfast.

Our dogs allowed us to finish our meal in tranquillity. They were sleeping by our side; but I remarked, that their late encounter with the jackalls had not concluded without their receiving several wounds, which I now, for the first time, observed in various parts of their body, and principally round their necks. Fearing the heat might bring on inflammation, I desired Jack, the valiant, to wash a small quantity of the butter thoroughly in fresh water, and then to anoint the wounds with it while they continued sleeping. This he effected with much skill and tenderness. The dogs awoke, but did not attempt the least resistance, seeming to be sensible of the benefit he was conferring on them; they themselves assisted the cure, by frequently licking the parts; so that in a few days they were as well as before.

One of the things we must not forget to look for in the vessel, said Fritz, is a spiked collar or two for our dogs, as a protection to them, should they again be called upon to defend themselves from wild beasts, which I fear it is too probable will be the case.

Oh! says Jack, I can make some spiked collars, if my mother will give me a little help.

That I will most readily, my boy; for I should like to see what new fancy has come into your head, cried mamma.

Yes, yes, pursued I, as many new inventions as you please; you cannot better employ your time; and if you produce something useful, you will be rewarded with the commendations of all. But now we must think of setting ourselves to some occasion. You, Mr. Fritz, who, from your superior age and discretion, enjoy the high honour of being my privy counsellor, must make haste and get yourself ready, and we will undertake to-day our voyage to the vessel, to save and bring away whatever may be passible. You younger boys will remain here, under the wing of your kind mother; I hope I need not mention that I rely on your perfect obedience to her will, and general good behaviour.

While Fritz was getting the boat ready, I looked about for a pole, and put a piece of white linen to the end of it; this I drove into the ground, in a place where it would be visible from the vessel; and I concerted with my wife, that in case of any accident that should require my immediate presence, they should take down the pole and fire a gun three times as a signal of distress, in consequence of which I would immediately return. But I gave her notice, that there being so many things to accomplish on board the vessel, it was very probable that we should not be able to return the same day; in which case I, on my part, also promised to make them signals. My wife had the courage and good sense to consent to my plan. Though she was well aware that it could not but be dangerous to pass a night alone with the children, without my protection, she yet preferred the risk, to that of my returning late from the vessel. She, however, extorted from me a promise that we should pass the night in our tubs, and not on board the ship. We took nothing with us but our guns and a recruit of powder and shot, relying that we should find plenty of provisions on board; yet I did not refuse to indulge Fritz in the wish he expressed to let him take the young monkey, he feeling the most eager impatience to see how the young creature would like some milk from the cow or from a goat.

We embarked in silence, casting our anxious looks on the beloved objects we were quitting. Fritz rowed steadily, and I did my best to second his endeavours, by rowing from time to time, on my part, with the oar which served me for a rudder. When we had reached to a considerable distance, I remarked, that besides the opening by which we had the first time made land, there was another that formed the mouth of the river, and the current of which was visible a good way into the sea.

To take advantage of this current, and to husband our strength by means of it, was my first thought and my first care. Little as I knew of the management of sea affairs, I however succeeded in keeping our boat in the direction in which it ran, by which means we were drawn gently on, till it had conducted us to within a short distance of the vessel, without our having any other trouble than that of keeping in the same line: at length, in consequence of the gradual diminution of the force of the current, we were again obliged to have recourse to our oars; but our arms having now rested for some time, we were ready for new exertions. A little afterwards we found ourselves safely arrived at the cleft of the vessel, and fastened our boat securely to one of its timbers.

Scarcely had we got out of the boat, than Fritz proceeded with his young monkey on his arm to the main deck, where he found all the animals we had left on board assembled. I followed him with great readiness, well pleased to observe the generous impatience he betrayed, to relieve the wants of the poor abandoned creatures, who, one and all, now saluted us by the cry or the sounds natural to its species! It was not so much the want of food, as the desire of seeing once more their accustomed human companions, which occasioned them to manifest their joy in this manner, for they had a portion of the food and water we had left them, still remaining. The first thing we did was to put the young monkey to one of the goats, that he might suck; and this he did with such evident pleasure and such odd grimaces, that he afforded us much amusement.—We next examined the food and water of the other animals, taking away what was half spoiled, and adding a fresh supply, that no anxiety on their account might afterwards interrupt our enterprise. Nor did we neglect the care of renewing our strength by a plentiful repast.

While we were seated, and appeasing the calls of hunger, Fritz and I consulted what should be our first occupation;

when to my great surprise, the advice he gave was that we should immediately contrive a sail for our boat. In the name of Heaven, cried I, what makes you think of such a thing at so critical a moment, and when we have so many other things of indispensable necessity to arrange? We will think of a sail when we have leisure, with all my heart, for it is an affair that will take a considerable time to accomplish. In reality, I experienced great uneasiness at the thought of passing the night at a distance from my family.

All you say is true, father, said Fritz; but let me confess the truth, which is that I found it very difficult to perform the task of rowing for so long a time, though I assure you I did my best, and did not spare my strength. I observed that, though the wind blew strong in my face, the current nevertheless carried us on. Now, as we cannot be benefitted on our return by the current, I was thinking that we might make the wind supply its place. Our boat will be very heavy when we have loaded it with all the useful things we mean to take away, and I am afraid I shall not be strong enough to row to land. Now do you not think that a sail would be a good thing just now?

Ah ha, Mr. Fritz! So you wish to spare yourself a little trouble, do you? But to speak seriously, I perceive much good sense in your argument, and feel obliged to my privy counsellor for his good advice. The best thing we can do is, to take care and not overload the boat, and thus avoid the danger of sinking, or of being obliged to throw some of our stores over-board. We will, however, set to work upon your sail, which, though it save your labour in rowing, will be at least a little troublesome at present. But come, let us look about for what we want.

I assisted Fritz to carry a pole strong enough to serve for a mast, and another not so thick for a sail-yard. I directed him to make a hole in a plank with a chisel, large enough for the mast to stand upright in it. I then went to the sail-chamber, and cut off from an ample piece of sail-cloth enough to make a triangular sail: in the edges I made holes, and passed cords through them. I then sought for a pulley, that I might fasten it to the top of the mast, and thus be enabled to raise and lower my sail at pleasure. Thus prepared, I hastened to join Fritz, who was earnestly working at the mast. As soon as he had done, we placed the plank that he had perforated, upon the fourth of our tubs, and made it fast. The pulley was suspended from a ring at the top of the mast, and the cord, attached to the sharpest angle of the sail, was passed through it. The sail formed a right-angle triangle, one side of which touched the mast, and was fastened to it. The shortest side was also fastened with cords to a pole, stretching from the mast beyond the circumference of our bark, and of which one end was fastened to the mast, and the other, by means of a cord, to the helm, in such a manner that I could, from my position, either weather the sail, or let it go altogether. In the foremost and hindmost bench of our little bark, we made holes with a piercer, and passed cords through them, by means of which we could guide the sail from the right to the left side of us, and back again, without being obliged to turn the boat entirely round.

While I was thus occupied, Fritz had been taking observations through a telescope of what was passing on land, and which we had already done several times. He imparted the agreeable tidings that all was still well with our dear family. He had distinguished his

JOHANN DAVID WYSS

mother walking tranquilly along the shore. He soon after brought me a small streamer, which he had cut from a piece of linen, and which he entreated me to tie to the extremity of the mast, and he appeared as much delighted with the streamer as with the sail itself. He gave to our machine the name of *The Deliverance*; and in speaking of it, instead of calling it a *boat*, it was now always denominated *the little vessel*. I could not withhold a smile at vanity like this, in such a situation as ours; it gave me too an opportunity of observing the operation of this prominent feature of human nature, in a lad of fourteen years of age. I myself took great pleasure in seeing the little streamer floating in the air, and in the respectable appearance of our machine altogether.

But now, father, said Fritz, looking kindly on me as he spoke, as you have eased me of the labour of rowing, it is my turn to take care of you. I am thinking about making you a better-contrived rudder; one that would enable you to steer the boat both with greater ease and greater safety. Your thought would be a very good one, said I, but that I am unwilling to lose the advantage of being able to proceed this way and that, without being obliged to veer. I shall therefore fix our oars in such a manner as to enable me to steer the raft from either end. Accordingly, I fixed bits of wood to the stem and stern of the machine, in the nature of grooves, which were calculated to spare us a great deal of trouble.

During these exertions the day became far advanced, and I perceived that we should be obliged to pass the night in our tubs, without having begun our task of emptying the vessel. We had promised our family to hoist a flag as a signal of our intention to pass the night from home, and we decided that our streamer was precisely the thing we wanted for this purpose.

We employed the rest of the day in emptying the tubs of the useless ballast of stones, and putting in their place what would be of service, such as nails, pieces of cloth, and different kinds of utensils, etc. etc. The Vandals themselves could not have made a more complete pillage than we had done. The prospect we seemed to have of an entire solitude, made us devote our principal attention to securing as much powder and shot as might fall in our way, that we might thus secure the means of catching animals for food, and of defending ourselves against wild beasts to the latest moment possible. Utensils for every kind of workmanship, of which there was a large provision in the ship, were also objects of incalculable value to us. The vessel, which was now a wreck, had been sent out as a preparation for the establishment of a colony in the South Seas, and for that reason had been provided with a variety of stores not commonly included in the loading of a ship. Among the rest, care had been taken to have on board considerable numbers of European cattle; but so long a voyage had proved unfavourable to the oxen and the horses, the greatest part of which had died, and the others were in so bad a condition that it had been found necessary to destroy them. The quantity of useful things which presented themselves in the store chambers, made it difficult for me to select among them, and I much regretted that circumstances compelled me to leave some of them behind. Fritz, however, already meditated a second visit; but we took good care not to lose the present occasion for securing knives and forks and spoons, and a complete assortment of kitchen utensils. In the captain's cabin we found some services of silver, dishes and plates of high-wrought metal, and a little chest filled with bottles of many sorts of excellent wine. Each of these articles we put into

PLATE 5
"The Vandals themselves could not have made a more
complete pillage than we had done."

our boat. We next descended to the kitchen, which we stripped of gridirons, kettles, pots of all kinds, a small roasting-jack, etc. Our last prize was a chest of choice eatables, intended for the table of the officers, containing Westphalia hams, Bologna sausages, and other savoury food. I took good care not to forget some little sacks of maize, of wheat, and other grain, and some potatoes. We next added such implements for husbandry as we could find;—shovels, hoes, spades, rakes, harrows, etc. etc. Fritz reminded me that we had found sleeping on the ground both cold and hard, and prevailed upon me to increase our cargo by some hammocks, and a certain number of blankets: and as guns had hitherto been the source of his pleasures, he added such as he could find of a particular costliness or structure, together with some sabres and clasp knives. The last articles we took, were a barrel of sulphur, a quantity of ropes, some small string, and a large roll of sail-cloth. The vessel appeared to us to be in so wretched a condition, that the coming on of the least tempest must make her go to pieces. It was then quite uncertain whether we should be able to approach her any more.

Our cargo was so considerable, that the tubs were filled to the very brim, and no inch of the boat's room was lost. The first and last of the tubs were reserved for Fritz and me to seat ourselves in and row the boat, which sunk so low in the water, that, if the sea had been otherwise than quite calm, we should have been obliged to ease her of some of the loading: we, however, used the precaution of putting on our swimming-jackets, for fear of any misfortune.

It will easily be imagined that every moment of the day had been laboriously employed. Night suddenly surprised us, and it was no longer possible to form a hope of returning to our family the same evening. A large blazing fire on the shore soon after greeted our sight,—the signal we had agreed upon for assuring us that all was well, and to bid us close our eyes in peace. We returned the compliment by tying four lanterns with lights in them to our mast-head. This was answered on their part, according to agreement, by the firing of two guns; so that both parties had reason to be satisfied and easy.

After offering up our earnest prayers for the safety and happiness of all, yet not without some apprehension for the night, we resigned ourselves to sleep in our tubs, which, it must be confessed, did not afford us a very enviable place of rest: they were, however, safer than the vessel, and more convenient for guarding our heavily loaded machine. At the least cracking of the vessel, we might cut the rope in an instant, and get out to sea. Our night, thank God, passed tranquilly enough: my boy Fritz slept as soundly as if he had been in a bed; while I, notwithstanding my fatigue, could neither close my eyes, or keep them from the direction of the shore, perpetually haunted by the recollection of the nocturnal visit of the jackalls, some of whose race I feared might come and enter the tent. I had, however, great reliance that my valiant dogs would do their duty, and was thankful to Heaven for having enabled us to preserve so good a protection.

# VI

# A TROOP OF ANIMALS IN CORK JACKETS

ARLY THE NEXT MORNING, THOUGH IT WAS SCARCELY LIGHT enough to distinguish the coast, I was already on the deck of the vessel, endeavouring to gain a sight of the beloved inhabitants of the tent through a spying-glass. Fritz speedily prepared a good substantial breakfast of biscuit and ham; but before we sat down to this refreshment, we recollected that in the captain's cabin we had seen a telescope of a much superior size and power, and we hastily conveyed it upon the deck. While this was doing, the brightness of the day had succeeded to the imperfect light of an earlier hour. I eagerly fixed my eye to the glass, and discovered my wife coming out of the tent and looking attentively towards the vessel, and we at the same moment perceived the motion of the flag upon the shore. A load of care and solicitude was thus taken from my heart; for now I had obtained the certainty that the beloved beings I had left were all in good health, and had escaped the dangers of the night. Fritz, said I to my boy, I thought this morning that it would be impossible for me to remain another moment on board the vessel, without returning to see what was passing at the tent; but now that I have had a sight of your mother, and an assurance of their being well and safe, my compassion is awakened for the poor creatures on board who are in so wretched a condition, and every hour in danger of destruction: a great object of my anxiety now, is to endeavour to save the lives of some of them at least, and to take them with us to the shore.

Would it be impossible to construct a raft, to get them all upon it, and in this way afford them a conveyance? said Fritz.

But recollect, my boy, what a difficulty we should find in completing such a raft, and that a greater still would be to induce a cow, an ass, and a sow, either to get upon a raft, or, when there, to remain motionless and quiet. The sheep and goats one might perhaps find means to remove, they being of a more docile temper; but for the larger animals, I am at a loss how to proceed. Do you consider of it, and tell me what thoughts occur to your young and active imagination.

My advice, father, is, to tie a long rope round the sow's neck, and throw her without ceremony into the sea: her immense weight will be sure to sustain her above water; and we can easily get hold of the other end of the rope and draw her after the boat.

Your idea is excellent, my boy: but unfortunately it cannot be applied to any of the animals except the pig; and I confess, she is the one I care the least about preserving.

Then here is another idea, father: let us tie a swimming-jacket round the body of each animal, and contrive to throw one and all into the water; you will see that they will swim like fish, and we can draw them after us in the same manner.

Right, very right, my boy; your invention is admirable: let us therefore not lose a moment in making the experiment.

We accordingly hastened to the execution of our design: we fixed on a jacket to one of the lambs, and threw it into the sea; and full of fear, of hope, and anxious curiosity, I followed the poor animal with my eyes. He sunk at first under water, and I thought he was drowned; but he soon re-appeared, shaking the water from his head, and in a few seconds we perceived that he had learned completely the art of swimming. After another interval, we observed that he appeared fatigued, gave up his efforts, and suffered himself without resistance to be borne along by the course of the water, which conducted and sustained him to our complete satisfaction. Victory! exclaimed I, hugging my boy with delight: these useful animals are all our own; let us not lose a moment in adopting the same measures with those that remain: but take care not to lose our little lamb. Fritz now would have jumped eagerly into the water to follow the poor creature, who was still floating safely on the surface; but I stopped him till I had seen him tie on one of the swimming-jackets, and then I suffered him to go. He took with him a rope, first making a slip knot in it, and, soon overtaking the lamb, threw it round his neck, and drew him back to our boat; and then, to his great content, drew him out of the water.

We then went and looked out four small casks, such as had been used for keeping the fresh water for the vessel. I first emptied them of their contents, and then carefully closed them again; next I bound them together with a large piece of sail-cloth, the two ends of which I nailed to each. I strengthened this with a second piece of sail-cloth, and this machine I destined to support the cow and the ass, two casks to each, the animal being placed in the middle with a cask on either side. The weight of the animal pressed down the sail-cloth, and would have brought the casks into close contact on each side, but that I took care to insert a wisp of hay or straw to prevent injurious friction or pressure. I added a thong of leather, stretching from the casks across the breast and haunches of the animal, to make the whole secure; and thus in less than an hour, both my cow and my ass were equipped for swimming.

It was next the turn of the smaller animals: of these, the sow gave us the most trouble; we were first obliged to put her on a muzzle to prevent her biting; and this being done, we tied a large piece of cork under her body The sheep and goats were more accommodating, and we had soon accoutred them for the expedition. And now we had succeeded in assembling our whole company on the deck, in readiness for the voyage: we tied a cord to either the horns or the neck of each animal, and to the other end of the cord a piece of wood similar to the mode used for marking nets, that it might be easy for us to take hold of the ropes, and so draw the animal to us if it should be necessary. We struck away some more of the shattered pieces of wood from the side of the vessel, which only served to encumber the cleft by which we had entered, and were again to pass when we should have completed our last work of throwing the animals into the sea. We began our experiment with the ass, by conducting him as near as possible to the brink of the vessel, and then suddenly shoving him off. He fell into the water, and for a moment disappeared; but we soon saw him rise, and in the action of swimming between his two barrels, with a grace which really merited our commendation.

Next came the cow's turn; and as she was infinitely more valuable than the ass, my fears increased in due proportion.

The ass had swum so courageously, that he was already at a considerable distance from the vessel, so that there was sufficient room for our experiment on the cow. We had more difficulty in pushing her overboard, but she reached the water in as much safety as the ass had done before; she did not sink so low in it, and was no less perfectly sustained by the empty barrels, and she made her way on the surface with gravity, and, if I may so express it, a sort of dignified composure. According to this method we proceeded with our whole troop, throwing them one by one into the water, where by and by they appeared in a group floating at their ease, and seemingly well content, at a short distance from the vessel. The sow was the only exception; she became quite furious, set up a loud squalling, and struggled with so much violence in the water, that she was carried to a considerable distance, but fortunately in a direction towards the landing place we had in view. We had now not a moment to lose. Our last act was to put on our cork-jackets; and then we descended without accident through the cleft, took our station in the boat, and were soon out to sea, surrounded by our troop of quadrupeds. We carefully took up from the water, each of the floating bits of wood which we had fastened to the ropes round the animals, and thus drew them all after us by fastening the bits of timber to the boat. When every thing was adjusted, and our company in order, we hoisted our sail, which soon filling with a favourable wind conducted us and our escort safe to the land.

We now perceived how impossible it would have been for us to have succeeded in our enterprise without the assistance of a sail; for the weight of so many animals sunk the boat so low in the water, that all our exertions to row to such a distance would have been ineffectual; while by means of the sail, and the improvement I had invented for the steering, she proceeded completely to our satisfaction, bearing in her train our suite of animals, and producing altogether the most singular effect. Proud of the success of so extraordinary a feat, we were in high spirits, and seated ourselves in the tubs, where we made an excellent dinner. Fritz amused himself with the monkey, while I was wholly occupied in thinking of those I had left on land, and of whom I now tried to take a view through my telescope. My last act on board the vessel had been to take one look more at those beloved beings, and I perceived my wife and the three boys all in motion, and seeming to be setting out on some excursion; but it was in vain that I endeavoured, by any thing I saw, to conjecture what their plan might be. I therefore seized the first moment of quiet to make another trial with my glass, when a sudden exclamation from Fritz filled me with alarm. O heavens! cried he, we are lost! a fish of an enormous size is coming up to the boat. And why lost? said I half angry, yet half partaking of his fright. Be ready with your gun in an instant, and the moment he is close upon us, let us both fire upon him at the same instant. Our guns were each loaded with two balls, and we got up from our tubs to give the intruder a hearty reception. He had nearly reached the boat, and with the rapidity of lightning had seized the foremost sheep: at this instant Fritz aimed his fire so skilfully, that the balls were lodged in the head of the monster, which was an enormous shark. The fish half turned himself round in the water and hurried off to sea, leaving us to observe the lustrous smoothness of his belly, and that as he proceeded, he stained the water red, which convinced us he had been severely wounded. I determined to have the best of our guns at hand the rest of the way, lest we should be again attacked by the same fish, or another his species.

Fritz had great reason to be proud of the achievement of having forced the shark to retreat; whilst I on my part rather felt surprise; for I had always understood that this kind of sea-monster was not easily to be frightened from his purpose, and that the heaviest load of shot was rarely known to do him any injury, the creature being extremely voracious of his prey, and his skin so hard, as to present an extraordinary degree of resistance to all attacks of this kind. For this time, however, the animal left us in tranquillity; I resumed the rudder; and as the wind drove us straight towards the bay, I took down the sail, and continued rowing till we reached a convenient spot for our cattle to land. I then untied the end of the cords, which had been fastened to the boat, and they stepped contentedly on shore. Our voyage thus happily concluded, we followed their example.

I had already been surprised and uneasy at finding none of my family looking out for us on the shore, and was at a loss to conjecture on what they could be occupied to prevent them: we could not, however, set out in search of them, till we had disen-cumbered our animals of their swimming apparatus. Scarcely had we entered upon this employment, when I was agreeably relieved by the exclamations and joyful sounds which reached our ears, and filled our hearts with rapture. It was my wife and the young-est boys who uttered them, the latter of whom were soon close up to us, and their mother followed not many steps behind; each and all of them in excellent health, and eager for our salutations. When the first burst of happiness at meeting had subsided, we all sat down on the grass, and I began to give them an account of our occupations is the vessel, of our voyage, and of all our different plans, and their success, in the order in which they occurred. My wife could find no words to express her surprise and satisfaction at seeing so many useful animals round us, and her language respecting them had such a vein of affectionate simplicity, as greatly to increase the gratification it could not otherwise but inspire. I had been ransacking my poor brains, said she, every moment of your absence, to conceive some means by which you might succeed in protecting the poor animals; but I could fix on none that seemed to promise the least success.

Yes, said Fritz a little consequentially, for this once the privy-counsellor has tried his talents at invention.

This indeed is very true, replied I; in all humility have I to confess, that to Fritz alone all praise belongs, and that to his sagacity it is, that we are indebted for our success. His mother could not refrain from giving him a hearty kiss. Our gratitude is due to both said she; for both have laboured to give us the possession of this troop of animals, an acquisition beyond any other agreeable and serviceable to us, in the situation in which it has pleased Providence to place us.

Ha ha! cried little Francis, what is that I see in your boat? Look, mamma, there is a sail and a new flag floating about in the air. How pretty they are! I like the sail and the flag much better than the ass and the cow.

Little blockhead! said his mother, you will change your mind when I give you every morning a cocoa-nut full of delicious milk.

Ernest and Jack now ran also to the boat, and bestowed no less admiration than Francis had done upon the mast, the sail, and the flag, desiring their brother to explain to them how all the things they saw had been effected, and what he had himself done towards them. In the mean time we began to unpack our cargo, which was by no means a trifling undertaking; while Jack, who had no fancy for the occupation, stole aside and amused himself with the animals, took off the jackets from the sheep and goats, bursting from time to time into shouts of laughter at the ridiculous figure of the ass, who stood before them adorned with his two casks and his swimming apparatus, and braying loud enough to make us deaf. Jack tried a long time to disengage the ass from his incumbrances, but constantly found difficulties he knew not how to overcome; till at last, tired out with so many fruitless endeavours, and longing to be in some way a more effectual actor in the scene, he got upon the ass's back between the casks, and kicked and stirred so violently against his sides, that he at last succeeded in causing the animal to advance to the place where we were all assembled.

We were much amused, and laughed heartily at the sight of so singular an equipage; when, as I was assisting him to get down from the ass's back, I perceived, with surprise, that he had round his waist a belt of metal covered with yellow skin, in which were fixed a pair of pistols.

In the name of Heaven! exclaimed I, where did you procure this curious costume, which gives you the look of a smuggler?

From my own manufactory, replied he; and if you cast your eyes upon the dogs, you will see more of my specimens.

Accordingly I looked at them, and perceived that each had on a collar similar to the belt round Jack's waist, with, however, the exception of the collars being armed with a number of nails, the points of which were outwards, and exhibited a most formidable appearance. And is it you, Mr. Jack, cried I, who have invented and executed these collars and your belt?

Yes, father, they are indeed my invention, with a little of mamma's assistance where ever it was necessary to use the needle.

But where did you get the metal and the thread and the needle?

Fritz's jackall furnished the first, answered my wife; and as to the last, a good mother of a family is always provided with them. You men think only of more serious concerns, while those of less importance fall to the care of a wife, and are frequently more useful. Then have I not an enchanted bag, from which I draw out such articles as I stand in need of? So, if you have a particular fancy for any thing, you have only to acquaint me with it. I tenderly embraced my wife, to express my thanks for this effort to amuse by so agreeable a raillery, and Jack too came in for his share both of the caresses and our most hearty commendations. But Fritz was somewhat angry and discontented on finding that Jack had taken upon him to dispose of his jackall, and to cut his beautiful skin into slices. He, however, concealed his ill humour as well as he could; but, as he stood quite near to his brother, he called out suddenly, holding his nose as he spoke: What a filthy smell! it is enough to give me the plague! Does it perchance proceed from you, Mr. Currier? Is this the perfume we may expect from your manufactory? It is rather yours than mine, replied Jack in a resentful tone; for it was your jackall which you hung up in the sun to dry.

And which would have been dried in a whole skin, if it had not pleased your sublime fancy to cut it to pieces, instead of leaving me the power to do what I please with my own booty.

Son Fritz, said I in a somewhat angry tone, this is not generous on your part. Of what importance is it, whether it was your brother or yourself who cut up the skin of the jackall, if by so doing it has contributed to our use? My dear children, we are here in this desert island, in just such a situation as that of our first parents when they were driven out of the garden of Eden; it was still in their power to enjoy happiness in the fertile land in which God permitted them to live; and this happiness was to proceed from their obedience, from the work of their hands, and the sweat of their brow: a thousand and a thousand blessings were granted for their use, but they suffered the passions of jealousy, envy, and hatred to take root in their bosoms; Cain killed his brother Abel, and thus plunged his unhappy parents into the deepest affliction, so that he and his race were cursed by God. This is the horrid crime to which the habit of disputing may conduct. Let us then avoid such an evil, let us share one with the other in every benefit bestowed upon us, and from this moment may the words *yours* and *mine* be banished from our happy circle! What is discovered or procured by one of you, should be equally for the service of all, and belong to all, without distinction. It is quite certain, Jack, that the belt round your waist, not being dry, has an offensive smell; the pleasure of wearing what you had ingeniously contrived, makes you willing to bear with the inconvenience: but we should never make our own pleasure the pain of another. I therefore desire that you will take it off and place it in the sun to dry, and take care that it does not shrink during the operation; and then you can join your brothers, and assist them to throw the jackall into the sea.

Fritz's ill humour was already over; but Jack, whose temper was less docile, persisted in keeping on the belt, assuming an air of importance which was meant to express that he was not disposed to yield. His brothers however continued their warfare, by pretending to avoid him, and crying out—What a smell! What a smell! till at length Jack, tired with the part he had been acting, suddenly stripped off the belt, and ran to assist his brothers in dragging the dead jackall to the sea, where he no longer occasioned us any inconvenience.

Perceiving that no preparations were making for supper, I ordered Fritz to bring us the Westphalia ham, for that I was hungry. The eyes of all were now fixed upon me with astonishment, for every one believed that I could only be in jest; when Fritz returned, jumping and displaying with exultation a large and excellent ham, which we had begun to cut in the morning. A ham! cried one and all; a ham! and ready drest! What a nice supper we shall have! said they, clapping their hands to give a hearty welcome to the bearer of so fine a treat.—It comes quite in the nick of time too, interrupted I; for, to judge by appearances, a certain careful steward I could name, seems to have intended to send us supperless to bed, little thinking, I suppose, that a long voyage by water is apt to increase the appetite.

I will tell you presently, replied my wife, what it was that prevented me from providing a supper for you all at an early hour: your ham, however, makes you ample amends; and I have something in my hand with which I shall make a pretty side dish; in the twinkling of an eye you shall see it make its entrance. She now showed us about a dozen of turtle's eggs, and then hurried away to make an omelette of some of them.

Oh! look, papa, said Ernest, if they are not the very same sort which Robinson Crusoe found in his island! See, they are like white balls, covered with a skin like wetted parchment! We found them upon the sands along the shore.

Your account is perfectly just, my dear boy, said I: by what means did you make so useful a discovery? Oh, that is a part of our history, interrupted my wife; for I also have a history to relate, when you will be so good as to listen to it.

Hasten then, my love, and get your pretty side-dish ready, and we will have the history for the dessert. In the mean while I will relieve the cow and the ass from the encumbrance of their sea accoutrements, for I am sure they will be glad to get rid of them. Come along, boys, and give me your help. I got up, and they all followed me gaily to the shore, where the animals had remained. We were not long in effecting our purpose with the cow and the ass, who were both animals of a quiet and kind temper; but when it was the turn of the grunting sow, our success was neither so easy nor so certain; we had no sooner untied the rope than she escaped from us, and with so much rapidity that none of us could get hold of her. The idea occurred to Ernest of sending the two dogs after her, who caught her by the ears and brought her back, while we were half deafened with the hideous noise she made; but at length she suffered us to take off her cork jacket quietly enough. We now laid the swimming apparatus across the ass's back, and returned to the kitchen; our slothful Ernest being highly delighted at finding that he was likely in future to have our loads carried for us by a servant.

In the mean while, my kind wife had prepared the omelette, and spread a tablecloth on the end of the cask of butter, upon which she had placed some of the plates and silver spoons we had brought from the ship. The ham was in the middle, and the omelette and the cheese opposite to each other; and all together made a figure not to be despised by the inhabitants of a desert island. By and by the two dogs, the fowls, the pigeons, the sheep, and the goats, had all assembled round us, which gave us something like, the air of sovereigns of the country. It did not please the geese and ducks to add themselves to the number of these our curious-looking subjects: they seemed to prefer their natural element, and confined themselves to a marshy swamp, where they found a kind of little crabs in great abundance: these animals furnished a delicious food for them, and relieved us of the care of providing for their support.

When we had finished our repast, I bade Fritz present our company with a bottle of Canary wine, which we had brought from the captain's cabin, and I then desired my wife would indulge us with the promised history. I first requested her to taste our wine, and then she began her narrative, as will be seen in the ensuing.

# VII

# SECOND JOURNEY OF DISCOVERY PERFORMED BY THE MOTHER OF THE FAMILY

Y OU PRETEND, SAID MY WIFE WITH A LITTLE MALICIOUS SMILE, to be curious about my history, and for all that, you have not let me speak a single word in all this time; but the longer a torrent is pent up, and interrupted in its course, the longer it flows when once let loose. Now then, that you will have the condescension to attend, I shall give vent to a certain little movement of vanity, which is fluttering at my heart. Not, however, to intrude too long upon your patience, we will skip the first day of your absence, in the course of which, nothing new took place, except my anxiety on your account, which confined me for the most part to the spot from whence you embarked, and from which I could see the vessel. But this morning, after the gratifying sight of the signal you had promised, and having set up mine in return, I looked about, before the boys were up, in hopes to find a shady place, in which I might sit down and rest myself: but not an inch of ground appeared of this description, for there is not a single tree in any direction near us, and the only bit of shade which presented itself, was behind our tent. This occasioned me to reflect a little seriously on our situation. It will be impossible, said I to myself, to remain in this place, scorched, during the whole of the day, by the burning heat of the sun, without any other shelter than a miserable tent, under which the heat is even more excessive than without. Courage then! said I, my husband and my eldest son are at this moment actively employed in the vessel for the general good; why should not I, on my part, be active and enterprising also? why not undertake, with my youngest sons, to do something that shall add some one comfort to our existence? I will pass over with them to the other side of the river, and with my own eyes examine the country respecting which my husband and Fritz have related such wonders. I will try to find out some well shaded agreeable spot, in which we may all be settled. I now cast another look towards the vessel; but perceiving no sign of your return, I determined to share a flight dinner with the boys, and to set out resolutely on a journey of discovery for a habitation which might afford us more convenience, and a better shelter from the sun.

In the course of the morning, Jack had slipped away to the side of the tent where Fritz had hung his jackall, and with his knife, which he sharpened from time to time upon the rock, he cut some long slips of skin, lengthways, from the back of the animal, and afterwards set about cleaning them with great attention. Ernest discovered him employed in this uncleanly occupation; and as he is, as we all know, a little delicate and afraid to soil his fingers, he not only refused to give Jack any assistance, but thought fit to sneer a little at the currier-like trade which he had engaged in. Jack, who, as we also know, has not the most patient temper in the world, raised his hand to give him a little cuff. Ernest made his escape, more alarmed, I believe, by Jack's dirty hands, than by the expected blow; while I, for my part, ran to set them right, and to give a mother's reproof to both. Jack persisted that he had a justification full and undeniable, in the great usefulness of the said dirty work; for, observed he, it is intended to make some collars, which I shall afterwards arm with spikes, and the dogs will wear them for our defence. I saw in an instant that Ernest had been the aggressor, and on him fell the reproof; I represented how little a squeamish delicacy like his, suited with the difficulties of our situation, in which one and all were called upon to assist in any employment that should promise to contribute to the general good.

Jack returned to his strips of skin, the cleaning of which he completed very cleverly. When he had finished this part of his undertaking, he looked out from the chest of nails, those that were longest, and which had the largest and flattest heads: these he stuck through the whole of the bit of skin intended for the collar, at small distances. He next cut a strip of sail-cloth the same breadth as the leather, and, laying it along on the heads of the nails, politely proposed to me the agreeable occupation of sewing them together, to prevent the head of the nails from injuring the dogs. I begged leave to be excused; but observing afterwards the good-humour with which he set about trying to sew them for himself, and that with all his good-will it was too difficult for a boy to execute, I conquered my repugnance to the wild fetid smell of the leather, and rewarded him by completing the job myself;—a mother seldom refuses the sacrifice of a little personal convenience, if it can afford delight to a virtuous child.

But now having yielded the first time, I found I had made myself liable to a further claim on my good-nature. The next thing was a belt for himself, which he had manufactured of the same materials, and was impatient to see completed,—it being intended to contain his two pistols. We shall see, said he, strutting about as he spoke, if the jackalls will dare to attack us now. But, my dear Jack, you do not foresee what will happen;—a piece of skin not entirely dry, is always liable to shrink when exposed to the heat. So, after all the disagreeable task you have imposed upon me, you will not be able to make use of it. My little workman, as I said this, struck his forehead, and betrayed other marks of impatience. What you say is true, said he, and I had not well considered; but I know of an effectual remedy. He then took a hammer and some nails, and stretched his strips of leather on a plank, which he then laid in the sun to dry quickly, thus preventing the possibility of their shrinking. I applauded his invention, and promised him I would not fail to give you a full account of his proceedings.

I next assembled them all three round me, and informed them of my plans for an excursion, and you may believe I heard nothing like a dissenting voice. They lost not a moment in preparing for our departure; they examined their arms, their game-bags, looked out the best clasp knives, and cheerfully undertook to carry the provision bags; while I, for my share, was loaded with a large flask of water and a hatchet, for which I thought it likely we might find a use. I also took the light gun which belongs to Ernest, and gave him in return a carbine, which might be loaded with several balls at once. We took some refreshment and then sallied forth, attended by the two dogs for an escort. Turk, who had already accompanied you in the direction I intended to take, seemed well aware that he knew the way, and proceeded at the head of the party in quality of a conductor. We arrived at the place at which you had crossed the river, and succeeded in passing over as securely as you had done, not however without considerable difficulty.

As we advanced, I reflected that our safety depended in some measure on the two boys, because it was they only who knew how to use the guns. I now for the first time began to feel how fortunate it was, that you had accustomed them from infancy to face danger of every kind; in our own country I had sometimes blamed you for allowing them the use of guns, and showing them how to fire. I was averse to their conceiving a partiality to field sports, and apprehended numberless accidents that might happen to them. But at present I am convinced that every parent who adopts a hardy scheme of education acts the wisest part. Let me now resume the passing of the river.

Ernest was first in reaching the other side, and met with no accident. The little Francis entreated me to carry him on my back, which appeared difficult enough, as I must have left the things with which I was loaded, on the shore, and have returned to fetch them. At length we found means to manage pretty well, thanks to Jack, who relieved me of my gun and the hatchet. But for himself, finding he was scarcely able to stand under his added weight, he resolved to go straight into the water at once, rather than run the risk of slipping, by stepping on the loose wet pieces of stone, when so heavily loaded. I myself had great difficulty to keep myself steady with the dear little burden at my back, who joined his hands round my neck, and leaned with all his weight upon my shoulders. After having filled my flask with river water, we proceeded on our way; and when we had reached to the top of the ascent on the other side, which you described to us as so enchanting, I myself experienced the same effect from the delightful scenery around. I continued for some time to look and admire in silence; and for the first time since the event of our dreadful accident at sea, I felt my heart begin to open to a sense of enjoyment and of hope.

In casting my eyes over the vast extent before me, I had observed a small wood of the most inviting aspect. I had so long sighed for a little shade, that I resolved without hesitation to take our course towards it: for this, however, it was necessary to go a long way through a strong kind of grass, which reached above the heads of the little boys; an obstacle which, on trial, we found too difficult to overcome. We therefore resolved to pursue a direction along the river, till it was necessary to turn upon the wood. We found traces of your footsteps, and took care to follow them till we had come to a turn on the right, which seemed to lead directly to it; but here again we were interrupted by the extraordinary height and thickness of the grass, which nothing but the most indefatigable endeavours could have enabled us to get through. Jack was now loitering a little behind, and I frequently turned round to observe what he could be doing: at last I saw him tearing off some handfulls of grass, and wiping his clothes with it; and then I perceived him shake his pocket-handkerchief, which was wet, and lay it on his shoulders to dry. I hastened back to him, to inquire what had happened.

Oh, mother, said he, I believe all the water of the river we have crossed, has got into my pockets: only see, every thing I had in them is wet, pistols, turfs, every thing.

Good heavens! interrupted I in great alarm, had you put your pistols in your pocket? They were not loaded, I hope?

I am sure I do not know, mother; I only put them there while my belt was drying, that I might always have them about me.

Thoughtless, yet fortunate boy! exclaimed I. Do you know what an escape you have had? If with the suddenness of your motions the pistols had gone off, they would infallibly have killed you. Take care, I entreat you, not to commit such an imprudence in future. There is nothing, I believe, to fear, mother, for this time, replied he, holding the pistols so as to let the water run out of them. And in reality I perceived, by the condition they were in, that there was little danger of their going off. While we were conversing about what had happened, our attention was interrupted by a sudden noise, and looking about, we perceived a large bird issuing from the thickest part of the grass, and mounting in the air. Each of the boys prepared to fire, but before they could be ready, the bird was out of the reach of shot. Ernest was bitterly disappointed, and instantly exchanged the gun for the carbine I had given him, crying: What a pity! If I had but had the lightest gun! if the bird had not got away so fast, I would lay any wager I should have killed him.

The mischief was, no doubt, that you did not let him know beforehand that it was your pleasure he should wait till you could be quite ready, observed I, laughing.

But, mother, how could I possibly suppose that the bird could fly away in less than the twinkling of an eye? Ah, if one would but come at this very moment!

A good sportsman, Ernest, always holds himself in readiness, this being, as I understand, one of his great arts; for you must know, that birds never send messages to give notice of their coming.

I wish I could but know, said Jack, what bird it was; I never saw any the least like it. I am sure it was an eagle, said the little

Francis, for I have read in my book of fables that an eagle can carry off a sheep; and this bird was terribly large.

O yes, said Ernest scoffingly, as if all large birds must be eagles! Why, do you not know that there are some birds much larger even than eagles? the ostrich for example, which travellers sometimes name the Condor or the Candor. I must confess it would have afforded me the highest pleasure to have examined this bird minutely.

If you had had time to examine him, you would have had time to kill him, said I: but, as the opportunity is gone, let us look for the place in the grass from which he mounted; we may judge at least of his size by the mark he will have left there. The boys now all scampered away to the place; when suddenly a second bird, exactly like the first, except that he was a little larger, rushed out with a great noise and mounted above their heads.

The boys remained stupid with astonishment, following him with their eyes and open mouths without speaking a word, while for my own part I could not help laughing heartily. Oh! such fine sportsmen as we have here! cried I: they will never let us be in want of game, I plainly perceive. *Ah! if one would but come at this very moment!* these were your own words, Ernest, and behold one came, and you have let him escape: it is not of much use, methinks, to load your guns . . . Ernest, always a little disposed to vent uneasiness by crying, now began to sob; but Jack, with a curious mixture of a tragi-comic bravery upon his features, darted his eager eyes upon the mountain traveller, and taking off his hat made a profound bow, roaring out, as if for the bird to hear: Have the goodness, Mr. Traveller, to indulge me once more with, a little visit, only for a single minute: you cannot imagine what good sort of people we are: I entreat that we may have the pleasure of seeing you once again . . . We now minutely examined the place from which the birds had mounted, and found a kind of large nest formed of dry plants, and the workmanship of which was clumsy enough; the nest was empty, with the exception of some broken shells of eggs. I inferred from this, that their young had lately been hatched; and observing at this moment a rustling motion among some plants of shorter growth, at some distance from the spot on which we stood, I concluded that the young covey were scampering away in that direction; but as the motion soon ceased, we had no longer a guide to conduct us to their retreat. We had now then a moment for remark. Ernest, assuming his professor tone, began: You see clearly, I suppose, Francis, that these large birds which we have met with, cannot possibly be eagles, for that species of birds was never known to make their nests in the grass; neither are their young ones capable of taking care of themselves, so soon after being hatched; the only birds that can walk without help as soon as they come out of the shell, are partridges and quails.

Give me leave, interrupted I, to add to your list, all birds of the gallinaceous kind, such as the turkey, the peacock, and the Guinea fowl; and no doubt many other wild fowls have the same feature in their description.

But, mother, replied he, birds of the gallinaceous kind have not white feathers on the belly, and slate-coloured wings, like those which have just escaped us. I, for my part, am of opinion, that they were the great bustard; the second bird having a small mustachio on the side of the beak, which answers to the description I have seen of him in my engravings.

What you have seen, Ernest, is always in engravings, said Jack. For my part, I should like for once to see a real original that you had had the skill to vanquish. If Fritz had been with us, I can tell you, the said birds would now be lying dead before us, and then you would have an opportunity of comparing them with your engravings.

I, for my part, observed I, most heartily rejoice that things have happened as they did, and that those poor little birds which stand so much in need of their parents' care, have not been deprived of them. What would be your own sensation, if a cruel savage of this country should attack your father or your mother, with an intention to destroy them?

I can more easily tell you, mother, what I would do, than what I should feel, said Jack, straightening his arm as he held the pistol: young as I am, I think I can answer, that if such a bird as that should come in my way, he should meet with a reception that would not much incline him to repeat his visit.

I thank you, my good fellow: but this would not be so easy as you imagine; for though you have arrived at the prodigious age of your tenth year, there would be some difficulty in conquering one who would have twice your own strength. But now for a little grave advice:—Take care, my excellent children, to guard against the growth of the insensible and cruel disposition, which a passion for field-sports is so apt to inspire; it is for this reason that I have never wished my family to be fond of them. It has always appeared to me that no animals ought to be destroyed, but those who do injury to man, or are indispensably necessary for his support.

Discoursing thus, we reached the little wood; and here our son Ernest had an opportunity of recognising many of the originals of the engravings in his books of natural history, and of displaying his knowledge, or his ignorance, to his heart's content. A prodigious quantity of unknown birds were skipping and warbling on the branches of the trees, without betraying the least alarm at our vicinity. In spite of the lesson in morality which I had so lately been pronouncing, the desire of firing upon them again possessed their hearts; but this I absolutely forbade, and with the less scruple, as the trees were of so enormous a height as to be out of gun-shot reach.—No, my dear husband, you cannot possibly form an idea of the trees we now beheld! You must somehow have missed this wood; or so extraordinary a sight could not have escaped your observation; in my whole life I have never seen a single tree of so immense a size. What appeared to us at a distance to be a wood, was only a group of about fourteen of them, the trunks of which seemed to be supported in their upright position, by arches on each side, these arches being formed by portions of the roots of the tree, of great thickness and extent. Meanwhile the tree itself is further supported by a perpendicular root issuing from the others, and of a smaller compass, while the projecting roots extend themselves on every side of the tree, and double the circumference it would have.

Jack climbed with considerable trouble up on one of these arch-formed roots, and with a packthread in his hand measured the actual circumference of the tree itself. He found that it measured more than fifteen braches (the brache is equal to twenty-two inches and a half). I made thirty-two steps in going round one of those giant productions at the roots; and its height from the ground to the place where the branches begin to shoot, may be about thirty-six braches. The twigs of this tree are strong and thick; its leaves moderately large in size, and bearing some resemblance to the hazel-tree of Europe; but I was unable to discover that it bore any fruit. The soil immediately round the tree and under its branches, produced in great abundance a short thick kind of plant, unmixed with any of the thistle kind, and of a perfectly smooth surface. Thus every circumstance seemed to concur in inviting us to use this spot as a place of repose; and my predilection for it grew so strong that I resolved to go no further, but to enjoy its delicious coolness till it should be time to return. I sat down in this verdant elysium with my three sons around me. We took out our provision-bags; a charming stream, formed to increase the coolness and beauty of the scene, flowed at our feet, and supplied us with a fresh and salutary beverage. Our dogs were not long in reaching us; they had remained behind, sauntering about the skirts of the wood. To my great surprise, they did not ask for any thing to eat, but lay down quietly, and were soon asleep at our feet. For my own part, I felt that I could never tire of beholding and admiring this enchanting spot; it occurred to me, that if we could but contrive a kind of tent that could be fixed in one of the trees, we might safely come and make our abode here. I had found nothing in any other direction that suited us so well in every respect; and I resolved to look no further. When we had shared our dinner among us, and well rested from our fatigue, we set out on our return, again keeping close to the river, half expecting to see along the shore, some of the pieces or other vestiges of the vessel, which the waves might have washed on shore there.

But before we left our enchanting retreat, Jack entreated me to stay a little longer, and finish sewing the linen strips to his leather belt. The little coxcomb had so great an ambition to strut about and exhibit himself in this new ornament, that he had taken the trouble to carry the piece of wood on which he had nailed his skin to dry, along with him, through the whole of our expedition. Finding that the skin was really dry, I granted his request, preferring, since it appeared that work I must, to do it now when I had the advantage of being in the shade, than after I should be returned to the scorching of the sun outside our tent. When I had finished my task, he eagerly fastened the belt round him, and placed his pistols in it; he set himself before us in a marching step, with the knuckles of his hand turned back upon his hip, leaving to Ernest the care of putting on the dogs' collars, which he insisted should be done, for it would give them, he said, a martial air. The little hero was all impatience for you and Fritz to see him in his new accoutrement; so that I had enough to do to walk quick enough to keep sight of him; for, in a country where no track of the foot of man is to be found, we might easily lose each other. I became more tranquil respecting him when we had got once more all together on the sea-shore; for, as I expected, we found there pieces of timber, poles, large and small chests, and other articles which I knew had come from the vessel. None of us however were strong enough to bring them away; we therefore contented ourselves with dragging all we could reach to the dry sands, beyond the reach of the waves at the highest state of the tide. Our dogs, for their part, were fully employed in fishing for crabs, which they drew with their paws to the shore, as the waves washed them up, and on which they made an excellent repast. I now understood that it was this sort of prey which had appeased their hunger before they joined us at dinner. Heaven be praised, cried I, that our animals have found means to procure sustenance at so cheap a rate! for I really began to think that, with their enormous appetites, they might some day have taken it into their heads to eat their masters.

Eat us! exclaimed my brave son Jack, you surely forget; am I not here to defend you with my pistols?

Silly young pretender! they would swallow you if they had a mind, as easily as you would swallow a pill; but in reality they are kind excellent creatures, who love us, and will never do us any harm. By swallowing us, I meant that they would so considerably diminish our provisions, that in this respect they would inflict upon us a serious misfortune.

We now suddenly cast our eyes on Ponto, whom we perceived employed in turning over a round substance he had found in the sands, some pieces of which he swallowed from time to time. Ernest also perceived what he was about, and did us the favour, with his usual composure, to pronounce just these words:—They are turtles' eggs!

Run, my children, cried I, and get as many of them as you can; they are excellent, and I shall have the greatest pleasure in being able to regale our dear travellers on their return, with so new and delicious a dish. We found it a little difficult to make Ponto come away from the eggs, to which he had taken a great fancy. At length, however, we succeeded in collecting near two dozen of them, which we secured in our provision-bags. When we had concluded this affair, we by accident cast our eyes upon the boundless ocean, and to our great astonishment we perceived a sail, which seemed to be joyfully approaching towards the land. I knew not what to think; but Ernest, who always thinks he knows every thing, or can guess at every thing, exclaimed that it was you and Fritz; but little Francis was terribly afraid that it must be the savages come to eat us up, like those described in Robinson Crusoe's Island. We soon, however, had the happiness of being convinced that Ernest was right, and that it was indeed our well-beloved! We ran eagerly towards the river, which Jack and Ernest recrossed as before, by leaping from one great stone to another; while I also resumed my burden of little Francis at my back, and in this manner soon arrived at the place of your landing, when we had nothing further to do but to throw ourselves into your arms! This, my dear husband, is a faithful and circumstantial narration of our journey of discovery; and now, if you wish me a great deal of happiness, you will not refuse to conduct me and your sons, with our whole train of animals, to the spot I have described, where we cannot fail to find a more agreeable asylum than here, under these scorching rocks.

And these giant trees are then the asylum you have chosen for our future abode! And you would have a tent set up in one of them, at a distance of more than sixty-six feet from the ground, where we should be perched like parrots! And pray by what means are we to ascend this tree? for at present I have no clear view of this important part of the subject.

Alas! my dear husband, I see the objections against my plan as plainly as you can do; but after all, we cannot but be considerable gainers by the change: for my part, I dared not venture further without having my dear protector at my side. Who knows, were we to set out together, upon another expedition, if we should not find a still more convenient spot, in which we could take up our abode?

I perceived a tear stealing into my wife's eyes, on finding that she could not prevail upon me to think as favourably as she wished of her discovery, and that I treated the subject of her giant trees with so little respect: I therefore endeavoured by every means to sooth and relieve her somewhat wounded sensibility. I assured her how much I admired her courage, and that I considered her adventure as a proof that women possess that fine quality in as great perfection in their hearts, as some men exhibit instances of it in their conduct. Do not then distress yourself, my love, but tell me if I shall make you a balloon of sail-cloth, to enable you to arrive at your country seat amongst the branches.

Yes, yes, said she, laugh as much as you like, if it amuses you; but I assure you my plan is not so silly as you imagine: one advantage, at least, it is certain we should derive,—the being out of reach of jackalls and other wild beasts. Do you recollect the large lime-tree in the public walk of the town we lived in, and the pretty little room which had been built among its branches, and the flight of stairs which led to it? What should hinder us from effecting such a contrivance in one of my giant trees, which afford even superior facilities in the enormous size and strength of their branches, and the peculiar manner of their growth?

Well, well, we shall see about it. In the mean while, my boys, let us extract a little lesson in arithmetic, from the subject of these marvellous trees; for this, at least, will be deriving a real benefit from them. Tell me, learned Mr. Ernest, how many feet there are in thirty-six braches? for that, your mother assures us, is the height of the trees.

*Ernest.*—To answer this question, I must know first how many feet or inches the brache contains.

*Father.*—I thought you knew long ago as much as this; but, as usual in young heads, what goes in at one ear goes out at the other. I must then remind you, as you have forgot, that the brache, or half-ell, contains one foot ten inches, or twenty-two inches. Now then make your calculation.

*Ernest.*—I do not find it so easy as I thought. You must help me, Fritz, you are older than I am.

*Fritz.*—With all my heart. First we take thirty-six braches; then multiply thirty-six by twenty-two, the number of inches each brache contains, and you have 792; divide this by twelve, the number of inches in a foot, and it will give us sixty-six for the number of feet. Is that right, father?

*Father.*—Yes, quite right. So, my dear wife, you will have every evening to climb sixty-six feet to get to bed, which, as we have no ladder, is not the easiest thing imaginable. Now then let us see how many feet the tree is in circumference, taking it round the roots. Your mother found that she walked round it in thirty-two steps. Tell us then, Ernest, how many feet do you think these thirty-two steps would make?

*Ernest.*—You always ask me the things that I know nothing at all about: you should tell me, at least, how many feet there are in a step.

*Father.*—Well, say two feet and a half to each step.

*Ernest.*—Twice thirty-two makes sixty-four; the half of thirty-two is sixteen; which added to sixty-four makes eighty feet.

*Father.*—Very well. Tell me now, if you recollect the proper term in geometry for the circumference of a circle, or say of a tree, since we are talking of trees.

*Ernest.*—Oh, you may be sure that I could not forget that it is called the periphery.

*Father.*— Right. And what is the term for any line which may be drawn from one point of the periphery to another, passing through the centre? Now, Jack, you may show us what a great geometrician you intend to be.

*Jack.*—I believe it is called the diameter.

*Father.*—So far right. Next, can you tell me what is the diameter of a periphery of eighty feet, and what distance there is between the extremities of the roots of the giant tree and its trunk?

The boys all began to reckon, and soon one said one number, one said another, at random; but Fritz called out louder than the rest, that the distance was twenty-six feet.

*Father.*—You are pretty near. Tell me, did you make a calculation, or was it a mere guess?

*Fritz.*—No, father, not a guess; but I will tell you. In the town in which we lived, I have often taken notice that the hatter, when he was about to bind the edge of a hat, always measured three times the length of the diameter, and a trifle over, for the quantity of ribbon he should use: thus I had no difficulty in finding that the third of eighty was about twenty-six; and adding a couple of feet for the over measure, we may call it twenty-eight.

*Father.*—I am glad to see you did not lose such an opportunity for calculation; but a great boy like you, who have advanced in your studies, ought not to be under obligations to the hatter for the answer. But now let us go back to the measure of our trees, which are really of a most extraordinary size. Height from the ground to the branches, sixty-six feet; thickness, eight feet in diameter, and twenty-eight feet distance from the extremities of the roots to the trunk. They really, with propriety, may be called giant trees.

Having finished our conversation, we performed our devotions, and retired to rest, grateful and well satisfied to find ourselves once more together, and in health. We soon closed our eyes, and enjoyed tranquil slumbers till break of day.

# VIII

# CONSTRUCTION OF A BRIDGE

HEN MY WIFE AND I WERE AWAKE NEXT MORNING, WE RESUMED the question of our change of abode. I observed to her, that it was a matter of great difficulty, and required mature consideration; otherwise we might hereafter have reason to repent the useless labour and inconvenience we should have brought upon ourselves, by a fruitless removal. My own opinion is, said I, that, upon the whole, we had better remain here, where Providence seems to have conducted us; the situation of the place affords conveniences, both with respect to our personal safety and being so near to the vessel, from which we may continue to enrich ourselves. See how completely we are on all sides protected by the rocks; it is an asylum, inaccessible but by sea or by the passage of the river, which is not easily accomplished. Let us then have patience yet a little longer, at least, till we have got all that can be removed, or that would be useful to us from the ship.

Nothing can be sounder than your reasons, my love, replied my wife; but indeed no patience can endure the intense heat of these sands, which is even increased by the vicinity of the rocks. It is not easy for you to conceive how great my sufferings are from this cause; for you have generally been out on some voyage of discovery, and have been occasionally relieved by the shade of trees. Another consideration is, that by remaining here, we must renounce all hope of procuring fruits of any kind, and must live on oysters, to which we have all a great aversion, or on such wild birds as that which you found so unpalatable. And, for the safety you boast of, the rocks did not prevent our receiving a visit from the jackalls; nor is it improbable that tigers or other animals might follow their example. Lastly, in regard to the treasures we might continue to draw from the vessel, I renounce them with all my heart. We are already in possession of a great abundance of provisions and other useful things; and, for my part, my heart is always filled with the most distressing apprehensions, whenever you and Fritz are exposed to the danger of that perfidious element the sea.

Upon my word, my love, the shade of your giant trees has inspired you with a most powerful eloquence; and I perceive that nothing so effectually animates the language of a female, as an ardent desire and a fixed determination to carry a particular point; I see that the affair will end by my submitting to your will. You are, as you ought to be, the director of our plans; but let us have a well-digested scheme of operation before we leave this spot for your favourite wood.—First, we must contrive a place among the rocks, that may serve both for a fortress and a storehouse, where we can leave our provisions and other things, and to which, in case of any danger from invasion in the wood, we can immediately retreat.—Come then, this agreed, the next thing is to throw a bridge across the river, if we are to pass it with all our family and baggage.

A bridge! exclaimed my wife; can you possibly think of such a thing? If we stay while you build a bridge, we may consider ourselves as fixt here for life. What reason can there be, that we should not cross the river as we did before? The ass and the cow will carry all our goods upon their backs.

But do you recollect, that to preserve dry what they carry, they must not perform their journey as they did from the vessel? For this reason, then, if for no other, we must contrive a bridge. We shall want also some sacks and baskets to contain our different matters; you may therefore set about making these, and I will undertake the bridge, which the more I consider, the more I find to be of indispensable necessity; for the stream will, no doubt, at times increase, and the passage become impracticable in any other way. At this moment it would be found so for our shortest-legged animals, and I am sure you would not wish to see them drowned. But even our own boys, at least the youngest, will derive a means of safety from my bridge; for it is not quite certain that they would always succeed so well as they did the first time, in their jumping from stone to stone.

Well, then, a bridge let there be, said my wife; I see I must consent. But let us not allow ourselves a moment of leisure till we have completed all that is necessary for our departure. You will leave our stock of gunpowder here, I hope; for I am not easy with a large quantity of it so near us; a thunder-storm, or some thoughtless action of one of the boys, might expose us to serious danger.

You are right, my love; and I will carefully attend to your suggestion. We will keep on hand only a sufficient quantity for daily use; I will contrive a place in the rock for the rest, where it will be safe from the chance of fire or dampness. It is an article which, according to the use which is made of it, may become on the one hand, a most dangerous enemy, and, on the other, a most useful friend.

Thus, then, we decided the important question of removing to a new abode; after which we fixed in concert upon a plan of labour for the day, and then awaked the boys. Their ecstasy on hearing of our project may easily be conceived; but they expressed their fear that it would be a long while before a bridge could be built; a single hour appearing an age to them, with such a novelty in view as the prospect of removing to the wood, to live under the giant trees. They, in the fullness of their joy, entreated that the place might be called, *The Promised Land.*

We now began to look about for breakfast; Fritz taking care not to neglect his monkey, who sucked one of the goats as quietly and as contentedly as if she had been its mother. My wife undertook to milk another, and then the cow, and afterwards gave some of the milk to each of the children: with a part of what remained she made a sort of soup with biscuits, and the rest she put into one of the flasks, to accompany us in our expedition. During this time, I was preparing the boat for another journey to the vessel, to bring away a sufficient quantity of planks and timbers for the bridge. After breakfast we set out; and this time I took with me Ernest as well as Fritz, that we might accomplish our object in a shorter time. We rowed stoutly till we reached the current, which soon drew us on beyond the bay; but scarcely had we passed a little islet, lying to one side of us, than we perceived a prodigious quantity of sea-gulls and other birds, whose various and discordant rounds so disagreeably assailed us, that we were obliged to stop our ears. Fritz would instantly have fired upon them, if I had not prevented him. I had a great curiosity to discover what could possibly be the reason of so numerous an assembly of these creatures. I therefore steered to the spot; but, finding that the boat made but little way, I hoisted my sail, that we might have the assistance of the wind.

To Ernest our expedition afforded the highest delight. He was in ecstasies at seeing the sail begin to swell, and the motion of the streamer in the air. Fritz, on his part, did not for a moment take his eyes from the islet where the birds had assembled. Presently he suddenly exclaimed: I see what it is; the birds are all pecking, tooth and beak, at a monstrous fish, which lies dead upon the soil.

Tooth! brother Fritz, replied Ernest: it must be curious to see birds with teeth. Fritz, however, was right; I approached sufficiently near to step upon the land, and after fringing the boat to an anchor with a heavy stone, we walked cautiously and gently up to the birds. We soon perceived that the object which attracted them was in reality an enormous fish, which had been thrown by the sea upon the islet, and whose dead body lay invitingly there for all the birds which should pass that way. Indeed, so eagerly were they occupied with the feast, that though we were within the distance of half gunshot, not one of them attempted to fly off. We observed with astonishment the extreme voracity of this plumed group; each bird was so intent upon its prey, that, nothing could have been more easy than to have killed great numbers of them with our sticks alone: we did not, however, envy them their prize. Fritz did not cease to express his wonder at the monstrous size of the animal, and asked me by what means he could have got there.

I believe, answered I, you were yourself the means; there is every appearance that it is the very shark you so skilfully wounded yesterday. See, here are the two balls which you discharged at its head.

Yes, yes, it is the very same, said my young hero skipping about for joy; I well remember I had two balls in my gun, and here they are, lodged in his hideous head.

I grant it is hideous enough, continued I; its aspect even when dead makes one shudder with disgust, particularly when I recollect how easy it would have been for him to have devoured us. See what a horrible mouth he has, and what a singular kind of mustachio projecting above! and what a rough and prickly skin! one might almost use it for a file. Nor is he small of his species; for I would lay any wager that he measures more than twenty feet, from head to tail. We ought to be thankful to Providence, and a little to our Fritz also, for having delivered us from such a monster! But let us each take away with us a bit of his skin; for I have an idea that it may in some way or other be useful to us. But how to drive away these eager intruders, so as to get at him, is the difficulty.

Ernest instantly drew out the iron ramrod from his gun, and in a few moments killed several, by striking among them to right and left, while all the others took their flight. Fritz and I then advanced and cut several long strips of the skin from the head of the shark, with which we were proceeding to our boat, when I observed, lying on the ground, some planks and timbers which had recently been cast by the sea on this little island. On measuring the longest, we perceived they would answer our purpose, and with the assistance of the crow and a lever which we had brought with us, found means to get them into the boat, and thus spare ourselves the trouble of proceeding further to the vessel. With great exertion of our strength, we contrived to bind the timbers together, with the planks, upon them, in the manner of a raft, and tied them to the end of the boat; so that, through this adventure, we were ready to return in four hours after our departure, and might boast of having done a good day's work. I accordingly pushed again for the current, which soon drove us out to sea; then I tacked about, and resumed the direct route for the bay and for our place of embarkation, thus avoiding the danger of touching upon shallows. All this succeeded to my utmost wishes; I unfurled my sail, and a brisk wind soon conveyed us to our landing place.

While we were sailing, Fritz, at my request, had nailed the strips of skin we cut from the shark, to the mast to dry. Ernest had been examining the birds he had killed with his ramrod. I cannot imagine, father, said he, why you should think they are not good to eat. What is their name?

I believe they are called sea-gulls, a bird that lives upon the carcases of other animals, and whose flesh for that reason must have contracted a bad flavour; there are many kinds of them, and all of so senseless a nature, as to fly down in flocks upon dead whales, even while the fishermen are round them cutting them up; the birds try to seize upon small pieces of the fat, as they hold them in their hands; and they suffer themselves to be killed, rather than let go their prize.

They must indeed be stupid creatures, said Fritz, to have let Ernest kill them with the ramrod. But look here, father, you were wrong in telling me to nail my skins to the mast; for they have curled round in drying, and I cannot make them flat again.

That was precisely my intention, replied I, they will be much more useful to us round than flat; besides, you have still some left which you may dry flat; and then we shall have a fine provision of shagreen, we can find out a good method to rub off the sharp points, and afterwards to polish it.

I thought, said Ernest, that shagreen was made of ass's skin. And you were not mistaken, rejoined I; the best shagreen is made in Turkey, Persia, and Tartary, from skin taken from the back of the ass and of horses. While the skin is yet moist, it is stretched upon a kind of hard fat; they then beat the skin, by which means the fat is incorporated, and gives the surface the appearance of a kind of file: but very good shagreen is also made from the skin of sea-fish, particularly in France.

Ernest asked his brother if he knew why the mouth of the shark is not, as in other animals, placed in the middle of the snout, but directly under. Fritz confessed his inability to answer this question. And for my part, continued he a little consequentially, all I know is how to kill them when the occasion presents itself. So pray, learned brother, be kind enough to let us share your information on the subject, for I take for granted, your question means that you can answer it yourself.

I suppose, rejoined Ernest, that the mouth of the shark is thus placed, with the intention of preventing him from depopulating the sea and the land. With so excessive a voraciousness of appetite as he possesses, nothing would escape him, if he had the power to seize his prey without turning his body; but as it is, there is time enough for a smaller animal to make his escape.

Well reasoned, my young philosopher, cried I; and, though we should not always be able to comprehend the intention of the

Creator in the objects which surround us, at least the conjectures we are induced to form respecting them, cannot fail of being a useful exercise to the mind.

I have already said we were once more landed safely on our shore, but no one of our family appeared. We called out to them as loud as we could, which was answered by the same sounds in return, and in a few minutes my wife appeared between her two little boys returning from the river, a rising piece of ground having concealed her from our sight: each carried a handkerchief in hand, which appeared filled with some new prize; and little Francis had a small fishing-net formed like a bag and strung upon a stick, which he carried on his shoulder. No sooner did they hear our voices, than they flew to meet us, astonished at our quick return. Jack reached us before the rest; and his first act was to open the handkerchief he held, and pour out a large number of lobsters at our feet: their mother and little Francis produced each as many more, forming all together a prodigious heap, and all alive; so that we were sure of excellent dinners for some days at least. Some of the animals tried to escape in different directions; and the boys in following them, were kept in full chase, sometimes, pleased and sometimes angry; sometimes laughing, sometimes scolding at the bootless trouble they were engaged in; for no sooner had they seized on one deserter, than ten more had followed his example.

Now, have I not been very lucky, papa? said little Francis; for you must know it was I who found them out! Look, there are more than two hundred of them, and see how large they are, and what fine claws they have! I am sure they will be quite delicious!

*Father.*—Excellent indeed, my little fellow, and particularly if it was your industry that first discovered them.

*Jack.*—Yes, father, it was Francis who saw them first; but it was I who ran to tell mamma, and it was I who fetched the net and put it to rights, and it was I who went up to my knees in water to catch them.

*Father.*—You make a charming story of it together, my boys; but as it is an interesting subject, you may tell me as many particulars as you please; it is indeed an event of some importance for our kitchen, and I have great pleasure in looking forward to partaking of a dish of your providing.

*Jack.*—Well, papa, I will tell you. As soon as you were gone, mamma sat down outside the tent and began to work, while Francis and I took a little walk towards the river, to find out a proper place for you to begin the bridge.

*Father.*—Bravo! Mr. Architect, it is you then who will direct the workmen; but joking apart, I am much gratified to find that careless head of yours for once employed upon a useful subject. Well then, did you find a proper place for me to begin the bridge?

*Jack.*—Yes, father, yes. But listen, and you will know all. We were advancing towards the river, and Francis was amusing himself with taking up some parti-coloured stones, calling out whenever he found one that seemed extraordinary: Jack, Jack, look what a beautiful stone I have found, all yellow! I am sure it must be gold, so I shall pound it, and make sand of it for my writing. As we reached the river we saw a stone of this kind just upon the brink, and kneeling down with his head out over to take it up, he all at once cried out: Jack, Jack, Fritz's jackall is covered all over with lobsters! Run as fast as you can. I sprang to him in an instant, and I saw not only the jackall covered with them, but legions more coming in with the stream. I ran to tell mamma, who immediately got the net which you brought from the vessel. Partly with this net, and partly with our hands, we caught those you see in a very few minutes; and we should have caught a much larger number if we had not heard you call, for the river is quite full of them. You took quite enough for once, my boy, said I: A little at a time is the maxim that suits us best, and I should even advise your taking the smallest of them back to the river, where they will grow larger; we shall still have sufficient for several magnificent repasts. This, then, said I to myself, is a new source for our support: even here, in these arid regions, we find means to procure, not only the necessaries of life, but luxuries in abundance. May we never cease to evince our gratitude to Providence, by the exercise of a more than ordinary care and industry!

It was now our turn to relate the events of our voyage on the water. Ernest gave an account of his sea-gulls, but it did not inspire his mother with a desire for one of them for our next day's dinner. We now put our remaining lobsters into the handkerchiefs and the net, and the boys took them to the place allotted for keeping our provisions. My wife set about dressing some of them, and in the mean time Fritz and I employed ourselves in untying the raft of timbers and planks, and in moving them from the boat. I then imitated the example of the Laplanders, in harnessing their reindeer for drawing their sledges. Instead of traces, halters, etc., I put a piece of rope with a running knot at the end, round the neck of the ass, and passed the other end between its legs, to which I tied the piece of wood which I wished to be removed. The cow was harnessed in the same manner, and we were thus enabled to carry our materials, piece by piece, to the spot which our architect Jack had chosen at the river, as the most eligible for our bridge; and to say the truth I thought his judgement excellent; it was a place where the shore on each side was steep, and of equal height; there was even on our side, an old trunk of a tree lying on the ground, on which I rested my principal timber.

Now then, boys, said I, the first thing is to see if our timbers are long enough to reach to the other side: by my eye I should think they are; but if I had a surveyor's plane, we might be quite sure, instead of working at a venture.

But my mother has some balls of packthread with which she measured the height of the giant tree, interrupted Ernest, and nothing would be more easy than to tie a stone to the end of one of them, and throw it to the other side of the river; then we could draw it to the very brink, and thus obtain the exact length that would be required for our timbers.

Your idea is excellent, cried I; nothing gives me more pleasure than to see you exercise your invention; run quickly and fetch the packthread. He returned without loss of time; the stone was tied to its end, and thrown across as we had planned; we drew it gently back to the river edge, marking the place where the bridge was to rest; we next measured the string, and found that the distance from one side to the other was eighteen feet. It appeared to me necessary, that to give a sufficient solidity to the timbers, I must allow three feet at each end of extra length for fixing them, amounting therefore in all to forty feet; and I was fortunate enough to find that many of those we had brought, did not fall short of this length. There now remained the difficulty of conducting them across the stream; but we determined to discuss this part of the subject while we ate our dinner, which had been waiting for us more than an hour.

We all now proceeded homewards, and entering the kitchen, we found our good steward had prepared a large dish of lobsters for us; but before she would let us taste them, she insisted we should see another useful labour she had been employed about; she accordingly displayed two sacks intended for the ass, which she had seamed with packthread; the work she assured us, had with difficulty been accomplished, since for want of a needle large enough to carry packthread, she had been obliged to make a hole with a nail for every stitch: we might therefore judge by her perseverance in such a task, of the ardour with which she longed to see her plan of a removal executed. She received on this occasion, as was well her due, abundance of compliments and thanks from her companions, and also a little good-humoured raillery. For this time, we hurried through our meal, all being deeply interested in the work we were about to undertake, and concerning which, each gave his advice without the least ceremony. The impatience we all felt to begin, scarcely left us time to strip the lobsters of their shells, each thinking only of the part which might be assigned him towards the execution of the *Nonpareil*; for this, for mutual encouragement, was the name we gave our bridge, even before it was in existence.

Having consulted together as to the means of laying our timbers across the river, the first thing I did, was to attach one of them to the trunk of the tree of which I have already spoken, by a strong cord, long enough to turn freely round the trunk; I then fastened another cord to the other end of the beam; this cord I fastened round a stone, and then threw the stone across the river. I next passed the river as I had done before, furnished with a pulley, which I secured to a tree; I passed my second cord through the pulley, and recrossing the river with this cord in my hand, I contrived to harness the ass and the sow to the end of the cord. I next drove the animals from the bank of the river; they resisted at first, but I made them go by force of drawing. I first fixed one end of the beam firm to the trunk of the tree, and then they drew along the other end, so as gradually to advance over the river: presently, to my great joy, I saw it touch the other side, and at length become fixt and firm by its own weight. In a moment Fritz and Jack leaped upon the timber, and, in spite of my paternal fears, crossed the stream with a joyful step upon this narrow but effective bridge.

The first timber being thus laid, the difficulty of our undertaking was considerably diminished; a second and a third were fixt in succession, and with the greatest ease. Fritz and I, standing on opposite sides of the river, placed them at such distances from each other, as was necessary to form a broad and handsome bridge: what now remained to be done, was to lay some short planks across them quite close to each other, which we executed so expeditiously, that our whole undertaking was completed in a much shorter time than I should have imagined possible. The reader should have seen our young workmen, to form the least conception of the delight they felt: they jumped, and danced and played a thousand antics, and uttered a thousand joyful sounds upon their bridge. For my own part, I could hardly restrain myself from joining in these demonstrations of their perfect happiness; and my wife, who had been the mover of all our operations, was as little disposed to a silent calm enjoyment of our success, as any of the rest: she ran to one, and then to another, embracing each in turn, and was never tired of passing and repassing on our piece

PLATE 6
"What now remained to be done was to lay some
short planks across them."

of workmanship, which was every where safe and even, and at least ten feet in breadth; I had not fastened the cross planks to each other, for they appeared to be close and firm without it; and besides, I recollected that in case of danger from any kind of invasion, we could with the greater ease remove them, and thus render the passage of the river more difficult. Our labour however had occasioned us so much fatigue, that we found ourselves unable for that day to enter upon new exertions; and the evening beginning to set in, we returned to our home, where we partook heartily of an excellent supper, and went to bed.

# IX

# CHANGE OF ABODE

A S SOON AS WE WERE ALL UP AND HAD BREAKFASTED, THE NEXT morning, I assembled all the members of my family together, to take with them a solemn farewell of this our first place of reception from the horrible disaster of the shipwreck. I confess that for my awn part I could not leave it without much regret; it was a place of greater safety than we were likely again to meet with; it was also nearer to the vessel: but it was sufficient for me to know that the kind and faithful companion of my misfortunes had conceived an unalterable distaste for it, to incline me to yield my own opinion and my wishes. I should indeed consider myself unworthy of such a partner, if I could have felt hesitation in a point of so much interest to her feelings. I thought it right to represent strongly to my sons, particularly to the youngest, the danger of exposing themselves as they had done the evening before, along the river. We are now going, continued I, to inhabit an unknown spot, which is not so well protected by nature as that we are leaving; we are unacquainted both with the soil and its inhabitants, whether human creatures or beasts; it is therefore necessary to use the utmost caution, to make it a rule never to remain separate from each other; particularly you young ones must take care not to run on before, or stay too far behind. This you must promise, my boys. Having unburdened my mind of this necessary charge, we prepared for setting out; I directed my sons to assemble our whole flock of animals, and to leave the ass and the cow to me, that I might load them with the sacks as before concerted; I had filled these at the two ends, and made a slit longways in the middle of each of them, and to each side of the slits I tied several long pieces of cord, which crossing each other and being again brought round and fastened, served to hold the sacks firmly on the back of the animal. We next began to put together all the things we should stand most in need of for the two or three first days, in our new abode; working implements, kitchen utensils, the captain's service of plate, and a small provision of butter, etc. etc. I put these articles into the two ends of each sack, taking care that the sides should be equally heavy, and then fastened them on. I afterwards added our hammocks and other coverings to complete the load, and we were about to begin our march when my wife stopped me. I cannot prevail upon myself, said she, to leave our fowls behind us to pass the night by themselves; for I fear they would infallibly become the prey of the jackalls. We must, somehow or other, contrive a place for them among the luggage, and also one for our little Francis, who cannot walk so far, and on that account would not fail to interrupt our speed. There is also my enchanted bag, which I recommend to your particular care, said she, smiling, for who can tell what may yet pop out of it for your good pleasure!

Women, for their part, never fail to have more things to carry than there are places to put them in, said I, also laughing: however, let us see how handsomely I shall be able to provide for what belongs to you, my love. Fortunately, I had already thought of making the ass's load as light as possible, foreseeing that it would be necessary he should carry our little one a part of the way. I now accordingly placed the child upon his back, fixing the enchanted bag in such a way as to support him, and I tied them together upon the ass with so many cords, that the animal might even have galloped without any danger of his falling off.

In the mean while, the other boys had been running after the cocks and hens and the pigeons, but had not succeeded in catching one of them; so they returned empty-handed and in ill-humour. Little blockheads! said their mother, see how you have heated yourselves in running after these untractable creatures! I could have put you in a way to catch them in a moment; come along with me, and see.—Yes, yes, you may think so, mother, said Jack, a little sulky, but I will give you leave to roast me in the place of the first fowl that you shall be able to catch. Poor Jack, said she laughing, you will then soon be on the spit, I can tell you; which would really be a pity, considering what better things we might do with you; though, to say the truth, you have not shown that you have more brains than a goose, in thinking to catch the animals by running after them in this manner. She now stepped into the tent, and brought out two handfuls of peas and oats, and by pronouncing a few words of invitation in the accustomed tone, the birds all flocked round her in a moment. She then walked slowly before them, dropping the grain all the way, till they had followed her into the tent. When she perceived that they were all in the inside, and busily employed in picking up the grain, she shut the entrance, and caught one after the other without the smallest difficulty. The boys looked at each other half ashamed, though much amused with the adventure. Grant me a reprieve from the spit, mother, cried Jack, and I will do all I can to help you in securing your prisoners. Accordingly, he set himself to work, and had soon caught the whole. They were then tied by the feet and wings, put into a basket covered with a net and placed in triumph on the top of our luggage. Ernest suggested the placing two bent sticks arch-ways across the basket, and throwing a blanket over it, that the want of light might incline them to repose; for, with the clatter they made, it was impossible to hear each other speak.

We packed up every thing we were obliged to leave, and placed it in the tent, which we carefully closed, and, for greater security, fastened down the ends of the sailcloth at the entrance, by driving stakes through them into the ground. We ranged a number of vessels, both full and empty, round the tent, to serve as a rampart, and thus we confided to the protection of heaven our remaining treasures. At length we set ourselves in motion: each of us, great and small, carried a gun upon his shoulder, and a game bag at his back. Children are always fond of a change of place; ours were full of joy and good-humour; nor was their mother less affected with the same cause; she walked before with her eldest son, the cow and the ass immediately behind them; the goat conducted by Jack came next; the little monkey was seated on the back of his nurse, and made a thousand grimaces. After the goats, came Ernest, conducting the sheep, while I, in my capacity of general superintendant, followed behind and brought up the rear; the dogs for the most part paraded backwards and forwards, thus seeming to play the part of adjutants. Our march was slow, and there was something solemn and patriarchal in the spectacle we exhibited; I fancied we must resemble our forefathers journeying in the deserts, accompanied by their families and their possessions. Now then, Fritz, cried I, you have the specimen you wished for of the patriarchal mode of life; what do you think of it? I like it much, father, replied he: I never read the Bible without wishing I had lived in those good times.

And I too, said Ernest, I am quite delighted with it, I cannot help fancying myself not merely a patriarch, but a Tartar, or an Arab, and that we are about to discover I know not how many new and extraordinary things. Is it not true, father, that the Tartars and the Arabs pass their lives in journeying from one place to another, and carrying all they have about them?

It is certainly for the most part true, Ernest, replied I, and they are denominated wandering tribes; but they generally perform their journeys attended by horses and camels, by means of which they can proceed a little faster, than if, like us, they had only an ass and a cow. For my part, I should not be sorry if I were quite sure that the pilgrimage we are now making would be our last.

And I too am of your way of thinking, cried my wife, and I hope that in our new abode we shall be so well satisfied with the shade of such luxuriant trees, that we shall not be inclined to rove. Let us, however, think as little as possible of the fatigue which seems to be our lot to-day, since to-morrow you will all be ready to thank me for having been the occasion of it.

Be assured, my dear, said I, that we have adopted your plans, and endure the fatigue they occasion, with cheerfulness, and that one and all are already grateful to you for their future happiness;

which happiness will be still increased by the reflection, that to your kind and anxious exertions it has been that we are indebted for it.

We had now reached our bridge, and advanced half way across it, when the sow for the first time took the fancy of joining us, and by the uncouth and listless figure she made, contributed to the pictorial effect of our procession. At the moment of our departure, she had shown herself so restive and indocile, that we had been compelled to leave her behind us; but when she saw that we had all left the place, she set out voluntarily to overtake us: but she took care to apprize us, by her continual grunting, that she disapproved of our migration.

On the other side of the river, we experienced an inconvenience wholly unexpected. The nutritious aspect of the grass, which grew here in profusion, was too strong a temptation for our animals, who, unable to resist, strayed from us in every direction to feed voluptuously upon it; so that, without the assistance of our dogs, we should not have been able to bring them back to the line of our procession. These active creatures were of great use to us on this occasion; and when every thing was restored to proper order, we were able to continue our journey. For fear however of a similar occurrence, I directed our march to the left, along the seaside, where the produce of the soil was not of a quality to attract them.

But scarcely had we advanced a few steps on the sands, when our two dogs, which had stayed behind among the grass, set up a loud barking, mixt at intervals with howling, as if they had been wounded, or were engaged in an encounter with some formidable animal. Fritz in an instant lifted his gun to his cheek, and was ready to fire; Ernest, always somewhat timid, drew back to his mother's side; Jack ran bravely after Fritz with his gun upon his shoulder; while I, fearing the dogs might be attacked by some dangerous wild beast, prepared myself to advance to their assistance. But youth is always full of ardour; and in spite of all my exhortations that they would proceed with caution, the boys, eager for the event, made but three jumps to the place from which the noise proceeded. In an instant Jack had turned to meet me, clapping his hands and calling out, Come quickly, father, come quickly, here is a monstrous porcupine!

I soon reached the spot, and perceived that it was really as they said, bating a little exaggeration. The dogs were running to and fro with bloody noses, about the animal; and when they approached too near him, he made a frightful noise, and darted his quills so suddenly at them, that a great number had penetrated the skins of the valiant creatures, and remained sticking in them; and it was no doubt the pain they occasioned, which made them howl so violently.

While we were looking on, Jack determined on an attack, which succeeded marvellously well. He took one of the pistols which he carried in his belt, and aimed it so exactly at the head of the porcupine, that he fell dead the instant he fired, and before we had a notion of what he was about. This success raised Jack to the height of joy and vanity; while Fritz, on the other hand, felt a sensation of jealousy almost to shedding tears. Is it right, Jack, said he, that such a little boy as you should venture to fire off a pistol in this manner? How easily might you have wounded my father or me, or one of the dogs, by so rash an action! Oh yes, to be sure, and what do you suppose hindered me from seeing that you were all behind me? Do you think I fired without taking care of that? Do you take me for an idiot? The porcupine could tell you about that, brother Fritz, if he could but speak. My first fire—pop—dead as a herring! This is something like, brother Fritz, and you would be glad enough to have had such a chance yourself!

Fritz only replied by a motion of his head. He was out of humour because his younger brother had deprived him of the honour of the day; and he sought a subject of complaint against him, as the wolf did with the poor little lamb. Come, come, boys, said I, let me hear no envious speeches and no reproaches; luck for one to-day, for another to-morrow; but all for the common good. Jack was, perhaps, a little imprudent, but you must allow that he showed both skill and courage; let us not therefore tarnish the glory of this action. We now all got round the extraordinary animal, on whom nature has bestowed a strong defence, by arming his body all over with long spears. The boys were absolutely at a loss what means to use for carrying away his carcase. They thought of dragging it along the ground; but as often as they attempted to take hold, there was nothing but squalling, and running to show the marks made by his quills on their hands. We must leave him behind, said they; but it is a great pity.

Not for an empire, cried Jack, shall he be left there, for my mother must have a sight of him. In saying this, he tied one corner of his handkerchief round the neck of the animal, and drew him by the other to the place where we had left his mother in care of our possessions, and who had been in great uneasiness at our long absence.

Here is the monster, mother, said he, armed with his hundred thousand spears; but I was a match for him, and at one fire too! His flesh is excellent food; at least papa says so.

Ernest began, with his usual coolness, to examine the animal minutely. After having looked at him a long while, he said: He is a most singular animal: his mouth contains the *dentes incisores*, and his ears and feet are much like those of a man.

Ah! said Jack, if you had seen how he darted out all his quills against the dogs, and the noise they made, rattling one against another! He is a most terrible creature but what of that? I did not mind going up to him, and I dispatched two or three balls at his head, and it was over with him in an instant!

He cannot be so terrible an animal, said Ernest, if it was so easy for a mere child to destroy him. *A mere child!* replied Jack, much mortified, and drawing up his head. It was plain that his conquest had added half a foot to his height, in his own imagination.

While the boys were disputing, my wife and I had hastened to relieve the dogs, by drawing out the quills and examining their wounds. Having done this, we joined the group which surrounded the porcupine; Jack taking upon him to do the honours, as if he was showing the animal at a fair. Observe, cried he, what a terrible creature it is! how long and hard his quills are! and see what strange feet he has! I am sure he must have run like a hare: but I killed him for all that! And what a singular sort of crest he has on his head! Upon my word, I like my day's work vastly.

That, said I, is the reason why naturalists call him the crested porcupine. But now tell me, my young hero, were you not afraid, in going so near him, that he would dart some of his quills at you?

*Jack.*—Oh no, papa, I knew that the stories about his quills were merely fabulous.

*Father.*—But you saw that many of them had stuck in the dogs, and this, surely, was no fable.

*Jack.*—That was because the dogs attacked the animal furiously from behind, thus putting themselves exactly in the way of his quills, so that it is not extraordinary that they should be wounded by them; but I took care to attack him in front, in which direction I knew he would not shoot them, so I had no reason to be afraid. Is it not also a fable, father, that when they escape the hunter, they throw their quills as they run, and sometimes kill him with them?

*Father.*—This account is, I believe, in a great measure untrue; but it is not improbable that it was such an occurrence as we just now met with, which first gave rise to the notion. An observation no less singular than true, has been made, that natural history, whose basis ought to be the strictest truth, has given birth to more fables than mythology itself. In general, mankind are fond of the marvellous, and the composed march of nature is uninteresting to them, from its simple uniformity. They accordingly dress her with all the singularities and extravagancies of their own imaginations. But tell me, Jack, what you mean to do with your prize? Are we to take it with us, or leave it here?

*Jack.*—Oh, take it with us, take it with us, father, I entreat, for you say its flesh is good to eat.

I could not resist his pressing importunity, and I resolved to lay the porcupine on the back of the ass, behind little Francis, having first wrapped his bloody head in a quantity of grass, and then rolled him up in a blanket to protect my boy from his quills. We now resumed our journey, but had not proceeded far, when the ass began lo kick furiously with his hind legs; tore himself away from my wife, who was guiding him, and set off full gallop, braying so loud as almost to deafen us, and scampering from side to side, in so extraordinary a way, that the boys were thrown into fits of laughter; in which my wife and I should probably have joined, if we had not conceived the idea, that the situation of our little Francis was not quite safe. A sign we made to the dogs, made them set off like lightning after the deserter, whom they in a moment overtook, and stopped his way with a tremendous barking. They would no doubt have attacked him violently, if we had not ourselves run quickly to the spot, to intimidate them. We took our boy from the ass's back, delighted to find that (thanks to the care I had taken in tying him on securely) he had kept his seat, and had scarcely even experienced any alarm. But tell me, Francis, said I jocosely, have you been clapping spurs to your horse, or what have you done to make him set off on a gallop in this manner? I no sooner pronounced these words, than suddenly I recollected the porcupine. I immediately examined if the quills had not penetrated through the covering in which I wrapped it: this I found to be the very thing: though I had, folded it three times double, the quills had pierced through all, and produced the effect of the sharpest spur on the poor animal. I soon found a remedy for this inconvenience, by placing my wife's enchanted bag, which was filled with articles of a nature to be absolutely impenetrable, between the ass's back and the dead animal. I now restored Francis to his place, exhorting him to keep in an upright posture, and we resumed our journey.

Fritz had run on before with his gun, hoping he should meet with some animal of prey. What he most desired, was to find one or two of those large bustards which his mother had described to him. We followed him at our leisure, taking care not to expose our health by unnecessary fatigue; till at last, without further accident or adventure, we arrived at the place of the giant trees. Such, indeed, we found them, and our astonishment exceeded all description. Good heavens! what trees! what a height! what trunks! I never heard of any so prodigious! exclaimed one and all. Nothing can be more rational than your admiration, answered I, measuring them with my eyes as I spoke. I must confess I had not myself formed an idea of the reality. To you be all the honour, my dear wife, for the discovery of this agreeable abode, in which we shall enjoy so many comforts and advantages. The great point we have to gain, is the fixing a tent large enough to receive us all, in one of these trees, by which means we shall be perfectly secure from the invasion of wild beasts. I defy even one of the bears, who are so famous for mounting trees, to climb up by a trunk so immense, and so destitute of branches.

We began now to release our animals from their burdens, having first thrown our own on the grass. We next used the precaution of tying their two fore legs together with a cord, that they might not go far away, or lose themselves. We restored the fowls to liberty; and then seating ourselves upon the grass, we held a family council on the subject of our future establishment. I was myself somewhat uneasy on the question of our safety during the ensuing night; for I was ignorant of the nature of the extensive country I beheld around me, and of what chance there might be of our being attacked by different kinds of wild beasts. I accordingly observed to my wife, that I would make an endeavour for us all to sleep in the tree that very night. While I was deliberating with her on the subject, Fritz, who thought of nothing but his sporting, and of his desire to take his revenge of the porcupine adventure, had stolen away to a short distance, and we heard the report of a gun. This would have alarmed me, if, at the same moment, we had not recognised Fritz's voice crying out, I touched him! I touched him! and in a moment we saw him running towards us, holding a dead animal of uncommon beauty by the paws. Father, father, look, here is a superb tiger-cat, said he, proudly raising it in the air, to show it to the best advantage. Bravo! bravo! cried I; bravo, Nimrod the undaunted! Your achievement will call forth the unbounded gratitude of our cocks and hens and pigeons, for you have rendered them what they cannot fail to think an important service. If you had not killed this animal, he would no doubt have demolished in the course of one night our whole stock of poultry. I charge you look about in every direction, and try to destroy as many of the species as fall in your way, for we cannot have more dangerous intruders.

*Ernest.*—I wish, father, you would be so good as to tell me why God created wild beasts, since man seems to be appointed to destroy them?

*Father.*—This indeed is a question I cannot answer, and we must be contented with taking care to arm ourselves against them: neither can I explain to you, why many other things, which to us appear to have only injurious qualities, have been created. With respect to beasts of prey, I am inclined to believe, that one of the ends of Providence, in giving them existence, is their embellishing and varying the works of the creation; of maintaining a necessary equilibrium among creatures endowed with life; and lastly, to furnish man who comes naked into the world, with materials for protecting himself from the cold, by the use of their skins, which become the means of exchange and commerce between different nations. We may also add, that the care of protecting himself from the attacks of ferocious animals, invigorates the physical and moral powers of man, supports his activity, and renders him inventive and courageous. The ancient Germans, for example, were rendered robust and valiant warriors, through their habitual exercises in the field, which enabled them, at a time of need, to defend their country and their liberty with as little difficulty as they would have experienced in killing a wolf or a bear.

*Jack.*—But what do you say of the insects, which feed on living human flesh, and who neither contribute their skins for the wants of man, nor to his health by exciting him to pursue them in the field! Of what use are such creatures as these?

*Father.*—They serve, my son, to exercise his patience, and to compel him to a constant cleanliness, which contributes to a perfect state of health. But let us return to the animal Fritz has killed. Tell me all the particulars of your adventure. How did you kill him?

*Fritz.*—With my pistol, father, as Jack killed the porcupine.

*Father.*—Was he on this tree, just by us?

*Fritz.*—Yes, father, I had been observing that something moved among the branches. I went softly as near as I could; and on seeing him, I knew him for a tiger-cat. I immediately fired, when he fell at my feet wounded and furious; and then I fired a second time and killed him.

*Father.*—You were very fortunate in escaping thus, for he might easily have devoured you. You should always take care in aiming at animals of this kind, to be at a greater distance.

*Fritz.*—Why so, father? I might have missed him if I had been further off. I, on the contrary, tried to be as near him as possible, and fired close to his ears.

*Father.*—This was acting in the same way as your brother Jack, whom you so much derided for his want of care, and may serve you as a lesson not to blame in your brothers, what you would yourself be perhaps obliged to do in the same situation; also not to interrupt their joy with unkind reflections, but rather to partake with them the pleasure of their success.

*Fritz.*—Well, father, all I now ask of Jack is, that he will be so good as not to spoil the beautiful skin of this animal, as he did that of the jackall. Only observe what beautiful figures it is marked with, and the fine effect of the black and yellow spots; the most richly manufactured stuff could not exceed it in magnificence. What is the exact name of the animal?

*Father.*—You may for the present give it the name of the tiger-cat. I do not, however, think that it is the animal which is so denominated at the Cape of Good Hope; I rather think it is the margay, a native of America, an animal of extremely vicious dispositions and singular voraciousness; he destroys all the birds of the forest, and neither a man, a sheep, or goat, that should fall in his way, could escape his rapacity; in the name of humanity, therefore, we ought to be thankful to you for having vanquished so formidable an enemy.

*Fritz.*—All the recompence I ask, father, is, that you will let me keep the skin; and I wish you would tell me what use I can make of it.

*Father.*—One idea occurs to me, and it is this:—you must skin the animal yourself, taking the greatest care not to injure it in the operation, particularly those parts which cover the fore legs and the tail. If you will do this, you may make yourself a belt with it, like your brother Jack's, except that it will be much more beautiful.

The odd pieces will serve admirably to make some cases to contain our utensils for the table, such as knives, forks, spoons; and as they will be light, we can easily carry them about with us, should we make any further excursions. It is not amiss, in such a situation as ours, to exercise ourselves in all kinds of trades and manual labour, and to do every thing with the utmost care, and in the best manner possible. Man, the lord of the creation, should always aim at perfection. Go, then, boy, and put away its bloody head, and we will see how to set about preparing the skin.

*Jack.*—And I too, father, will make some cases with the skin of my porcupine.

*Father.*—And why should you not, my boy? The skin of the tiger-cat can only furnish us with four, and we ought to have six at least, which will be one a-piece. So set to work, and show us quickly what you can perform. I should like for you to preserve some of the quills of your porcupine for me; for I think I can contrive to convert them into packing-needles, or into arrows; and what bits of skin are left, may serve to repair the dogs' collars when they begin to wear; or, which would be a masterpiece of invention, might be joined together and made into a sort of coat of mail, as a protection to them when they have to encounter wild beasts.

*Jack.*—Oh! yes, father, I will make the coat of mail, the coat of mail! Ernest, Fritz, did you hear what father said? Why, our dogs will look like a couple of knights of chivalry. The idea is most excellent; how I shall like to see them with a coat of mail!

The boys left me no moment of repose till I had shown them how to take off the skins of the animals without tearing them. In the mean while, Ernest looked about for a flat stone as a sort of foundation for a fireplace, and little Francis collected some pieces of dry wood for his mother to light a fire. Ernest was not long in finding what he wanted, and then he ran to join us and give us his assistance, or rather to reason, right or wrong, on the subject of skinning animals; and then on that of trees, making various comments and inquiries, respecting the real name of those we intended to inhabit. It is my opinion, said he, that they are really and simply, enormously large hazel trees; see if the leaf is not of exactly the same form. But that is no proof, interrupted I; for many trees bear leaves of the same shape, but nevertheless are of different kinds. Besides, it appears to me, that there is not so great a resemblance as you think, between the leaves of the trees which grow here, and those of the hazel, the former being of a paler colour, and white underneath. I recollect too, that there is the wild mango and also the fig-tree, whose roots grow in the same manner as our giant trees, forming a beautiful arch, and sometimes reaching to an immeasurable height.

*Ernest.*—I thought, father, that the mango tree only grew on the sea-shore, and in marshy soils?

*Father.*—You were not mistaken; it is the black mango tree which loves the water. But there is, besides, the red mango, which bears its fruit in bunches, something like our currant bushes. This kind of the mango tree is found at a considerable distance from the sea, and its wood is used for dyeing red. There is a third sort, which is called the mountain mango, or yellow wood, and this is the kind, whose roots produce the beautiful arches you now see around us.

We conversed thus as we proceeded with our work; for it was always my endeavour to compensate to my children, as much as I was able, our want of books for their instruction. Little Francis presently came running loaded with dry branches for his mother, with his mouth crammed full of something, and calling out, Mamma, mamma, I have found a nice fruit to eat, and I have brought you home some of it!

Little glutton! replied his mother quite alarmed, what have you got there? For Heaven's sake, do not swallow, in this imprudent manner, the first thing that falls in your way; for by this means you may be poisoned; and then you would die. She made him open his mouth, and took out with her finger what he was eating with so keen a relish. With some difficulty she drew out the remains of a fig. A fig! exclaimed I: where did you find it? Thank God, this is no poison! But nevertheless, remember, Francis, that you are never to put any thing into your mouth, without first showing it to your mother or to me. And now you may tell us where you got this fig.

*Francis.*—I got it among the grass, papa; and there are a great many more. I thought it must be good to eat, for the fowls and the pigeons, and even the pig, came to the place and ate them in large quantities.

*Father.*—You see then, my dear, said I to my wife, that our beautiful trees are fig-trees, at least the kind which are thus named at the Antilles; for they do not in the least resemble the tree called by that name in Europe, except that they both bear a fruit having some little resemblance to each other. I now recollect that the leaves of the mango tree are of a round form, and not oval like these. I took this occasion to give the boys another lesson on the necessity of being cautious in an unknown country, and never to venture on tasting any thing they met with, till they had seen it eaten by birds and monkeys. At the word monkeys, they all ran to visit the little orphan, whom they found seated on a root of a tree, and examining with the oddest grimaces and the most singular expression of curiosity, the half-skinned porcupine and the tiger-cat, which lay near him. Francis offered him a fig, which he first turned round and round, then smelled at it, and concluded by eating it voraciously. Bravo, bravo! Mr. Monkey, exclaimed the boys, clapping their hands; so then these figs are good to eat! Thank you, Mr. Monkey; for, after your wise decision we shall make a charming feast on them.

In the mean while, my wife had been employed in making a fire, in putting on the pot, and preparing for our dinner. She had put a large piece of the porcupine into it, and the rest she had laid in salt for another time. The tiger-cat was bestowed upon the dogs, who waited impatiently to receive it. While our dinner was dressing, I employed my time in making some packing-needles with the quills of the porcupine. I put the point of a large nail into the fire till it was red hot; then taking hold of it with some wet linen in my hand, by way of guard, I with great ease perforated the thick end of the quills with it. I had soon the pleasure of presenting my wife with a large packet of long, stout, needles, which were the more valuable in her estimation, as she had formed the intention of contriving some better harnessing for our animals, and had been perplexed how to set about them without some larger needles. I, however, recommended to her to be frugal in the use of her packthread, for which I should soon have so urgent a need, in constructing a ladder for ascending the tree we intended to inhabit.

I had singled out the highest fig-tree; and while we were waiting for dinner, I made the boys try how high they could throw their sticks and stones in it. I also tried myself; but the very lowest branches were so far from the ground, that none of us could touch them. I perceived, therefore, that we should be under the necessity of inventing some method to reach so far, as, otherwise, it would be impossible to fasten the ends of my ladder to them. I allowed a short pause to my imagination on the subject, during which I assisted Jack and Fritz in carrying the skins of the two animals to the adjacent stream, where we confined them under water with some large stones. By this time we were called to dinner, and we all partook with pleasure of our porcupine, which had produced an excellent soup, and had no fault but being a little hard. My wife, however, could not prevail on herself to eat of it, which occasioned Jack, who did the honours of the dish, a little mortification. But his mother could not be brought to relent, and made her dinner on a slice of ham and some bread and cheese, under the shade of the trees she had so much desired, and she found the plainest repast delicious.

# X

# CONSTRUCTION OF A LADDER

OUR REPAST BEING ENDED, I OBSERVED TO MY WIFE, THAT I did not think it would be possible for us to sleep that night in the tree, and that we should therefore be obliged to lie on the ground. I however desired her immediately to begin preparing the harness for the animals, that they might go to the seashore and fetch what pieces of wood or other useful articles might be thrown up to enable us to ascend the tree, if, contrary to my expectation, it should be found practicable. She lost not a moment in beginning her work; while I, in the mean time, set about suspending our hammocks to some of the arched roots of the trees, which I considered would be more convenient for passing the night, than on the ground. I next spread a piece of sail-cloth large enough to cover them, to preserve us from the dew and from the insects. Having thus made the best provision I could for my family, I hastened with the two eldest boys to the sea-shore, to examine the resources supplied by the waves, and to choose out such pieces of wood as were most proper for the steps of my ladder. The dry branches of the fig-tree

I would not use, for they appeared to me too fragile for the purpose; and I had not observed any other kind of wood growing near, that was sufficiently solid. There were, no doubt, on the sands, numberless pieces, the quality of which was fit for my object; but, unfortunately, there was none that would not require considerable labour to be adapted in all respects to my purpose; and thus my undertaking would have experienced a considerable delay, if Ernest had not been lucky enough to discover a number of bamboo canes in a sort of bog, where they lay half covered with sand and mud. I took them out, and, with the boys' assistance, completely cleared them from the dirt; and stripping off their leaves to examine them, I found to my great joy that they were precisely what I wanted. I then instantly began to cut them with my hatchet, in pieces of four or five feet long; the boys bound them together in faggots proportioned to their strength for carrying them, and we prepared to return with them to our place of abode. I next secured some of the straight and most slender of the stalks, to make some arrows with, of which I knew I should stand in need. At some distance from the place where we stood, I perceived a sort of thicket, in which I hoped to find some young pliant twigs, which I thought might also be useful to me; I determined, however, first to examine them. We proceeded to the spot; but apprehending, it might be the retreat of some dangerous reptile, or animal, we held our guns in readiness. Ponto, who had accompanied us, went before. We had hardly reached the thicket, when we observed him make several jumps, and throw himself furiously into the middle of the bushes; when instantly a troop of large-sized flamingoes sprang out, and, with a loud rustling noise mounted into the air. Fritz, always too ready with his gun, instantly fired, when two of the birds fell down among the bushes: one of them was quite dead, but the other was only slightly wounded in the wing: he soon got upon his feet, and giving himself a shake, and finding that he could not fly, he began to make use of his long legs, and to run so fast towards the water, that we were afraid he would escape us. Fritz, in the joy of his heart, ran to pick up the flamingo he had killed; he plunged up to his knees in the water, and with great difficulty was able to get out again; while I, warned by his example, proceeded more cautiously in my pursuit of the wounded bird.

Ponto came to my assistance, for without him I should have lost all trace of the animal; but he ran on before, caught hold of the flamingo, and held him fast till I reached the spot, and took him into my protection. All this was effected with considerable trouble; for the bird made a stout resistance, flapping its wings with violence for some time. But at last I succeeded in securing him.

Fritz was not long in extricating himself from the swamp; he now appeared holding the dead flamingo by the feet: but I had more trouble in the care of mine, as I had a great desire to preserve him alive. I had tied his feet and his wings with my handkerchief; notwithstanding which, he still continued to flutter about to a distressing degree, and tried to make his escape. I held the flamingo under my left arm, and my gun in my right hand. I made the best jumps I was able, to get to the boys, but at the risk of sinking every moment into the mud, which was extremely deep, and from which it would have been difficult to have released me. Attracted by the love of sporting, I had made my way through these dangerous places, scarcely observing their existence; but now, on my return, I shuddered on perceiving the danger to which I had exposed myself.

PLATE 7
"I proceeded more cautiously in my pursuit of
the wounded bird."

The joy of the boys was excessive, when they saw that my flamingo was alive. If we can but cure his wound and contrive to feed him, what a happiness it will be! said they. Do you think he will like to be with the other fowls?

I know, answered I, that he is a bird that may be easily tamed; and we will make our experiment upon him: but he will not thank you for such food as we give our fowls; he will make his humble petition to you for some small fish, a few worms, or insects.

*Ernest.*—Our river will furnish him with all these; Jack and Francis can catch as many as he will want; and very soon, with such long legs as he has, he may learn the way to the river and find them for himself.

*Father.*—I hope you will take great care of him, for I have a great desire to preserve him.

*Fritz.*—How delightful it will be, if we can catch some other sorts of wild birds, and have a yard to keep them in! But look, father, he is web-footed like aquatic birds, while his legs are long like the stork: is not this rare and extraordinary?

*Father.*—Not at all: many other birds, as well as the flamingo, possess the double faculty of running and of swimming.

*Ernest.*—But, father, are all flamingoes like this, of such a beautiful red colour, and the wings so exquisitely tinted with purple? I think I have seen the flamingo in my Natural History, and the colours were not like these: so perhaps this is not a flamingo at last?

*Father.*—I believe it is a flamingo, Ernest, and that this difference in the plumage denotes the age of the bird: when very young they are gray, at a more advanced age they are white; and it is only when they are full grown, that they are adorned with this beautifully tinted plumage.

*Ernest.*—This dead one, then, is an old fellow, and I am afraid by his colours that he will make but a tough dish: shall we not take him home to mamma?

*Father.*—Yes, certainly. I leave to you the care of carrying him in the best manner you can: in the mean time, I shall repeat my visit to the canes, for I have not done with them yet. I accordingly selected, now, some of the oldest of the stalks, and cut from them their hard pointed ends, which I had well considered would serve for the tips of my arrows, for which they are also used by the savages of the Antilles. Lastly, I looked for two of the longest canes, which I cut, for the purpose of measuring the height of our giant tree, about which I felt so deep an interest. When I told my sons the use I intended to make of the two longest canes, they indulged themselves in a hearty laugh at me, and maintained, that though I should lay ten such canes up the trunk of the tree, the last would not reach even the lowest branch. I requested they would oblige me by having a little patience; and I reminded them, that it was not long ago that they defied their mother to catch the fowls, because they themselves had not known how to set about it.

When I had done all I wanted, I began to think of returning. Ernest took the charge of all the canes; Fritz carried the dead flamingo, and I took care of the living one. We had not gone far, when Fritz, addressing himself to Ponto, said: Oho, lazy bones! so you think you are to be excused from any part of the burden; have the goodness to carry my flamingo on your back, with the same politeness as your companion Turk observed, towards my little monkey.

As he said this, he tied the dead bird upon his back, without the least resistance from the patient animal.

So then, said I, Mr. Fritz intends to return quite at his ease, and without any part of our load, while his old father and his young brothers carry each a heavy portion!

Your reproach is very just, father, said the excellent lad; give me, I entreat you, your live bird, and I will take the greatest care of him; only see if he does not already give me a kind look! and as for his long formidable beak; I am not the least afraid of it; he does not look as if he would bite me. That is the more generous on his part, replied I, for it was you who wounded him: but it is a known fact, that animals are often of a less revengeful nature than man, and you will see that this bird will attach itself to you very strongly: saying this, I put the flamingo carefully into his hands.

We were now returned to the spot where I had left the three bundles of bamboo-canes; and as my sons were sufficiently loaded, I took charge of them myself. Now you see, said I to Fritz, that in this instance kindness is its own reward; if you had not undertaken the care of the flamingo, you would have had to carry all these bundles, which are a much heavier load.

We were at length arrived once more at our giant trees, and were received with a thousand expressions of interest and kindness. Why, what have you there, Ernest, that is so beautiful a red?—and, Fritz, what is that in your handkerchief? All were delighted at the sight of our new conquests. My wife, with her accustomed disposition to anxiety on our account, immediately asked where we should get food enough for all the animals we brought home. You should consider, said I, that some of them feed us, instead of being fed; and the one we have now brought you, need not give you much uneasiness, if, as I hope, he proves able to find food for himself without our interference. I now began to examine his wound, and found that only one wing was injured by the ball, but that the other had also been slightly wounded by the dog's laying hold of him. I anointed them both with an ointment I composed of a mixture of butter and wine for the purpose, and which seemed immediately to ease the pain; I next tied him by one of his legs, with a long string, to a stake I had driven into the ground, quite near to the stream, that he might go in and wash himself when he pleased.

In the mean time, my little railers had tied the two longest canes together, and were endeavouring to measure the tree with them; but when they found that they reached no further than the top of the arch formed by the roots, they all burst into immoderate fits of laughter, assuring me, that if I wished to measure the tree, I must think of some other means. I however sobered them a little, by recalling to Fritz's memory some lessons in geometry and land surveying, which he had received in Europe, and that by means of these useful sciences, the measure of the highest mountains, and their distance from each other, may be ascertained by the application of triangles and supposed lines. I instantly proceeded to this kind of operation, fixing my canes in the ground, and making use of some string, which Fritz guided according to my directions. I will not fatigue the reader with a minute account of the geometrical process I adopted, as a substitute for the proper instruments; it is sufficient to let him know, that the means I used, answered my purpose and that I found that the height of the lower branches of our tree was forty feet: this particular of its height I was obliged scrupulously to ascertain, before I could determine the length of my ladder. I now set Fritz and Ernest to work, to measure our stock of thick ropes, of which I wanted no less than eighty feet for the two sides of the ladder: the two youngest I employed in collecting all the small string we had used for measuring, and carrying it to their mother. For my own part, I sat down on the grass, and began to make some arrows with a piece of the bamboo, and the short sharp points of the canes I had taken such pains to secure. As the arrows were hollow, I filled them with moist sand, to give them a little weight; and lastly, I tipped them with a bit of feather from the flamingo, to make them fly straight. Scarcely had I finished my work, than the boys came jumping round me, uttering a thousand demonstrations of joy: A bow, a bow, and some real arrows! cried they, addressing each other, and then running to me.—Tell us, father, continued they, what you are going to do with them; do let me shoot one;— and me; and me too, cried one and all as fast as they could speak.

*Father.*—Have patience, boys; I say, have patience. This once I must claim the preference for myself, in order to make trial of my work, which I undertook rather for use than for amusement; so now I will try one of them. Have you, my dear, any strong thread? said I to my wife; I want some immediately. We shall see, said she, what my enchanted bag, which has never yet refused its aid, can do for you. She then threw open its mouth. Come, said she, pretty bag, give me what I ask you for; my husband wants some thread, and it must be very strong. . . . See now, did I not promise you should have your wish? . . . See, here is a large ball of the very thread you want.

*Ernest.*—But I do not see much magic, however, mother, in taking out of a bag, exactly what we had before put into it.

*Father.*—If we are to discuss the matter seriously, Ernest, I cannot but allow that your observation is a just one; but in a moment of dreadful apprehension, such as we experienced on leaving the vessel, to think of a variety of little things that might be useful to one or all of us, was an act that we may truly call an enchantment; and it is a conduct, of which, only the best of wives and the best of mothers could be capable: it is, then, something like a truth, that your mother is a good fairy, who constantly provides for all our wants: but you young giddy things think little of the benefit you thus enjoy.

Just at this moment, Fritz joined us, having finished measuring the string; he brought me the welcome tidings that our stock, in all, was about five hundred fathoms, which I knew to be more than sufficient for my ladder. I now tied the end of the ball of strong thread to an arrow, and fixing it to the bow, I shot it off in such a direction, as to make the arrow pass under one of the largest branches of the tree, and fall again to the ground from the upper side of the same branch. By this method I lodged my thread across the main branch, while I had the command of the end and the ball below. It was now easy to tie a piece of rope to the end of the thread, and draw it upwards, till the knot should reach the same branch. We were thus enabled again to measure the height it was from the ground, and it again proved to be forty feet, as had appeared by my former mode of measuring. Having now made quite sure of being able to raise my ladder by means of the string already suspended, we all set to work with increased zeal and confidence. The first thing I did was to cut a length of about a hundred feet from my parcel of ropes, an inch thick; this I divided into two equal parts, which I stretched along on the ground in two parallel lines, at the distance of a foot from each other. I then directed Fritz to cut portions of sugar-cane, each two feet in length. Ernest handed them to me, one after another; and as I received them, I inserted them into my cords at the distance of twelve inches respectively; fixing them with knots in the cord, while Jack, by my order, drove into each a long nail at the two extremities, to hinder them from slipping out again. Thus in a very short time I had formed a ladder of forty rounds in length, and in point of execution firm and compact, and which we all beheld with a sort of joyful astonishment. I now proceeded to fasten it firmly to one end of the rope, which hung from the tree, and pulled it by the other, till one end of our ladder reached the branch, and seemed to rest so well upon it, that the joyous exclamations of the boys and my wife resounded from all sides. All the boys wished to be the first to ascend upon it; but I decided that it should be Jack, he being the nimblest and of the lightest figure among them. Accordingly, I and his brothers held the end of the rope with all our strength, while our young adventurer tripped up the ladder with as much ease as if he were a cat, and presently took his post upon the branch; but I observed that he had not strength enough to tie the rope firmly to the tree. Fritz now interfered, assuring me that he could ascend the ladder as safely as his brother: but, as he was much heavier, I was not altogether without apprehension. I gave him instructions how to step, in such a way as to divide his weight, by occupying four rounds of the ladder at the same time, with his feet and hands; I made him take with him some large nails and a hammer, to nail the ladder firmly to the branch. He set out courageously upon the undertaking, and was almost instantly side by side with Jack, forty-feet above our heads, and both saluting us with cries of exultation. Fritz immediately set to work to fasten the ladder, by passing the rope round and round the branch; and this he performed with so much skill and intelligence, that I felt sufficient reliance to determine me to ascend myself, and well conclude the business he had begun. But before I ascended, I tied a large pulley to the end of the rope, and carried it with me. When I was at the top, I fastened the pulley to a branch which was within my reach, that by this means I might be able the next day to draw up the planks and timbers I might want for building my aerial castle. I executed all this by the light of the moon, and felt the satisfaction of having done a good day's work. I now gently descended my rope ladder, and joined my wife and children.

As I found an inconvenience in being three of us together on the branch, I had directed the boys to descend first. My astonishment, therefore, on reaching the ground, and finding that neither Fritz nor Jack had made their appearance, it is easier to conceive than to describe; their mother, as she assured me, having seen nothing of them since they ascended the ladder. While I was endeavouring to conjecture where they could be, we suddenly heard the sound of voices which seemed to come from the clouds, and which chanted an evening hymn. I soon recognised the trick our young rogues had played me, who seeing me busily employed in the tree, instead of descending as I had desired them, had climbed upwards from branch to branch till they reached to the very top. My heart was now lightened of my apprehensions for their safety, and I called out to them as loudly as I could, to take great care in coming down. It was almost night, and the light of the moon scarcely penetrated the extreme thickness of the foliage. They presently descended, and joined their anxious relations without any accident. I now directed them to assemble all our animals, and to get together what dry wood we should want for making fires, which I looked to as our defence against the attacks of wild beasts. I explained to them all my reasons for this, informing them that in Africa, a country remarkable for its prodigious numbers of ferocious animals, the natives secure themselves from their nocturnal visits, by lighting large fires, which all these creatures are known to dread and avoid.

When these preparations were finished, my wife presented me with the day's work she had performed; it was some traces and a breast-leather each for the cow and the ass. I promised her, as a reward for her zeal and exertion, that we should all be completely settled in the tree the following day. And now we began to think of our supper, in which she and Ernest and little Francis had been busily and effectually engaged. Ernest had made two wooden forks, and driven them into the ground to support a spit, upon which was a large piece of the porcupine, which he kept turning at the fire. Another piece of the animal was boiling in the pot for soup; and both together exhaled an odour which gave us an excellent appetite.

All our animals had now come round us, one after the other. My wife threw some grain to the fowls, to accustom them to assemble in a particular spot; and when they had eaten it, we had the pleasure of seeing our pigeons take their flight to the top of the giant tree, and the cocks and hens perching and settling themselves, and cackling all the time, upon the rounds of the ladder. The quadrupeds we tied to the arched roots of the tree, quite near to our hammocks, where they quietly laid down on the grass to ruminate in tranquillity. Our beautiful flamingo was not forgotten, Fritz having fed him with some crumbs of biscuit soaked in milk, which he ate very heartily; and afterwards putting his head under his right wing, and raising his left foot, he abandoned himself with confidence to sleep.

At last we had notice that our supper was served. We had laid together in different heaps, a quantity of dried branches and pieces of wood, in readiness to light, when my wife summoned us to our meal, which we had waited for with impatience, and now greedily devoured. My wife, still keeping her resolution of not tasting the porcupine, contented herself with the more sober fare of bread and cheese. The children brought us some figs for the dessert, which they had picked up under the trees, and of which we all partook with pleasure. And now the gaping of one of the boys, and the out-stretched arms of another, gave us notice, that it was time for our young labourers to retire to rest. We performed our evening devotions. I set fire to several of the heaps, and then threw myself contentedly upon my hammock. My young ones were already cased in theirs, and we were soon greeted with their murmurs at being obliged to lie so close to each other, that they could not move their limbs. Ah, gentlemen, cried I, you must try to be contented; no sailor is ever better accommodated than you are now, and you must not expect beds to drop from the clouds on your behalf! I then directed them how to put themselves in a more convenient posture, and to swing their hammock gently to and fro. And see, added I, if sleep will not visit you as soon in a hammock, as on a bed of down. They profited by my advice, and all, except myself, were soon asleep.

# XI

# THE SETTLING IN THE GIANT TREE

I HAD THOUGHT IT NECESSARY TO KEEP WATCH DURING THIS first night, for the protection of my family. Every leaf that stirred, gave me the apprehension that it was the approach of a jackall or a tiger, who might attack some member of my family. As soon as one of the heaps was consumed, I lighted another; and at length, finding that no animal appeared, I by degrees became assured, and at last fell into so sound a sleep, that I did not awake early enough for the execution of my project for that day. The boys were all up and about me. We took our breakfast, and fell to our work. My wife, having finished her daily occupation of milking the cow, and preparing the breakfast for the family, and for all the animals, set off with Ernest, Jack, and Francis, attended by the ass, to the sea-shore; they had no doubt of finding some more pieces of wood, and they thought it would be prudent to replenish our exhausted store. In her absence, I ascended the tree with Fritz, and made the necessary preparations for my undertaking, for which I found it in every respect convenient; for the branches grew extremely close to each other, and in an exactly horizontal direction. Such as grew in a manner to obstruct my design, I cut off either with the saw or hatchet, leaving none but what presented me with a sort of foundation for my work. I left those which spread themselves evenly upon the trunk, and had the largest circuit, as a support for my floor. Above these, at the height of forty-six feet, I found others, upon which to suspend our hammocks; and higher still, there was a further series of branches, destined to receive the roof of my tent, which for the present was to be formed of nothing more than a large surface of sail-cloth.

The progress of these preparations was considerably slow. It was necessary to raise certain beams to this height of forty feet, that were too heavy for my wife and her little assistants to lift from the ground without great effort. I had, however, the resource of my pulley, which served to excellent purpose. My wife and the boys fastened the beams firmly to pieces of cord above, while Fritz and I contrived to draw them up to the elevation of the tent, one by one. When I had already placed two beams upon the branches, I hastened to fix my planks upon them; and I made my floor double, that it might have sufficient solidity if the beams should be in any way warped from their places. I then formed a wall something like a park-paling, all round, to prevent accidents to ourselves or children. This operation and a third journey to the sea-shore to collect the timber necessary, filled our morning so completely, that not one of us had thought about dinner. For this once it was requisite to be content with a simple provision of ham and milk. Dinner ended, we returned to work to finish our aerial palace, which now began to make an imposing appearance. We unhooked our hammocks, etc. from the projecting roots from which they had at first been suspended; and, by means of my pulley, contrived to hoist them up to our new habitation. The sail-cloth roof was supported by the thick branches above; and as it was of great compass, and hung down on every side, the idea occurred to me of nailing it to the paling on two sides, and thus getting not only a roof, but two walls also; the immense trunk of the tree forming a third, while a fourth side contained the entrance of our apartment: and this I left entirely open, both as a means of seeing what passed without, and for admitting a current of air to cool us in this burning temperature. We also on this side enjoyed an extensive and uninterrupted view of the vast ocean, and its lengthening shore. The hammocks were soon suspended from the branches above, and now every thing was ready for our reception that very evening. Well satisfied with the execution of my plan, I descended with Fritz, who had assisted me throughout the whole; and as the day was not far advanced, and I observed we had still some planks remaining, we set about contriving a large table to be placed between the roots of the tree, and surrounded with benches; and this place, we said, should be called our dining-parlour. For this time, we performed our task but slightly, for I confess I was much fatigued. The table, on the whole, however, was such as might be well endured, and the view of it gave my wife considerable satisfaction as she looked on, busied with preparations for our supper. In the mean time, the three youngest boys collected all the pieces of wood we had thrown down from the tree, and put them together to dry in a heap, at a small distance from our fire-place. I also tied together a quantity of small wood which we had collected, and which served to augment our store for making fires.

Entirely exhausted by the fatigues of the day, I threw myself at full length on a bank, saying to my wife, that as I had worked like a galley-slave today, I should allow myself some rest to-morrow. My wife answered, that not only I was entitled to a day of rest, but that it was a duty incumbent on me to take it on the following day; for, said she, I have calculated that to-morrow is Sunday. Unfortunately we had already passed one sabbath-day without recollecting that it was so.

*Father.*—I thank you, my dear, for making this discovery, and I promise you that the day shall be celebrated by us, as it ought to be. It was not unknown to me that we had passed over one Sunday without a due observance of the duties it imposes; but I confess it appeared to me, that being caused by the extraordinary exertions we had to make for the preservation of our lives in a desert place, to which it had pleased God to conduct us, it was a pardonable omission; but now that we seem to have surmounted many difficulties, and to have secured ourselves an habitation, we should indeed be culpable not to celebrate in a solemn and particular manner, the day he has consecrated to himself.

*My Wife.*—Be assured, my dear, that I shall heartily join you in rendering thanks to God, who in so imminent a danger preserved all that was dear to me, and affords us here, in a strange and desert land, not only the necessaries of life, but many of its comforts also. I could no where have met with an habitation more to my fancy, than that you have effected for us in the tree. I will mount the ladder this evening with you, for I feel almost a child's joy at the idea of passing the night up in the air, as we may call it. Let us quickly eat our supper and go to bed, without dropping a word about its being Sunday to-morrow. It will be a great pleasure to me to surprise the boys with the news of a day of rest from labour which they did not expect.

And I, for my part, said I, am rejoiced to find you thus contented and resigned to your fate, and entertaining no contempt for our imperfect contrivances. But now let us see what you have prepared for our reward; and let us call the children around us; I feel in want of such a restorative after my fatigue.

The little company was soon assembled round the table. The mother followed holding in her hand an earthen pot, which we had before observed upon the fire, and the contents of which we were all curious to be informed of. She took off the cover, and with a fork drew out of it the flamingo which Fritz had killed. She informed us that she had preferred dressing it this way, to roasting, because Ernest had assured her that it was an old bird, which would prove hard and tough, and had advised her to improve it by stewing. We rallied our glutton boy on this foible of his character, and his brothers gave him the name of the cook. We, however, had soon reason to know, that he had conferred upon us an important obligation; for the bird, which roasted, we perhaps should not have been able to touch, now appeared excellent, and was eaten up to the very bones.

While we were thus enjoying our repast, the live flamingo stalked up to the place where we were sitting, in the midst of our flock of fowls, to receive his part of the repast, little thinking that it was his late companion that had furnished it. The live flamingo had now become so tame, that we had released him from the stake. He took his walks gravely from place to place, and looked perfectly contented with his company. His fine plumage was a most pleasing sight; while, on the other hand, the sportive tricks and the grimaces of our little monkey, afforded the most agreeable spectacle imaginable. The little animal had become quite familiar with us; jumped from the shoulder of one to that of another; always caught adroitly the meat we threw him, and ate it in so pleasant a way as to make us laugh heartily. To increase our merriment, the old sow, which hitherto had shown an unconquerable aversion to our society, and which we had missed for two whole days, was now seen advancing towards us, grunting at every step. For this time, however, her grunting indicated her joy at having found us once more: and the joy was mutual; of which my wife gave her a substantial proof, by serving her instantly with what remained of our daily allowance of milk.

I confess I thought her a little too generous, till she explained to me that it was necessary to contrive some utensils proper for making butter and cheese, and that till this was done, it was better to turn the milk to profit in this way, than, in so hot a climate, to let it be spoiled; and it was the more necessary, she added, as our grain began to run short, and that, as pigs are very fond of milk, it might be a means of preventing her wandering from us again.

I always find you right, my dear, said I. It shall not be long ere we again undertake another visit to the vessel, to fetch a new provision of grain for your poultry.

Again the subject of the vessel, said she, with a sort of reproachful regret; I shall never enjoy a moment's happiness till it is gone to the bottom, and you shall have entirely banished it from your thoughts! You never make a voyage that does not leave me filled with agonizing alarm for your safety.

I cannot deny, replied I, that there may be some reason for this; but I must remind you that we always choose a day of calm and settled weather for our excursion; and in my opinion we should he unpardonable, if we allowed ourselves to be so subdued by causeless alarms, as to neglect the means of obtaining a variety of useful things, which Providence seems to have reserved for our use.

During this conversation, the boys, by my direction, had lighted one of the heaps of wood for the protection of our animals. This being done, we tied long ropes loosely round the necks of our dogs, purposing to mount to our tent with the ends in my hand that I might be able to let them loose upon the enemy at the first barking I should hear. Every one was now eager to retire to rest, and the signal for ascending the ladder, was given. The three eldest boys were up in an instant; then came their mother's turn, who proceeded slowly and cautiously, and arrived in perfect safety. My own ascension was the last, and the most difficult; for I carried little Francis on my back, and the end of the ladder had been loosened at the bottom, that I might be able to draw it up in the tent during the night: every step, therefore, was made with the greatest difficulty, in consequence of its swinging motion. At last, however, I got to the top, and, to the admiration of the boys, drew the ladder after me. It appeared to them that we were in one of the strong castles, of the ancient chevaliers, in which, when the draw-bridge is raised, the inhabitants are secured from every attack of the enemy. Notwithstanding this apparent safety, I kept our guns in readiness for whatever event might require their use. We now abandoned ourselves to repose; our hearts experienced a full tranquillity; and the fatigue we had all undergone induced so sound a sleep, that day-light shone full in front of our habitation, before our eyes were opened.

# XII

# THE SABBATH AND THE PARABLE

ON AWAKING IN THE MORNING, WE WERE ALL SENSIBLE OF AN unusual refreshment, and a new activity of mind. Well, young ones, cried I jocosely, you have learned, I see, how to sleep in a hammock, I heard not a single complaint all the night! no disputing about room from any one of you; all was still and tranquil. Ah, answered they, stretching and yawning as they spoke, we were so heartily fatigued yesterday, that it is no wonder we slept soundly.

*Father.*—Here then, my children, is another advantage derived from labour; that of procuring a sweet and peaceful sleep.

Yes, yes, father, that is very true, said they, so let us go to work again to-day: What is there to do? What will you give each of us to do?

*Father.*—Nothing at all; you will do no work with your hands for the whole day.

*The Boys.*—Oh, father, you are joking now, I see you are; you are laughing at us because we slept a little too long.

*Father.*—No, my dear boys, I am not joking. This day is Sunday, and God said, *Six days shall thou labour, but the seventh is the Sabbath of the Lord thy God*; and we will therefore celebrate it as we ought.

*Jack.*—Sunday! What, are there Sundays here? That is quite delightful! Oh, I will go and shoot my arrows, and I will walk about and play, and I will do no work the whole day.

*Father.*—Do you think, then, that it was solely for the purpose that people might amuse themselves, and indulge in idleness that God reserved Sunday to himself? You mistake; what he intended was, that there should be a day set apart for worship and thanksgiving for all his goodness; and such an employment of our time ought to be our greatest pleasure.

*Ernest.*—I thought, father, that the worship of God consisted in going to church to hear a sermon and sing hymns: we have no church here, how then can we properly observe Sundays?

*Francis.*—And we have no organ either, and I am very sorry, for I like very much to hear it.

*Jack.*—You see then, papa, that it is not possible for us to celebrate Sunday in the way you propose.

*Fritz.*—How childishly you talk! Do you think that father, who made sermons for us in our own country, cannot make them here? Is not God in every place, as certainly as in a church? And what should hinder us from singing without an organ? When there were soldiers encamped near our town, they had neither church nor organ, and yet the service of the church was performed to them: we have a good minister, and that is the principal thing.

*Father.*—Your brother is quite right, my boys; God is indeed every where, and the best worship consists in thinking of him, and of his holy will, and resolving to fulfil it. In this sense, there is no place in the world that may not serve for a church, because we may entertain pious sentiments everywhere; and this majestic arch of heaven, the immediate work of the Almighty, ought more effectually to raise the soul and touch the heart, than an edifice of stone made by the hand of man! We will, therefore, perform divine service this morning; we shall have no sermon to-day, those I know by heart being beyond your comprehension: young persons should be addressed on the subject of the Supreme Being, according to their feeble understanding, and not as we would address an audience whose judgement and reason are matured. I will hereafter compose a sermon that shall be suitable for you; to-day we will repeat the prayers, and sing one of those one affecting hymns of adoration which your mother taught you. I will then relate to you a parable, of the Great King, which is well adapted to awaken pious thoughts and sentiments in your minds.

*The Boys.*—A parable, a parable! What, like that of the Sower in the Testament! Ah, yes, do, father; we will listen for ever to that; do begin directly.

*Father.*—Every thing in its turn, if you please: first, let us perform our usual morning devotions; then we will descend to breakfast, and take care of our animals, a work which God permits us to engage in even on Sundays: in the mean while, I will reflect a little on the history I am to relate, and then I will call you round me.

Accordingly, after prayer, we descended the ladder, and breakfasted on warm milk; we served the animals also with their meal, and then we all sat down on the tender grass; the boys full of impatient curiosity; their mother absorbed in silent reflection, her hands joined and her eyes turned towards the sky; while I was penetrated with the most lively desire to impress upon the young minds of my children, a subject I considered of the highest importance for their well-being, both in this world and in that which is to come.

All now standing up, I repeated aloud the church service, which I knew by heart, and we sung some verses from the hundred and nineteenth psalm, which the boys had before learned; after which we sat down, and I began as follows:

"My dear children, there was once a Great King, whose kingdom was called The country of Light and Reality, because the purest and softest light of the sun reigned there continually, which caused the inhabitants to be in a perpetual state of activity. On the furthest borders of this kingdom, northward, there was another country which also belonged to the Great King, and the immense extent of which, was unknown to all but himself. From time immemorial, a plan the most exact of this country, had been preserved in the royal archives. This second kingdom was called The kingdom of Obscurity or of Night, because every thing in it was gloomy and inactive.

"In the most fertile and agreeable part of his empire of Reality, this Great King had a residence called the Heavenly City, in which he lived and kept his court, which was the most brilliant that the imagination can form an Idea of. Millions of guards and servants in high dignity, remained for ever round him, and a still larger number held themselves in readiness to receive his commands. The first of these were clothed in robes of cloth that was lighter than silk, and white as snow; for white, the image of purity, was the favourite colour of the Great King. Others of his attendants carried flaming swords in their hands, and their garments displayed the most brilliant colours of the rainbow; each of these stood in waiting to execute the will of the King, with the rapidity of lightning, on receiving from him the slightest sign. All were happy to be admitted into his presence; their faces shone with the mildest joy, and wore the impression of a calm serenity, and of the absence of all inquietude and pain: there was but one heart, and one soul among them; the sentiment of paternal concord so united these beings, that no envy or jealousy ever arose among them. The common centre of all their thoughts, and all their sentiments, was devotion to their sovereign: it would have been impossible either to see or converse with them, without passionately desiring, even at any sacrifice, to obtain their friendship, and to partake their lot. Among the rest of the inhabitants of the Heavenly City, there were some less close in their attendance upon the Great King; but they were all virtuous, all happy, all had been enriched by the beneficence of the monarch, and, what is of still higher price, had received constant marks of his paternal care; for his subjects were all equal in his eyes, and he loved them and treated them as if they had been his children.

"The Great King had, besides the two kingdoms I have been describing, an uninhabited island of considerable extent; it was his wish to people and cultivate this island, for all within it was a kind of chaos: he destined it to be for some years the abode of such future citizens as he intended to receive finally into his residence, to which only such of his subjects were admitted, as had rendered themselves worthy by their conduct. This island was called Earthly Abode; he who should have passed some time in it, and by his virtues, his application to labour, and the cultivation of the land, should have rendered himself worthy of reward, was afterwards to be received into the Heavenly City, and made one of its happy inhabitants.

"To effect this end, the Great King caused a fleet to be equipped, which was to transit the new colonists to this island. These he chose from the kingdom of Night, and for his first gift bestowed upon them the enjoyment of light, and the view of the lovely face of nature, of which they had been derived in their gloomy and unknown abode. It will easily be imagined that they arrived joyful and happy, at least they became so, when they had had been for a short time accustomed to the multitude of new objects, which struck their feeble sight. The island was rich and fertile when cultivated. The beneficent king provided each individual who was disembarked upon it, with all the things he could want in the time he had fixed for their stay in it, and all the means for obtaining the certainty of being admitted as citizens of his magnificent abode, when they should leave the Earthly Island. All that was required to entitle them to this benefit, was that they should occupy themselves unceasingly in useful labour, and strictly obey the commands of the Great King which he had made known to them. He sent to them his only son, who addressed them from his father in the following terms:

"'My dear children, I have called you from the kingdom of Night and Insensibility to render you happy by the gifts of life, of sentiment, and of activity. But your happiness for the most part will depend upon yourselves. You will be happy, if you wish to be so. If such is your sincere desire, you must never forget that I am your good king, your tender father; and you must faithfully fulfil my will in the cultivation of the country I have confided to your care. Each of you shall receive, on his arriving at the island, the portion of the island which is intended for him; and my further commands respecting your conduct, will be soon communicated to you. I shall send you wise and learned men, who will explain to you my commands, and that you may of yourselves seek after the light necessary for your welfare, and remember my laws at every instant of your lives, it is my will that each father of a family, shall keep an exact copy of them in his house, and read them daily to all the persons who belong to him. Further, each first day of the week, I require to be devoted to my service. In each colony, all the people shall assemble together as brothers in one place, where shall be read and explained to them, the laws contained in my archives. The rest of this day shall be employed in making serious reflections on the duties and destination of the colonists, and on the best means to fulfil the same: thus, it shall be possible to all, to receive instruction concerning the best manner and most effectual means, of improving the land which has been confided to your care: thus, you will each day learn to manure, to sow, to plant, to water, and cleanse the land from tares, and from all evil weeds that that may choke the good seed. On this same day, each of you may present his supplications, may tell me what he stands in need of, and what he desires to have, to forward the perfection of his labour; all these requests will appear before me, and I shall answer, by granting such as I shall think reasonable, and tending to a salutary end. If your heart tells you that the various benefits you enjoy, deserve your gratitude, and if you will testify it by doubling your activity, and by consecrating to me the day I have chosen for myself, I will take care that this day of rest, instead of being an injury to you, shall become a benefit, through the salutary repose of your body, and that of the animals given you to assist your labours, and who, as well as yourself, should enjoy repose on that day to recruit their strength. Even the wild animals of the field, and of the forests, ought on that day to be protected from the pursuit of the hunter.

" 'He, who in his Earthly Abode shall most strictly have observed my will, who shall have best fulfilled the duties of a brother towards his fellow inhabitants, who shall have preserved his land in the best order, and shall show the largest produce from it, shall be recompensed for his deeds, and shall become an inhabitant of my magnificent residence in the Heavenly City. But the neglectful and the idle man, and the wicked man, who shall have spent their time in interrupting the useful labours of others, shall be condemned to pass their lives in slavery, or, according to the degree of their wickedness, shall be condemned to live in subterraneous mines, in the bowels of the earth.

" 'From time to time, I shall send ships to fetch certain individuals from the Earthly Island, to reward or punish them, according as they have done well or ill; and as none will be warned beforehand, of the time of the coming, of my messenger, it will be well for you to keep watch, that you may be ready to perform the voyage, and worthy to be received into the Heavenly City. It will not be permitted for any one to pass by stealth on board the ship; and leave his abode without my orders; for such a one shall be severely punished. I shall have the most certain knowledge of all that passes in the Earthly Island, and no one will be able to deceive me. A magical mirror will at all times show me the actions of each individual in the island, and you shall be judged according to your most secret thoughts and actions.'

"All the colonists were well satisfied with the discourse of the Great King, and made him the most sacred promises. After a short time allowed for repose from the fatigue of the voyage, a portion of land and the proper instruments for labour, were distributed to each of the strangers. They received also seeds and useful plants, and young trees, for producing them refreshing fruits. Each was then left at liberty to act as he pleased, and increase the value of what was confided to his care. But what happened? After some time, each followed the suggestions of his fancy: one planted his land with arbours, flowery banks, and sweet-smelling shrubs; all pleasing to the sight, but which brought forth nothing. Another planted wild apple-trees, instead of the good fruit as the Great King had commanded; contenting himself with giving high-sounding names to the worthless fruit he had caused to be brought forth. A third had indeed sown good grain; but not knowing how to distinguish the tares that grew up along with it, he pulled up the good plants before they were mature, and left only the tares in his ground. But the greater part let their land lie fallow, and bestowed no labour upon it, having spoiled their implements, or lost their seed, either from negligence or idleness, or liking better to amuse themselves than to labour; many of them had wilfully misunderstood the instructions of the Great King, and sought by subtleties to change their meaning.

"Few, very few, worked with diligence and courage, and seeking to improve their land, according to the orders they had received. The great fault of these was, that they would not believe what the Great King had sent to tell them. All the fathers of families, had indeed a copy of the laws of the Sovereign, but most of them omitted to read in the book: some saying that it was useless to read it, for they knew it by heart, while they never employed their thoughts upon it. Others pretended that these laws were good for times past, but were no longer beneficial for the present state of the country. Some even had the audacity to assert, that it contained many inexplicable contradictions, that the laws it prescribed were merely supposed of falsified, and that they had therefore a right to deviate from them. Others among them maintained, that the magical mirror was a mere fable; that the King was of too merciful a nature to keep galleys; that there would be no such place as the subterranean mines; and that all would at last enter the Heavenly City. From habit they continued to celebrate the first day of the week, but by far the smallest part of it was consecrated to the honour of the Great King. Great numbers of them dispensed with going to the general assembly, either from idleness, or to employ themselves in occupations which had been expressly forbidden. By far the greater part of the people considered this day of repose as intended for pleasure, and thought of nothing but adorning and amusing themselves as soon as daylight appeared. There were only then a small number of persons who kept the day according to the decree; and even of those who frequented the assembly, many had their thoughts absent, or were sleepy, or engaged in forming empty projects, instead of listening to the words, which fell from the lips of the minister of the sovereign. The Great King, however, observed unalterably the laws he had laid down and announced, respecting them. From time to time some frigates appeared on their coasts, each bearing the name of some disastrous malady; and these were followed by a large ship of the line, named the *Grave*, on board of which, the admiral, whose name was *Death*, caused his flag of two colours, green and black, to be constantly floating in the air. He showed the colonists, according to the situation in which he found them, either the smiling colour of Hope, or the gloomy colour of Despair.

"This fleet always arrived without being announced, and seldom gave any pleasure to the inhabitants. The admiral sent the captains of his frigates, to seize the persons be was ordered to bring back with him. Many who had not the smallest inclination were suddenly embarked, while others, who had prepared every thing for the harvest, and whose land was in the best condition, were also seized. But these last took their departure cheerfully, and without alarm; well knowing that nothing but happiness awaited them. It was those who were conscious they had neglected to cultivate their land, who felt the most regret. It was even necessary to employ force to bring them under subjection. When the fleet was ready for departure, the admiral sailed for the port of the Royal Residence; and the Great King, who was present on their arrival, executed with strict justice both the rewards and punishments which had been promised to them. All the excuses alleged by those who had been idle, were of no avail. They were sent to the mines and to the galleys, while those who had obeyed the Great King and well cultivated their land, were admitted into the Heavenly City, clothed in robes of brilliant colours, one exceeding the other according to the degree of merit."——Here, my dear children, ends my parable. May you have thoroughly understood its meaning, and may you reap the advantage it is capable of affording you! Make it the subject of your reflections the whole of this day. You, Fritz, I see, are thoughtful; tell me what struck you most in my narration.

*Fritz.*—The goodness of the Great King, and the ingratitude of the colonists, father.

*Father.*—And you, Ernest, what is your thought?

*Ernest.*—For my part, I think they were great fools to have made so bad a calculation. What did they get by conducting themselves as they did? With a little pains they might have passed a very agreeable sort of life in the island, and would have been sure of going afterwards to the Heavenly City.

*Jack.*—To the mines, gentlemen, away with you! you have well deserved it.

*Francis.*—For my part, I should have liked best to have lived with the men who were drest in the colours of the rainbow. How beautiful they must have looked!

*Father.*— This is well, my boys. I perceive that each of you, according to his age and character, has seized the meaning of my parable. I have by this image endeavoured to represent to you the conduct of God towards man, and that of man towards God: let us see now if you have completely seized the sense.—I then put different questions to them, and explained what they had not perfectly comprehended; and after a short review of the principal parts of my discourse, I concluded it by a moral application.

"Human creatures," said I, "are the colonists of God; we are required to perform the business of probation for a certain period, and sooner or later are destined to be taken hence. Our final destination is Heaven, and a perfect happiness with the spirits of just men made perfect, and in the presence of the bountiful Father of us all. The piece of land intrusted to each is the soul! and according as he cultivates and ennobles it, or neglects or depraves it, will be his future reward or punishment. At present, dear children, that you know the true sense of my parable, each of you should make the application of it according to his own consciousness. You, Fritz, should think of the subjects who planted the wild apples, and wished to make them pass for sweet savoury fruit of a superior kind. These represent persons who make a parade of the natural virtues belonging to their character, and which are consequently exercised without any trouble to themselves; such as courage, strength, etc. who prefer them to more essential qualities acquired by others, with sacrifices and labour to themselves; and who, full of presumption and arrogance, consider themselves as irreproachable because nature has given them personal courage, and bodily strength, and a certain skill in the use of these qualities.

"You, Ernest, should think of the subjects of the Great King who cultivated their land so as to produce arbours, flowery banks, and sweet-smelling shrubs, and such productions in general as would please the eye, but which produced no fruit. These are they, who give their whole attention to the acquiring unfruitful knowledge, sciences, etc., and consider with a sort of contempt the things more immediately required for the conduct of life; who exert themselves solely for the understanding, and neglect the heart; whose principal aim it is, to obtain self-indulgences, and who neglect what is useful in society.

"You, Jack, and you, Francis, should apply to yourselves the case of those men who let their land lie fallow, or, in their thoughtlessness, mistook the grain, and sowed tares instead of wheat. These are the neglectful subjects, who neither think nor learn, but give to the winds what is taught them, or entirely forget instruction; who reject virtuous sentiments, and let the bad ones grow in their hearts. But for ourselves, one and all, we will adopt the model of the good and zealous labourers; and should our exertions be a little painful, we shall think of the reward which awaits us, when we shall have adorned our souls with all that is good, just, and praiseworthy. Thus, when death, which cannot fail to come at last, shall summon us, we may follow him with joy to the throne of the Good and Great King, to hear him pronounce these sweet and consoling words: O good and faithful servant! thou hast been tried, and found faithful in many things; enter thou into the joy of thy Lord." With these words, and a short prayer of benediction, I concluded the solemnity of our Sunday; and I had the satisfaction of seeing, that my four sons had not only listened attentively, but that they were struck with the application I had made to each of them. They remained for a short time reflecting in silence. Jack was the first to break it: You have explained to us every part of the parable, father, except the copy of the laws of the Great King, which was to be kept and read in every family: have you one of these copies? for you never read it to us.

*Father.*—Alas! my children, I have never been without such a copy; and not only one, but several, and we have read in it almost every day. This copy is the Holy Bible, which contains all God's laws, and which we ought constantly to study carefully. I cannot forgive myself for not having thought of bringing it from the vessel. Should we not be able to go another voyage, we shall for ever be deprived of this divine doctrine. I can hardly imagine how it could be possible for me, a minister of the Holy Gospel, and the father of a family, to be so occupied about things for the comfort of our poor mortal bodies, and forget what might console and sustain our immortal souls, and which was so necessary for the conduct of my children!

*My Wife.*—Have you then forgot my enchanted bag, which I have promised shall furnish every thing you can desire? You wish for a Bible. In a minute I will put one into your hands; and heartily do I rejoice in having the power to procure you so great a satisfaction.

*Father.*—O best and most excellent of women! how ashamed I am of myself in the comparison! While, in the midst of confusion and horrors, you thought of so many little things conducive to our comfort, and which we as males disdained to be occupied about, have you then also taken care of the most essential of all, the health of our souls? A thousand thanks are due to you! Give me the inestimable book, these laws of the Great King, which I have mentioned in my parable, and which from this moment, we will take for the rule of our lives. She opened her bag, and with joy I received from her the book of life. I opened it, and immediately read some passages from it to my family. In this solitude, in which for so long a time we had heard only our own thoughts expressed in an appropriate language, we were singularly affected with the voice from heaven, which now seemed to address us; we felt forcibly that, notwithstanding our exile, we were still connected with the community of mankind: by the invisible tie of the same religion, and the same Father, we were for ever numbered among the children of God, to whom he enjoins laws, and on whom he bestows his care, no less in a desert, than in an immense capital; our island, containing only our own family, was no doubt as interesting in his eyes, as whole nations of people. I explained with the utmost care what I read to them, and I gave the book in turn to each of the boys, that they might have the pleasure of reading for themselves. I chose in preference, such passages as were applicable to our circumstances. We then raised our hearts to God, to thank him for so signal a benefit as the preservation of our Bible. My young folks still remained thoughtful and serious; but by and by the gaiety natural to their age, prevailed, and each slipped away to seek the recreation he liked best. But as it had been enjoined them not to undertake any kind of labour, they rambled about from place to place, with more appearance of listlessness than of reflection. This gave me an opportunity of observing, that at their age, the soul is too feeble to sustain herself through the whole day without occupation. I recalled them, therefore, and observed that the Great and Good King did not require complete inaction from them, and that they might amuse and occupy themselves the rest of the day, without giving him offence, provided they should avoid unruly sports. Jack desired me to lend him my bow and arrows, as he wished to see how they would fly, now that they had been completed from the quills of his porcupine. Fritz had a great desire to be employed about the case he was to make of the skin of the tiger-cat, and asked my advice how to proceed. Little Francis, also, laid my activity under contribution, by requesting me to make him a bow and arrows, he being yet too young to be intrusted with a gun. I began with giving Jack the bow and arrows as he desired, and told him how to make the sand run out, and to put the sharp points at the end, and tie them securely round with packthread, and then to dip them into some glue.

Yes, yes, I understand, said Jack wagging his head knowingly; I know how to do it very well, father. But will you be kind enough to tell me where there is a glue-shop, that I may step and buy some glue in a minute?

I will show you where, said little Francis, laughing as he spoke: ask mamma to give you one of her soup cakes, which are exactly like good strong glue.

Little blockhead! replied Jack, you think then it is enough to be like; what I want is glue, and not soup.

*Father.*—Not so much of a blockhead as you think, Jack, interrupted I. The truth often comes from the lips of children, and you will do well to follow his advice. I am of opinion, that one of the cakes, dissolved in a little water, and afterwards thickened upon the fire, would produce what would be an excellent substitute for glue; give yourself therefore the trouble of making the experiment. Put a soup cake over the fire in one of our cocoa-shells, and you will soon know the event.

While Jack was preparing his glue, and Francis, proud of being the inventor, was busied in assisting his brother, blowing the fire, etc., Fritz came to me for my advice about the making of his case. Run, said I, and fetch your skin, and we will work at it together. I sat down on the grass, took out my knife, and with the remains of a bamboo cane, began to make a bow for Francis. I was well satisfied to observe them one and all, take a fancy to shooting with an arrow, having been desirous to accustom them to this exercise, which constituted the principal defence of the warriors of old, and might possibly become our only means of protection and subsistence: our provision of powder must at last be exhausted; we might even, from moment to moment, be deprived of it by accident; it therefore was of the utmost importance to us, to acquire some other means of killing animals, or attacking our enemies. The Caribees, I recollected, were taught at a very tender age, to strike an object at the distance of thirty or forty steps; they hit the smallest birds perched on the top of the tallest trees. Why then should it not be possible for my boys to learn to do the same? I will at least, said I, provide them with bows and arrows, and try what can be done.

While I was silently reflecting on the subject, employed in finishing a bow for Francis, Ernest, who had been observing me for some time, slipped suddenly away; and Fritz coming up at the same moment, with the wetted skin of the tiger-cat in his hand, I paid no attention to the circumstance. I began my instructions to my eldest boy, respecting the trade of a tanner. I told him the method of getting rid of the fat of the skin, by rubbing it over with sand, and placing it in running water till it had no longer any appearance of flesh, or any smell; next to rub it with soft butter, to make it supple, and then to stretch the skin in different directions; and also to make use of some eggs in the operation, if his mother could spare them. You will not at first produce such excellent workmanship as I have seen of this kind from England; but with a little patience, regretting neither your time, nor your labour, you will have completed some decent-looking cases, which will give you the more pleasure, from being made from an animal of your own taking, and by the work of your own hands. When your skin shall have thus been prepared, cut certain small cylinders of wood of the size and length required; scoop these cylinders hollow so as to form a convenient case for a knife, a fork, or a spoon; then stretch your softened skin upon the surface of the cylinders, in such a manner, that the skin may reach a little beyond the extremity of the wood, and close at the top; you have nothing more to do, than to let the skin cling to, and dry upon these moulds. Your work will then be finished, and will turn out a neat and masterly production.

*Fritz.*—I understand perfectly, and I hope I shall succeed; but if I were to take some cork for my moulds, the cases would be lighter, and more convenient for carrying.

*Father.*—No doubt they would, but where can you get any cork? and how would you be able to cut it and scoop it out? It is a singularly impracticable material, and would resist the knife.

*Fritz.*—If you would let me take one of the cork jackets we keep for swimming, I could try by means of heating it, to render it fit for my purpose.

*Father.*—To this I have no objection; I like to see you inventive, and casting about for the means of success. In reality, we have a pretty considerable number of those jackets; and I am in hopes we shall not want them any more. You may get one of them, but take care not to hold it too long to the fire. But what is the matter, wife, that you shake your head? You seem dissatisfied with your boy's undertaking?

*My Wife.*—No, I am not dissatisfied with his work, provided he can accomplish it, but to the use for which it seems intended. Do you imagine that I shall let you have our silver table utensils to be dragged about at the risk of losing them, in your expeditions? In the first place, I do not consider them as our own; and what account should we have to give the captain, should we ever meet again?

*Jack.*—Oh, we should have accounts enough for him. We would tell him, that but for the pains we took to preserve them, they would all have gone to the bottom; that the last thing our friends the sharks would have thought of, would be to restore his silver spoons; and that, as we had all the trouble, they ought to be considered of our own earning.

*My Wife.*—So you have made a partnership with the shark, my boy! I hope, however, that you entertain a higher idea than you profess, of your own nature; and that upon more reflection you will perceive, that in equity and justice, we ought to consider not only these utensils, but all the other things of value we took from the vessel, as a trust committed to our care; and which we ought to use our utmost endeavours to preserve, I am, however, of opinion, that having rescued them at the risk of our lives, we have a right to use them for our own convenience, while we remain destitute of all human aid; but that, if we should ever find the persons to whom they belong, it is a duty incumbent on us to return them.

*Fritz.*—And I, for my part, am of opinion, that the captain, however great a man he may be, will not be sorry to receive them in a magnificent case made from the skin of the tiger-cat, with which I shall present him, in return for the use of his utensils.

I was laughing at the vanity of my young pretender, when suddenly, we heard the firing of a gun, which proceeded from our tent in the tree, and two birds at the same time fell dead at our feet. We were at once surprised and alarmed, and all eyes were turned upwards to the place. There we saw Ernest standing outside the tent, a gun in his hand, and heard him triumphantly exclaiming, Catch them! catch them there! I have hit them; and you see I did not run away for nothing. He descended the ladder joyfully and precipitately, and ran with Francis to take up the two birds; while Fritz and Jack mounted to our castle, hoping to meet with the same luck. I observed them when they were got near the top, and called after them—What are you going about? Have you already forgot the Great King, who commands that the birds of the air and the beasts of the field should rest on the day he has consecrated to himself?

These words suddenly interrupted the zeal of the young sports-men, and diminished the pleasure of Ernest. He blushed, and cast his eyes on the ground, without attempting an excuse; while his brothers quietly descended the ladder, and began to examine the birds which had fallen. One of the dead birds proved to be a sort of thrush, and the other was a very small kind of pigeon, which in the Antilles is called an ortolan: they are very fat, and of a deli-cious taste. We now observed, for the first time, on looking about, that the wild figs began to ripen, and that they attracted a great number of these birds. I foresaw, in consequence, that we were about to have our larder well stored, and our table furnished with a dish which even a nobleman might envy us. I consoled the boys for the reproach I had made them, by giving them permission to kill as many of these birds, in future, as they liked. I knew that, half roasted and put into barrels with melted butter thrown over them, it was a food that would keep a long time, and might prove an excellent resource in time of need. My wife set about strip-ping off the feathers of the birds Ernest had killed, to dress them for our supper. I seated myself by her side, and proceeded in my work of arrow-making for Francis; and observed to my wife, that she would find an excellent substitute in the figs, for the grain we should want to feed our fowls, who no doubt would be found to have as high a relish for them, as was evinced by the ortolans.

Thus finished our day of rest. The birds proved excellent; but in point of quantity, we ran no risk of indigestion. Supper ended, and prayers said, we ascended the ladder in procession; and each withdrew to his hammock to taste the sweets of a tranquil sleep, though unprompted by such fatigue as we had experienced the preceding day.

# XIII

# CONVERSATION, A WALK, AND IMPORTANT DISCOVERIES

J ACK HAD FINISHED THE TRIAL OF HIS ARROWS: THEY FLEW to admiration; and he practised his new art incessantly. Little Francis waited with impatience for the moment when he should do the same, and followed with his eyes every stroke I made. But when I had finished my bow, and prepared some little arrows for him, I must next undertake we make him a quiver; for, said he, an archer can no more be without a quiver, than a sportsman without a game-bag. I found I must submit. I took some bark from the branch of a tree, which came off in a round form; and folding the edges over each other, I stuck them together with some glue produced from the soup cakes, and which answered the purpose extremely well. I next stuck on a round piece to serve for the bottom; and then tied to it a loop of strings which I hung round his neck. He put his arrows into it; and, happy as a chevalier in full armour, he took his bow in his hand, and ran to try his skill by the side of his brother. Fritz had also cleaned and prepared his materials for the cases, when his mother summoned us to dinner.

We cheerfully placed ourselves under the shade of our tree, round the table I had manufactured. At the end of the repast, I made the following proposition to the boys, which I was sure would give them pleasure.

What think you, my good friends, said I, of giving a name to the place of our abode, and to the different parts of the country which are known to us? I do not mean a general name to the whole island, for who knows, but that some illustrious European traveller may have already bestowed on it that of either a great navigator, or of some saint; and that our island may not already make a figure in certain maps of geography? But this need not prevent us from also giving names to the objects we are concerned with, and which will make us better understand each other, when we are conversing about them: this ceremony will also present to us the soothing illusion, of inhabiting a country already known and peopled.

They all exclaimed, joyfully, that the idea was excellent.

*Jack.*—Oh! pray, papa, let us invent some very long names, and that are very difficult to be pronounced. I should be glad that those who shall read about us, should be a little puzzled to remember the names of the places and things that belonged to us. What pains has it not cost me to remember their *Monomolapa*, their *Zanguebar*, their *Coromandel*, and many other still more difficult appellations! Ah! now we shall take our revenge of them.

*Father.*—This would all be very well, if it were probable that our history in this country, and the names we shall have bestowed, were likely to be objects of public curiosity; but in the mean while, you forget that our own organs will be fatigued, by frequently pronouncing such barbarous words as you propose.

*Jack.*—How shall we manage then? What pretty names can we find?

*Father.*—We will do as all sorts of nations have done before us. We will name the places by different words from our own language, that shall express some particular circumstance with which we have been concerned.

*Jack.*—Well, so we will; I shall like this still better. Where shall we begin?

*Father.*—We shall naturally begin with the bay by which we entered this country. What shall we call it? What say you, Fritz? You must speak first, for you are the eldest.

*Fritz.*—Let us call it *Oyster Bay*: you remember what quantities of oysters we found in it.

*Jack.*—Oh, no! let it rather be called *Lobster Bay*; for you cannot have forgot what a large one it was that caught hold of my leg, and which I carried home to you.

*Ernest.*—Why then we may as well call it the *Bay of Tears*, for you must remember that you blubbered loud enough for all of us to hear you.

*My Wife.*—My advice would be that, out of gratitude to *God*, who conducted us hither in safety, we ought to call it *Providence Bay*, or the *Bay of Safety*.

*Father.*—This name is both appropriate and sonorous, and pleases me extremely. But what name shall we give to the spot where we first set up our tent?

*Fritz.*—Let us call it simply *Tent-House*.

*Father.*—That name will do very well. And the little islet at the entrance of *Providence Bay*, in which we found so many planks and beams that enabled us to make our bridge, how shall it be named?

*Ernest.*—It may be called *Sea-Gull Island* or *Shark Island*, for it was here we saw both those animals.

*Father.*—I am for the last of these names, *Shark Island*; for it was the shark that was the cause of the sea-gulls being there; and it will also be a means of commemorating the courage and the triumph of Fritz, who killed the monster.

*Jack.*—For the same reason we will call the marsh, in which you cut the canes for our arrows, *Flamingo Marsh*.

*Father.*—Quite right, I think; and the plain, through which we passed on our way to this place, *Porcupine Field*, in memory of your skilful encounter with him. But now comes the great question—What name shall we give to our present abode?

*Ernest.*—It ought to be called, simply, *Tree Castle*.

*Fritz.*—No, no, that will not do at all; that is the same as if, when we wanted to name a town, we called it *The Town*. Let us invent a more noble name.

*Jack.*—Yes, so we will. I say, *Fig Town*.

*Fritz.*—Ha, ha, ha! a noble name, it must be confessed! Let us call it *The Eagle's Nest*, which I am sure has a much better sound. Besides, our habitation in the tree, is really much more like a nest, than a town, and the eagle cannot but ennoble it, since he is the king of birds.

*Father.*—Will you let me decide the question for you? I think our abode should be called *The Falcon's Nest*; for, my boys, you are not yet arrived at the dignity of eagles, but are simply, poor birds of prey; and like the falcon, you also are, I trust, obedient, docile, active, and courageous. Ernest can have no objection to this; for, as he knows, falcons make their nests in large trees. All exclaimed, clapping their hands, Yes, yes, we will have it *The*

*Falcon's Nest*! the sound is quite chivalrous; so, Health to *Falcon's Nest Castle*! cried they all, looking up to the tree, and making low bows. I poured out a small quantity of sweet wine, and presented it to each, to solemnize our baptism. And how, said I, shall we name the promontory, where Fritz and I in vain wearied our eyes, in search of our companions of the vessel? I think it may properly be called *Cape Disappointment*.

*All*.—Yes, this is excellent. And the river with the bridge—

*Father*.—If you wish to commemorate one of the greatest events of our history, it ought to be called *The Jackall's River*; for these animals crossed it when they came and attacked us, and it was there that one of them was killed. The bridge I should name *Family Bridge*, because we were all employed in its construction, and all crossed it together in our way to this place. It will be quite a pleasure to converse about the country we inhabit, now that we have instituted names as if every thing belonged to us.

*Ernest*.—It will be just as if we had farms and country houses, all dependent upon our castle.

*Francis*.—It is the same as if we were kings.

*My Wife*.—And the queen-mother is not without hope, that her little slips of majesty will conduct themselves mercifully towards their subjects—the birds, the agoutis, the geese, and the flamingoes; the . . . What more shall I say? for I do not know the family name of all your vassals. Let me, therefore, end, by hoping that you will not depopulate your kingdom.

*Fritz*.—No, mother, we will take care of that. We will endeavour to extirpate, only those among our subjects, who are wicked.

In this pleasing kind of chat, the time of dinner passed agreeably away. We settled the basis of a geography of our own country; and amused ourselves with saying that it must go by the first post to Europe.

After dinner, Fritz again set to work upon his case; and, to my great astonishment, he had possession of one of the cork-jackets and was preparing to cut it to pieces, and use it as a lining to the cylinders. In the name of Heaven, cried I, where did you get the jacket? I was quite sure we had left them all at Tent-House; and when I gave you leave this morning, to take one of them, it was in the hope that, tired with waiting, you would use some other wood, and that the jacket would escape. As it is, I must shut my eyes while you cut it, for I will not retract my word. But tell me where you got it? It was I, said my wife, who placed it as a saddle on the ass's back, for little Francis to sit upon. You, it seems, did not observe it; but nothing escapes that lynx-eyed boy of ours, called Fritz.

Well, well, since it is thus, replied I, let him make use of it if he can; the cutting it will at least exercise his patience. I shall soon find how to manage it, said Fritz, by holding it near the fire. We let him do as he liked, and I went out to look for Jack, whom I met, dragging the skin of his porcupine with great difficulty along; for it was still armed with all the quills, with the exception of about a dozen, which we had taken for the arrows. He spread it at my feet, entreating me to assist him in making some coats of mail, or cuirasses, of it, for the dogs, as I had before recommended to him, and which he had taken care not to forget. After making him clean the skin completely on the inside, with some cinders and sand mixed together, I assisted him in cutting it, and his mother helped him in the sewing. When this was done, we put the first that was dried on the back of the patient Turk, which gave him a respectable warlike sort of an appearance, and no one could doubt that he was sufficiently well armed to encounter even an hyena.

His companion, Ponto, had less reason to be pleased with this new kind of spiked accoutrement. Turk, unconscious of one particular quality in his new dress, approached near to Ponto and lay down by his side, who sprang off in a fright, searching about, for some place where he might be sheltered from the perforating familiarities of his companion. Jack's concluding business, was, stripping the skin from the head of the porcupine, and stretching it on one of the roots of our trees to dry, intending to make a cap of it, like those worn by the savages, which, he said, would frighten our enemies should they approach; while, in the mean time, his friends if they liked it, might set it on a pole and make merry with it.

During our employment, Ernest and Francis had been exercising themselves in shooting their arrows: the evening was advancing, and the intense heat of the day began to diminish. I invited all my family to take a walk: Leave your work for this time, my boys, said I, and let us make a short excursion; and, as a suitable conclusion to the day, let us seek in the beautiful face of Nature, for traces of the wisdom and goodness of the Creator. Which way shall we direct our steps?

*Fritz.*—Let us go to Tent-House, father; we are in want of powder and shot for the little consumers of our figs; nor must we miss our dinner for to-morrow, or forget that we are to secure a supply for winter.

*My Wife.*—I too vote for Tent-House; my butter is nearly gone, for Fritz took an unreasonable share for his new trade of tanning; also, I have never failed to observe, that those who most zealously preach a life of frugality and economy, are at least as well satisfied as the rest, when I take care to present them with an excellent and well dressed dinner.

*Ernest.*—If we go to Tent-House, let us try to bring away some of the geese and ducks with us: they will look very well swimming about in our stream here, by Falcon's Nest.

*Jack.*—I will undertake to catch them, if any one will help to bring them home.

*Francis.*—And I will catch my handkerchief full of lobsters in the Jackall's River, and we will put them into Falcon's Stream, where, no doubt, they will thrive to admiration.

*Father.*—You really all of you assign such good reasons, that I see I must yield to them. To Tent-House, then, we will go; but we will not take our accustomed road along the sea-shore, but rather vary our pleasure, by trying to explore some other way. We will keep along our own little stream as far as the wall of rocks, whose agreeable shade will accompany us almost as far as the cascade formed by Jackall's River: it will, I hope, as we have no burden to carry, be easy for us to cross it, by jumping from stone to stone, and so to get to Tent-House: we will return with our provisions by the road of Family Bridge, and along the seashore; the sun, if not gone down, will then be at our backs. This new route may possibly furnish some additional discoveries.

My idea was highly applauded, and all was soon arranged for our setting out. Fritz was adorned with his fine tiger-cat-made belt, but he had not been able to finish his cases in time. Jack walked gravely on, his porcupine cap upon his head, and his jackall belt, armed with his two pistols, round his waist. Each carried a gun and a game-bag; even little Francis had his bow in his hand, and his quiver on his shoulder; and being both pretty and of a fair complexion, he resembled a little Cupid. Their mother was the only person not burdened with a gun; but she carried her large butter-pot, to fill it at our store-house. Turk marched before us with his coat of mail studded with spikes; but it was apparent that he felt intimidated and ill at ease; his step was therefore slow and quiet. The monkey also, having a great desire to accompany us, leaped without ceremony on his accustomed seat, the back of Turk. But when he perceived the formidable saddle and the projecting spikes, he sprang four times forward, making the most comical grimaces imaginable. He was not long, however, in choosing what to do. Ponto, he saw, was without such a frightful instrument; so he jumped upon him in a trice, and clung so closely to his back, that the dog could not shake him off: he therefore gave up the endeavour, and quietly submitted to carry him. Even our new friend, the flamingo, seemed to understand that some extraordinary movement was in agitation, and prepared to make one of the party. The pretty kind-tempered animal had become every day more tame, and attached himself to us with a confidence which increased our goodwill towards him. The boys, enchanted by the manner in which he placed himself in the ranks with us, all contended for being his companion; but the flamingo adopted the prudent measure of coming up to me, and showing his reliance on my protection, by walking gravely by my side.

Our route along the stream, was at first extremely agreeable, being sheltered by the shade of large trees, while the ground under our feet was a short and soft kind of grass. To prolong the pleasure of our walk, we proceeded slowly, amusing ourselves with looking about us to the right and left; the eldest boys made frequent escapes on before, so that we sometimes lost sight of them. In this manner we reached the end of the wood; but the country now appearing to be less open, we thought it would be prudent to bring our whole company together. On looking forward, we saw the boys approaching us full gallop, and this time, for a wonder, the grave Ernest was first. He reached me panting for breath, and so full of joy and eagerness, that he could not pronounce a single word distinctly; but he held out his hand, which contained three little balls of a light green colour.

We have found a prize, indeed, father, cried he at last, when he had recovered his voice; we have found some potatoe seed!

What say you? potatoe seed inquired I joyfully; have you really been so fortunate? Come, every one of you, and let me look at your little balls; for I scarcely dared believe in so happy an event, as the discovery of a plant which would place us for ever beyond the reach of hunger, and even of apprehension. It was you then, Ernest, who found the prize, and our grateful thanks are your due.

*Jack.*—I do not see any great merit there was in the case. I should have found them as soon as he, if I had been in the right place. I see no great talent in what he has done.

*My Wife.*—But, Jack, there is still less talent in your attempt to undervalue the useful discovery your brother has made, and in seeking to diminish the obligation, which we ought rather to feel a pleasure in acknowledging. This little movement of envy in your bosom occasions me uneasiness; I must add, that it is by no means certain that, even if you had been in the same place, you would have remarked the potatoes; that you, who are so thoughtless and unobserving, would have known the leaves for those of the potatoe plant. Ernest gives more attention to what he sees, and his discoveries are not merely the effect of hazard, but of observation also. Perhaps, too, you do not know a potatoe when you see it; and it is even possible that we may ourselves mistake the plant, from our great eagerness to meet the confirmation of our wishes; for there are, no doubt, other plants which also produce small green round balls upon their stalks.

*Francis.*—Why, do potatoe plants bear fruit on their branches as well as at the roots?

*Ernest.*—Little blockhead! do you think, then, that the roots bear blossoms? Do you not know that the vegetable called the potatoe is only the root of the plant, or at least a part of the root, and not a fruit? The fruit, in all plants, is the depository of the seed, which must ripen in the sun, and consequently above ground: these little green balls, therefore, are the real fruit which succeed to the blossom, and contain the seed.

I did not fail to applaud Ernest for this clear and sensible explanation. We all hastened to the place where he had seen these tubercles, and, with extreme joy, we found there a large plantation of potatoe plants; a number of them were covered with their lilac and yellow blossoms, the sight of which conveyed more pleasure to our hearts than if they had been the most fragrant roses; another portion of the plantation was in seed; and in several places, some younger plants were pushing through the earth. Our petulant Jack bawled out, jumping for joy, They are really potatoes! and though it was not I who discovered them, at least it shall be I who will dig them up. Saying this, he knelt down and began to scratch up the earth with all ten fingers of his feeble hands. He would not, however, have made much progress, if the monkey, excited by his example, had not also set himself to work. He dug up several with great dexterity; and after smelling at them, he was going to throw them to a distance: but Jack snatched them eagerly out of his paws, and gave them to his mother; and afterwards the monkey and he continued digging up the potatoes together, and soon obtained enough to serve up for a dinner. The rest of us, unwilling to be idle spectators, set to work also; with our knives and sticks we soon procured a sufficient number, to fill our bags and our pockets. When we were well loaded, we again began to think of our walk to Tent-House. Some of our company raised their voices in favour of returning immediately to Falcon Stream, to unload our cargo, and convert our booty into a delicious meal; but so many pressing motives presented themselves for proceeding to our store-house, that it was decided we should continue our route, which we accordingly resumed.

My children, said I, as we pursued our way, this discovery of the potatoes is one of inestimable value; it reminds me of a passage in the Bible, which is strikingly applicable to our situation, and ought to awaken a sentiment of the warmest gratitude in our hearts, towards our heavenly Father: it is a part of the hundred-and-seventh psalm, and these are the words:

"They wandered in the wilderness, in a solitary way; they found no city to dwell in: hungry and thirsty, their soul fainted within them: then they cried unto the Lord in their trouble, and he delivered them out of their distress: he led them forth by the right way, that they might go to the place of their habitation. He satisfieth the longing spirit, and filleth the hungry soul with his goodness."

*Fritz.*—This is truly applicable to our situation, and we will all return thanks to God for so inestimable a gift.

*Father.*—There are, no doubt, different kinds of vegetables, more succulent and more delicate than the potatoe; but it is precisely this plain tasteless kind of sustenance, that can be eaten for the longest time together, without satiety: accordingly, food of this nature, such as bread, rice, potatoes, obtains, on the whole, a preference over provisions possessing a higher flavour. Can you tell me, boys, the reason of this?

*Ernest.*—I know; it is because they are more wholesome.

*Jack.*—And because they occasion no disgust; I could eat potatoes every day of my life, without being tired of them.

*Father.*—All you say is true; in future they will serve us for bread, and often indeed for our whole dinner. But let us for the present dismiss the subject of our unexpected good fortune, and resume our expedition.

# XIV

# CONTINUATION OF THE PRECEDING CHAPTER, AND MORE DISCOVERIES

ONVERSING ON DIFFERENT SUBJECTS, WE REACHED THE LONG chain of rocks, over which our pretty Falcon Stream made its escape in the form of a cascade, whose gentle murmurs delighted the ear, as much as its wild and various aspect gratified the eye. We kept along the chain of rocks which led to Jackall's River, and from thence to Tent-House, having first, with difficulty, pushed through the high grass which presented itself in our path. Our fatigue, however, was relieved by the uncommon beauty of the scenery around: on the right hand was a boundless sea; on the left, the island, with the bay by which it was accessible, and the chain of rocks, presenting altogether, an assemblage of the picturesque, equal to what the liveliest fancy could desire. The view reminded me of the large flower-stands common in Europe; the shelvings, the projections, the cornices of which, instead of pots of flowers, were covered with plants most rare and contrasted, and in a vigorous state of vegetation. In the greatest number of these, were distinguishable the different families of grasses, many of them of the thorn-leaved species, and more flourishing than those which are cultivated in the green-houses of Europe. There was also in abundance the Indian fig, with its large broad leaf; aloes of different forms and colours; the superb prickly candle, or cactus, bearing straight stalks, taller than a man, and crowned with long straight branches, forming a sort of star. The broad plantain spread along the rocks its innumerable boughs twisted with each other hanging down perpendicularly, and ornamented with flowers, which grew in large tufts, and were of the brightest rose-colour; while that which pleased us best, and which was found there in great abundance, was the king of fruits, both for figure and relish, the crowned pine-apple. We immediately fell on this fruit with avidity, because we knew its value and its innocence, and because it was fit to be eaten without any further preparation than merely gathering it. The monkey was not the last to seize one for himself; and as he could make higher jumps than the boys, they formed the scheme of making him angry by little tricks, so as to induce him to fling pine-apples at them. This game they continued so long, that I thought it prudent to interrupt them, fearing that the unripe state of the fruit might affect their health. My wife and I ate one or two with great pleasure, and after bestowing the commendations so fine a fruit deserved, we agreed that we would frequently return to the place, and eat them as a dessert.

Soon after, I was fortunate enough to discover, among the multitude of plants which grew either at the foot or in the clefts of the rock, the karata (the Bromelia Karata of Linnæus), many of which were now in blossom, and of others the flowers had lately fallen off. They resembled young trees; and travellers have given so perfect a description of them in their books of natural history, that it was impossible I should mistake them. But what further confirmed their identity, was their straight slender stalk, crowned with blossoms, and proceeding from a tuft of leaves like the pine-apple, with its large foliage terminating in a sharp point, and forming altogether, a plant remarkably pleasing to the eye. I pointed out to the boys the immense size of these leaves, which were hollowed in the middle like a saucer, in which the rain is for a long time preserved; and also its beautiful red flowers. As I was acquainted with the properties of this useful plant, the pith of which is used as tinder by the Negroes, who also make a strong kind of thread from the fibres of its leaves, I was not less satisfied with my discovery, than I had been with that of the potatoes; and I did not hesitate to assure them, that I preferred it to the pine-apples. All answered me, their mouths at the same time full of the fruit, that they would resign those trees with all their flowers to me, if I would leave them the pine-apples. The pine-apples are better than all the rest, said they, even than the potatoes. What is a handsome-looking tree worth, if it does not bear any fruit? Your most devoted humble servant, Mr. Karata, but pine-apples for us!

Little gluttons! cried I, half angry, your preference is as sense-less as that of a man who prefers a woman with a handsome face, to one possessed of those valuable and lasting virtues which soothe the cares of human life. The flavour of the pine-apple gratifies your palate; but it is not of necessary use, and I will immediately give you a proof that I am not wrong in my preference of the karata. Ernest, take out my flint and steel, and strike me a light.

*Ernest.*—But, father, what am I to do for tinder? what can I put to receive the sparks?

*Father.*—This is precisely to the purpose. When the tinder which we brought from the vessel is all consumed, how shall we be able to make a fire? and without a fire, how shall we dress a dinner, or prepare numberless other matters we have occasion for?

*Ernest.*—Oh, I should not be in the least at a loss. We would do like the savages; rub two pieces of wood against each other, till at length they catch fire.

*Father.*—Many thanks for your information: but for us who are not savages, and not in the habit of such exercise, the expedient would be somewhat inconvenient. I would lay a wager, that if you were to rub two pieces of wood together for a whole day, you would not produce a single spark; or if you did, you would wait so long for the end you had in view, as to make it almost useless.

*Ernest.*—If this is the case, we must endeavour to have patience till we can find a tree that bears tinder, just as we found one that bears gourds.

*Father.*—We might make tinder by burning some linen rag, and putting it in a close box: but we have, unfortunately, none to spare; and, therefore, the best thing for us would be to find tinder ready prepared in some plant; and in this we may succeed by examining our new prize, the karata tree.

I then took a dried stalk of the tree, stripped off the bark, and there appeared a kind of dry and spungy substance, which I laid upon the flint; and then striking it with a steel, it instantly caught fire. The boys looked on with astonishment, and then began to caper about, exclaiming: Long live the tinder tree!

Here then, said I, we have an article of greater usefulness than if it served merely to gratify the appetite. Your mother will next inform us, what materials she will use for sewing your clothes, when her provision of thread from the enchanted bag is exhausted.

*My Wife.*—I have long been uneasy upon this very subject, and would willingly give all the pine-apples in the world, in exchange for some hemp or flax.

*Father.*—And your wish shall be accomplished, said I. For once I shall have the pleasure of presenting you with something you eagerly desire to have. If you examine, you will find some excellent thread under the leaves of this extraordinary plant, where all-provident nature has placed a store-house of this valuable article, though the lengths of thread will be found not longer than the leaf. I accordingly examined one of the leaves, and drew out of it a strong piece of thread of a red colour, which I gave to my wife. How fortunate it is for us, said she, that you have had the habit of reading and of study! None of us would have had a thought about this plant, or have conceived that it could be of any use; but will it not be a little difficult to draw out the little lengths of thread through the prickles that surround them?

*Father.*—Not in the least; we shall puts the leaves to dry, either in the sun, or by a gentle fire. The useless part of the leaf will then separate by being beaten, and the mass of thread will remain.

*Fritz.*—I see clearly, father, that we ought not to trust to appearances; it is the same with this tree as with mankind; the most merit is often found in an individual that was least supposed to possess it; but I believe it would be difficult to find any good qualities in the prickly plants which are growing here in all directions, and wounding the persons who go near them: of what use can they possibly be?

*Father.*—Again, my son, you form your judgement from appearances. The greatest part of these plants possess medicinal virtues; great use is made in pharmacy of the aloe, which produces such abundance of beautiful flowers, in green-houses in Europe, some have been seen to bear more than three thousand blossoms. At Carlsbad, upon the estates of Count de Limbourg, there was an aloe tree twenty-six feet in height; it had twenty-eight branches, which branches bore more than three thousand blossoms in the space of a month. At Paris, at Leyden, in Denmark, there have been also seen some exceedingly curious specimens of this tree; many of them are full of a resinous sort of sap, of which valuable gums are made. But look, here, too, is the Indian fig or prickly pear, a vegetable of no common interest; it grows in the poorest soils, and, as you see, upon the rocks; the poorer the soil, the more its leaves are thick and succulent; I should be tempted to believe that it was nourished by the air, rather than by the earth. It is also called the racket-tree, from the resemblance of its long, thick, flat leaves to that well-known instrument. This plant bears a kind of fig, which is said to be sweet and palatable, when ripened in its native sun, and it is both a salutary and refreshing food. This, then, is another plant of great utility. Scarcely had I pronounced these words, than our light-footed Jack was on the rock, trying to gather some of the fruit; but this time he had reason to repent his precipitation; for the fruit of this tree is covered with fine prickles, which assail the skin of the bold hand that dares to gather them. Poor Jack soon came down again, crying heartily, striking his feet upon the ground, and shaking his hand with the pain the prickles occasioned. I had not the courage to make this the moment for a lesson of morality founded upon the effects of his gluttony, for which he was sufficiently punished; and I reproved his brothers, who stood by laughing while I was drawing out the thorns. I then instructed them how to gather this fruit without incurring the same inconvenience. I threw up a stone, and brought down a fig, which I caught upon my hat; I cut off its two ends, and was thus enabled to hold it without injury, while I peeled off the skin. I then resigned it to the curiosity of my young companions.

The novelty, rather than the taste, of the fruit, made them think it excellent: they all found means to gather some of the figs, and each was busied in inventing the best method of taking off the skins: but that of Fritz had the best success; he gathered his figs, by plunging the sharp point of his stick into them, and then pulling the stick a little sideways to bring them down: he peeled them quite neatly while they were still on the stick, and presented several to his mother, who partook of them with pleasure.

In the mean time, I perceived Ernest holding a fig upon the end of his knife, turning it about in all directions, and bringing it close to his eye with a look of curious inquiry. I wish I could know, said at length our young observer, what little animals these are in the fig, which feed so eagerly upon and are as red as scarlet.

*Father.*—Ha, ha! this too will perhaps turn out a new discovery, and an additional source of usefulness, which this plant possesses. Let me look at your fig; I will lay a wager that it is the insect called the cochineal.

*Jack.*—The cochineal! what a droll name! What is the cochineal, father?

*Father.*—It is an insect of the kind called *suchers*, or *kermes*; he feeds upon the Indian fig, which, no doubt, is the cause of his beautiful colour, which forms an object of considerable importance in the trade of a dyer; for nothing else produces so fine a scarlet. In America, they stretch pieces of linen under the branches, and then shake the tree; and when the insects have fallen in great numbers, the ends of the linen are folded together to inclose them; the insects are sprinkled with vinegar or cold water, and then dried, and sent to Europe, for the use of dyers, who pay a high price for the commodity.

*Ernest.*—I now perfectly agree with you, that this plant is of ten times more use than the finest pine-apple: the latter, however, has also its merit, and we are not obliged to reject the one, if we choose the other: yet, as we have not any occasion for a scarlet dye, and that the fruit of the fig-tree is certainly inferior to the pine-apple, so I think it is but reasonable to prefer the last.

*Father.*—In this you are to blame; I have not yet mentioned a still superior usefulness peculiar to the Indian fig-tree; it serves as a protection to man.

*Fritz.*—As a protection to man! Why, how can that be, father?

*Father.*—It is used for making hedges round the habitations of man, its prickly surface effectually preventing the approach of animals; for you see, that besides the prickles which took such a fancy to Jack's hand, there is a large thorn at each of the knots, which appear in the plant.

*My Wife.*—The largest serve very well for pins, and even for nails; see how they keep my gown well fastened.

*Father.*—This, then, you see is a third usefulness the Indian fig-tree can boast, and of which I was not at first aware. You must perceive of what importance these inclosures are; and the rather, as they are made, with so little trouble; for, if you plant only one of its leaves in the ground, it immediately takes root, and grows with astonishing rapidity: it is therefore not only a defence against wild beasts, but against enemies in general; for they could not get over it without cutting through the hedge; and during such an operation, which also would be attended with some danger, the persons within, gain time to escape, or to prepare an effectual defence.

Jack, the king of the thoughtless race, asserted that this plant was extremely soft, and yielding in its nature; and that with the assistance of a knife, or even a stick, it would be easy to get over such a hedge: to prove his assertion, he began to cut down, with his clasp knife, a pretty large plant; striking every where to right and left with all his might, till at length one of the divided leaves fell with such violence on his leg, that the thorns struck into the flesh, and Jack roared out piteously, and quickly seated himself upon a stone to disengage it as quickly as possible. I could not now, as I assisted him to draw out the thorns, refrain from laughing a little at this second attack of the figs, which was caused solely by his obstinacy and his imprudence; I observed to him, how difficult it must be, for savages, who wear no clothes, to force such a barrier as they formed; and for this once, I had the pleasure of convincing him.

*Ernest.*—Ah, papa, do let us make such a hedge round our tree; we shall then have no further occasion to light fires to preserve us from wild beasts, or even from the savages, who from one day to another may arrive in their canoes, as they did on Robinson Crusoe's Island.

*Fritz.*—And we could, then, easily gather the cochineal, and try to make the beautiful scarlet colour.

*Father.*—We shall have time enough for many things, my dear children; but for the present, it is sufficient to prove to you, that

God has not made any thing to be wholly useless; and that it is the duty of men, on whom he has bestowed the gifts of wisdom and intelligence, to employ those faculties, in discovering the utility of the different productions he has allowed to exist.

*Jack.*—For my part, I have done with the Indian fig-tree, its fruit, its cochineal, and its ugly thorns, and I will never go near it again.

*Father.*—If the plant could speak, it would most likely say: That little boy shall not come near me any more. Without any reason, or any necessity, but purely out of contradiction to his father, he attacks and destroys me; me, who would have done him service, if he would but have treated me with kindness, and have been careful in coming near me. And now, Jack, if your leg is still painful, apply a leaf of the karata to it, for I recollect that the plant possesses the property of curing wounds. He accordingly took my advice, and in a few minutes was able to join us on our road to Tent-House.

Now then, said Ernest, I have had an opportunity of learning the valuable properties of the karata tree, and of the Indian fig-tree; but I wish I could also be informed respecting those tall plants which look like sticks covered with thorns, that I perceive every where about us; I see neither fruit nor insects on them: of what use then, father, do you think they can be?

*Father.*—It is not in my power, my dear boy, to explain to you the uses of all the plants in the world; I presume that many exist which have no other than that of contributing to the sustenance of different kinds of animals; and, as I have already told you, it is for man, by his superior intelligence, to discover those that can be applied to his own use. Many possess medicinal qualities of which I am ignorant, and which will become better known as the world advances in age. It occurred to me that one of the plants we saw today, named the prickly candle, is of the kind which Bruce describes in his *Travels to Abyssinia*, and of which he gives a drawing; the only difference that I perceive, being the size. They serve, says he, for food to the elephant and the rhinoceros; the first, with his strong teeth, or his trunk, and the latter with his horn, lays hold of this seeming stick, and rips it up from one end to the other; they then devour the pith, and sometimes the rind.

*Ernest.*—The palate of these animals must surely be made of iron, to be able to chew such a thorny substance without injury.

*Fritz.*—Why so? Camels and asses are very fond of thistles, and appear to digest them extremely well. It is probable, therefore, that the stomach of these animals is so formed that these prickly substances occasion in it only an agreeable excitation, favourable to their appetite and their digestion.

*Father.*—Your idea is not a bad one; and if it be not true, it is at least probable.

*Fritz.*—Will you tell me, father, the precise difference between *true* and *probable*?

*Father.*—Your question is one of those which have occupied the attention of philosophers for two thousand years. It would therefore be too tedious to discuss at this moment; I will, however, endeavour to make my answer such, as to be of use to you, in the science of logic, or the art of reasoning. Let us see, if you will understand it. What we call true, is that which cannot in any way be contradicted, and which exactly agrees, in every point, with the idea we conceive of a certain object, or as it really exists before our eyes: for example, when I make an impression with my seal on some warm wax, it is absolutely true that the figure impressed on the wax, is the same as that on the seal. A thing is probable, when we have a variety of motives for believing it true, without, however, being able to bring any proof. Again, we call *false*, that which is in positive contradiction to all our notions, our reason, and our experience. Is it *true*, *probable*, or *false*, that a man can fly up into the air?

*All.*—It is false, absolutely false.

*Father.*—How so?

*Jack.*—Because the thing is impossible.

*Father.*—Very well, my young philosopher, and why is the thing impossible?

*Jack.*—Because it is not possible.

*Father.*—Ha, ha, ha! here is a pretty round of *possible* and *impossible. It is false because no such thing can be done, and no such thing can be done, because it is not possible.* Presently you will tell me that it is impossible because it is false. Try again, my lads, we must have some better reasons. What say you, Ernest?

*Ernest.*—I say, that the thing cannot be done, because it is not in the nature of man to fly; that having no wings, he is not formed for flying.

*Father.*—Well, but if some one should assert, that a man is able to make a machine, by the assistance of which he can raise and support himself in the air without wings, and without the machine's resting upon any thing; would this be *probable* or *improbable*? What think you, Fritz?

*Fritz.*—I think I should have said *improbable* if I had not known that people have accomplished what you describe, by the invention of balloons.

*Father.*—And why should you have thought it *improbable*?

*Fritz.*—Because man is, in his nature, heavier than the air; and I should have supposed, that a machine of whatever kind, instead of diminishing, would only add to his weight.

*Father.*—Very well reasoned. But you would be told that this machine is of large dimensions, and composed of a close, light kind of silk, and that it is filled with air chemically prepared, which being much lighter than atmospheric air, tends perpetually to ascend, and supports the man in the air, as bladders support you upon the water. Do you understand all this, my boy? and what have you to say in answer?

*Fritz.*—Yes, father, I understand it; and I perceive how it might be probable, that since man has discovered a means to be sustained upon water, he might also find the means to raise and sustain himself in the air.

*Father.*—And when a multitude of persons of veracity, and of different ages, shall declare, that with their own eyes they saw a balloon, to which a parachute was fastened filled with men, and that all mounted in the air together, and disappeared above the clouds; should you still maintain that it is false that a man can fly?

*All.*—No, to be sure, we should say that it is quite true that he can fly.

*Father.*—And yet you all said but a minute ago, that it was absolutely false.

*Fritz.*—Ah! but we said that, father, of a man by himself, independently of any machine he might construct; for though nature has refused him wings, she has not failed to bestow on him an inventive mind, which more than compensates for that deficiency.

*Father.*—Your observation is perfectly just, and I hope you will not fail to profit by it. With the aid of his intelligence, and his reason, there is scarcely any thing which man cannot attain to. But to return to our example: you will find in it the definition of the words which you ask me about: it is *false*, that man of himself can fly; it is *probable* that by the aid of a machine of his own invention, he may be enabled to mount and sustain himself in the air; and it is *absolutely true*, that this has been effected by man, though without his having yet found a certain means of guiding these factitious wings; a defect, which in a great measure renders his discovery useless.

*My Wife.*—Well now we have had a long lesson upon the subject, during which I have not been able to put in one single little word; I am afraid you will make your boys so learned, that I shall not know on what subjects to converse with them.

*Father.*—There is no fear of that, my dear; for even should I teach them all I know myself, they would not be very learned. A man should always endeavour to acquire knowledge: if he lives in the world, he is in consequence the more esteemed, the more respected, and knows the better how to manage his affairs: if, as will most likely be the case with our sons, their lot is to live in a kind of solitude, it will be less tiresome to them, if they have cultivated the habit of thinking and reflecting; so that even the little information in my power to give them, may be of use. I have never had occasion to regret that I knew so much, but often that I knew too little, particularly in our present situation, where no other master can be obtained for them than myself and nature. If the boys could conceive what advantages they would derive from study, they would impose upon themselves the strictest application, while at the age when learning is so easy.

Conversing thus, we reached Jackall's River, which we crossed, stepping with great care from stone to stone, and very shortly arrived at our old habitation, where we found every thing in perfect order as we had left it; and we immediately dispersed, each in pursuit of what he intended to take away. Fritz loaded himself with powder and shot; I and my wife and Francis employed ourselves in filling our pot with butter, the carrying of which on our return it was agreed was to fall on me. Ernest and Jack looked about for the geese and ducks; but as they were become somewhat savage, the boys could not succeed in catching one of them. The idea then occurred to Ernest, of taking a small bit of cheese, and tying it to the end of a piece of string, and holding it to float in the water. The voracious animals hastened eagerly to seize it. In this way, Ernest drew them towards him, one by one, with the cheese in its mouth, till he had caught the whole: he put them in their pocket handkerchiefs, leaving only the head at liberty; and then we fastened them as a parcel to our game-bags, so that each had his share in carrying them.

We had thought of taking back with us a provision of salt; but we could not carry so much as we wished, the sacks being occupied with potatoes. I, however, thought of throwing in a certain quantity loose into one of them, to fill up the space between the potatoes. In this way we secured a tolerable supply; but it made the sack so heavy, that no one was willing to be incumbered with it. Fritz proposed that our faithful Turk should carry it; and accordingly we took off his superb coat of mail, and left it at Tent-House, and the sack was tied on the back of the quiet, kind-tempered animal. Ponto was to carry the monkey as before.

We set out on our return, loaded with, treasures, and the appearance of our caravan was even more amusing than it had been before: the ducks and geese with their heads and necks stretching out at our shoulders, cackling with all their might, gave us a truly singular and ludicrous appearance: we could not help laughing immoderately as we passed the bridge, one after the other, loaded in so strange a fashion. Our mutual jokes, and the general good humour which prevailed, served to shorten the length of the walk, and we none of us were sensible of fatigue, till we were seated under our tree at Falcon's Stream. My wife now prepared to console us, by putting some of the potatoes which we so eagerly desired to taste, immediately on the fire. She next milked the cow and the goat, and refreshed us with a draught of their warm milk, giving us a proof how the natural strength may be increased by the feelings of conjugal and maternal love. The kind-hearted woman was at least as much fatigued as any of us; yet she made no attempt to rest herself, till she had provided us with all she had to give for our refreshment. At length, after dining heartily on our potatoes, on which we bestowed abundance of commendation, we concluded the day with evening-prayers and then joyfully climbed our ladder to seek the blessing of repose in our aerial castle.

# XV

# THE IMAGINARY BEAR—THE SLEDGE—
# A LESSON IN NATURAL PHILOSOPHY

I HAD REMARKED THE EVENING BEFORE, ON OUR RETURN TO THE sea-shore, a quantity of wood, of which I thought I could make a kind of conveyance for our cask of butter and other provisions from Tent-House to Falcon's Stream. I had secretly determined to go early the next morning, before my family should be awake, to the spot. I had fixed upon Ernest for my assistant, thinking that his indolent temper required to be stimulated to exertion. I made him feel as a great favour the preference I gave him, and he promised to be ready at a very early hour. I was also desirous to leave Fritz with the family, as, being the tallest and strongest, he was more able to protect the rest.

As soon as I perceived the first dawn of morning, I quietly awoke Ernest. He raised himself, stretching and gaping in his hammock. We descended the ladder without being perceived by the rest of the family, who continued to sleep soundly. The first thing we had to do, was to awake the ass, who was to be of our party; and that he might not go without a load, I made him draw a very large branch of a tree, which I wanted for my undertaking. As we walked along, I asked Ernest if he was not a little out of humour at being obliged to get up so early, to set about a laborious occupation, instead of remaining with his brothers, to shoot at the thrushes and the pigeons on the fig tree?

*Ernest.*—Not in the least, father: now I am once up and dressed, I do not mind it at all; I like being with you, and assisting you, very much. My brothers will leave plenty of birds for me to shoot; for I will lay any wager, that their first fire at least will miss.

What makes you think so, my boy?

Because they will all forget to take the balls out of the guns, and to put in shot in their place: besides, I am sure that they will all fire from under the tree, and it is so high, that their shot cannot possibly reach it. I, for my part, have always fired from Tree Castle, which was the only way to succeed.

You may be right in your suspicions, answered I, but I have two remarks to make. The first is, that it would have been kinder and more generous in you, to have told your brothers these particulars, than to triumph in their ignorance; thus exposing them to spend their powder, which is so valuable an article, to no effect. The second is, that though it gives me pleasure to see you act with coolness and reflection, yet I am somewhat apprehensive of your falling into the habit of a certain slowness of decision, which may frequently prove injurious; there are occasions which require instant resolution, and cannot admit of a moment for reflection. He who, in a moment of alarm, of danger, or distress, preserves his presence of mind and decides instantly, has a great advantage over him who waits to calculate every possibility before he begins to act. This presence of mind, joined to great wisdom, is a quality of inestimable value, and it may be acquired by cultivating a habit of cool reflection and inquiry, as to how we should act under such or such a circumstance. If we do not acquire this habit, we suffer ourselves to be under the dominion of fear at the time of danger, and are consequently defeated. Let us see, for example, what would you do if we were suddenly surprised by a bear.

*Ernest.*—I almost believe I should run away as fast as I could.

*Father.*—And I believe so too; at least, you frankly assure me that it would be so. But if you were to reflect, you would conclude, that the bear having four legs, and you only two, he would run much faster and for a much longer time than you, and would therefore soon overtake you.

*Ernest.*—Then I would fire upon him, if I had my gun; and now that I reflect upon it, I will not go out any more without it.

*Father.*—This would still be acting without reflection; for your gun might easily miss fire, or you might only slightly wound the animal, and then you would have every thing to fear from his rage.

*Ernest.*—Well, then, I would wait with coolness till he should be only three steps from me; I would then fire my gun at his head, which would for ever cure him of the inclination to attack me.

*Father.*—It would cure either you or him, to a certainty; for you would run the risk of your gun's missing fire, and it would then be too late to try any other expedient; for you would be torn to pieces in a moment.

*Ernest.*—Well, then, I would try another way. I would lie down on the ground, hold my breath, and make believe I was dead, and the bear would turn me over and over; for it is said they will not touch a dead body.

*Father*.—This is a great mistake; I would advise you not to trust to it. Bears are often known to devour dead animals and that they are even a powerful attraction to them.

*Ernest*.—Oh, but I would be prepared with my clasp knife, with which I would settle him in a trice, or I would knock him on the head with the end of my gun.

*Father*.—All ineffectual means, I assure you. Do you think you would have strength enough to destroy so formidable a creature? or that you could penetrate so thick a hide with your clasp knife? Nor would you have the resource of climbing up a tree, for bears climb also. The only means you could use, and I confess it would be most cruel, would be to give up the ass to him, by keeping him before you in readiness. When the bear should begin the attack, you might try to shoot him with your pistol, or to plunge your knife into his throat. But I trust we shall have no such animal to encounter; for I should be sorry to sacrifice our poor ass, even in defence of our own lives.

*Ernest*.—And I too, father; but if there were no other means?

*Father*.—In such a case it is permitted to use the remedy, inhuman as it seems; while at the same time we should form a hope that it might be possible to save the ass also.

In this kind of conversation we reached the sea-shore; well content to have met with no bear, and at finding pieces of wood in great abundance, to obtain which was the object of our walk. I determined to cut such pieces as I wanted, of the proper length, and to lay them cross-ways on the branches which the ass had drawn to the place, and by this means to make them serve as a kind of sledge. We lost no time in setting to work, and we added to the load a little chest, which we found half buried in the sands, quite close to the waves. We also provided ourselves with some poles which lay there, that we might use them as rollers, should we stand in need of them for passing difficult places, and then we set out on our return to Falcon's Stream. When we were within a certain distance of our abode, we heard a loud firing, which informed us that the attack upon the ortolans was in good train; but on seeing us approach, the cries of joy which were uttered resounded in every direction, and all ran eagerly to meet us. The chest we had brought was soon opened by a strong hatchet, for all were eager to see what was within. It contained only some sailor's dresses and some linen, which was quite wet with the sea.

I had to account to my wife for having absented myself with one of the boys, without giving her notice, or bidding her adieu. She had been uneasy, and I confessed I had been to blame. In such a situation as ours, so many unforeseen and painful events might happen! She had discovered, however, that we had taken the ass with us, and this circumstance had consoled her. The sight of so many useful pieces of wood, and the promise of a sledge for better security in conveying her provisions for the table, soon appeased her discontent, and we sat down tranquilly to breakfast.

I next inspected the booty of the three sportsmen, who had shot, in all, no less than fifty ortolans and thrushes. As Ernest had foretold, their first fire missed; afterwards they had had various luck, now missing and now hitting, and had used so large a quantity of powder and shot, that when, by their brother's advice, they were about to get up the tree and fire from thence, my wife and I stopped them, recommending a more frugal use of those materials, as they were our only means of defence, or of procuring food in future, or at least till we could make another visit to the vessel.

I taught them how to make some snares to be suspended from the branches of the fig-tree, and advised them to use the thread of the karata, which is as strong as horse-hair, for the purpose. What is new always amuses young persons, and the boys accordingly took a great fancy to this mode of sporting. Jack succeeded in his very first attempt; I left Francis to assist him, and took Fritz and Ernest to help me in making the sledge. As we were all hard at work, for my wife had joined the youngest boys, we suddenly heard a prodigious clatter among the fowls; the cock crowed louder than all the rest together, and the hens ran to and fro, as if they were pursued by a fox. I wonder what is the matter with the creatures, said my wife, rising; every day I hear the hens clucking as if they had been laying eggs. At this moment Ernest happened to look at the monkey, and remarked that he fixed his piercing eyes on the hens; and when he saw my wife approaching, driving the hens before her, he jumped quickly into a hollow place, under one of the roots of the tree, and hid himself. Ernest ran to the place as soon as he, and was fortunate enough to seize him, seeing that he held a new-laid egg in his paw, which he was going to conceal in this place for a future regale. The monkey sprang immediately to such another hole, and Ernest followed; here also he found some eggs, and brought them in his hat to his mother, who received them with great pleasure. The monkey was so greedy of this food, that he was sure to seize the eggs as soon as the hens had laid them. We inflicted no other punishment upon him for this little piece of knavery, than that of tying him up when the hens were about to lay. By this means my wife soon collected a considerable number of eggs, and we waited with impatience for the time when the hens would sit, in the hope of seeing their species multiplied.

In the mean while, Jack had got up into the tree, and had suspended some of the snares to the branches, to catch the little devourers of our figs; he came down again to bring us the acceptable intelligence, that our pigeons, which we brought from the vessel, had made a sort of nest there of some dry grass, and that it already contained several eggs. I therefore forbade the boys from firing any more in the tree, for fear of alarming or wounding these gentle creatures. I also directed, that the snares should be frequently examined, to see that the pigeons were not caught in them, as they might be strangled in their efforts to get loose. I should now even have forbidden the use of the snares, if I had not myself made them known to the boys, and that so very lately. It is imprudent at all times, for a tutor to contradict himself, and thus prove to his pupils that he was wrong in issuing such or such a command; a single word revoked on the part of the tutor, will occasion ten to be revoked by the pupil. We should always duly reflect before we lay a command on a child; but when once the word is pronounced, it should never be recalled, whether from caprice, from a disposition to indulge the child, or even from conviction. My sons had all murmured at my prohibition, in regard to the gunpowder; and little Francis with his innocent face came running to tell me, that we need only to sow some of it, and that he and his brother were ready to bestow any labour, to have a large quantity of it at their own disposal. We all laughed heartily at the idea, and Professor Ernest did not overlook the advantage of the occasion, to display his science. My little sprig of wisdom, cried he, we may judge how much you know of what you are talking about; your field of gunpowder indeed! Do you think then, that gunpowder comes from seeds, like oats?

*Father.*—How else, then, is it produced, Mr. Professor? At least, you might be so good as to inform your little brother what you yourself know of its nature, since you laugh at his great ignorance on the subject.

*Ernest.*—I know that it is produced by art, but of the manner in which it is made, I confess I am myself ignorant. I imagine that it is prepared from charcoal, since it is so black, and that sulphur, of which it smells so strong, is mixed with it.

*Father.*—Add some saltpetre, and your answer will not be amiss; the saltpetre is in reality the principal ingredient; mixed with charcoal, it easily takes fire, and rarefies or expands the air that is mixed with it, by means of its elastic force. Touched with a spark of fire, it acts with extraordinary vehemence, and drives forward with astonishing force, whatever resists its action. So that balls or shot, impelled by this irresistible force, strike the object against which they impinge so as to take away life: as you and I, and Fritz and Jack, see happen to us every day in letting off our guns.

The boys now had a thousand questions to propose, which brought on a sort of lesson in natural philosophy, as well as I could make it such, with the degree of information I possessed, and without instruments for experiments. The eldest boys understood the lesson pretty well, having previously some notion of the subjects, but little Francis, on hearing me say that the heat contained in bodies was brought out by motion or friction, asked, ludicrously enough, whether, in running very fast, he should not be in danger of being set on fire and burnt?

Your ideas run too fast, my little fellow, said I; but this I can tell you, that when a young boy like you, uses violent exercise, he runs at least the risk of inflaming his blood, and getting into a fever, or some other dangerous disease; and there results something like the burning you talk of, that may prove no less dangerous. But my remark is almost equally applicable to a person who takes too little exercise, and abandons himself to idleness; for such habits tend to vitiate the humours, and to corrupt the blood. Thus, my dear children, in this, as in every thing else, it is advisable to observe a just medium.

During this conversation, I was busily employed upon my sledge, which was soon completed; and I found that necessity had converted a preacher of moderate talents into a tolerably good carpenter. Two bent pieces of wood, the segments of a circle, formed the outline of my machine, which I fixed in their places, by a straight piece of wood, placed across, and firmly fixed to the bent pieces in the middle, and at the rear. I then fastened two ropes to the front of my work, and my sledge was finished. As I had not raised my eyes from my work, I did not know what my wife and the two youngest boys had been about. On looking up, I perceived that they had been stripping off the feathers from a quantity of birds, which the boys had killed, and that they afterwards spitted them on an officer's sword, which my wife had turned into this useful kitchen utensil. I approved of the idea; but I blamed her profusion in dressing more birds at once than we could eat. She reminded me, that I had myself advised her to half roast the birds before putting them into the butter, to be preserved for future use. She was in hopes, she said, that as I had now a sledge, I should not fail of going to Tent-House after dinner, to fetch the cask of butter, and in the mean while, she was endeavouring to be ready with the birds. I had no objection to this, and immediately determined on going to Tent-House the same day, and requested my wife to hasten the dinner for that purpose. She replied that this was already her intention, as she also had a little project in her head, which I should be informed of, at my return. I, for my part, had one too, which was to take a bathe in the sea, and thus refresh myself from the heat and fatigue of my laborious occupations. I wished that Ernest, who was to accompany me, should bathe also; while Fritz was to remain at home for the protection of the family.

# XVI

# A BATHING, A FISHING, THE JUMPING HARE, AND A MASQUERADE

S SOON AS ERNEST AND I HAD DINED, WE PREPARED FOR OUR departure. Fritz presented each with one of the best cases of his own workmanship, which we stuck through our belts, and which, in reality, were ingeniously contrived for holding spoons and knives and forks, while room was left in the middle for a little hatchet. I praised Fritz for having thus brought his idea to perfection, and for contriving to make two cases with his skin instead of one. He had used the skin of the two fore-legs of the animal for one, and of the two hind-legs for the other, and reserved the place in the middle, for the hatchet. Ernest showed a warmth of gratitude for his share in the benefit, of which I had not thought him capable.

We now set about harnessing the ass and cow to our sledge; each took a piece of bamboo-cane in hand, to serve as a whip; and resting our guns upon our shoulders, we began our journey. Ponto was to accompany us, and Turk to remain behind. We bade adieu to our companions, and put our animals in motion. We took the road by the sea-shore, where the sands afforded better travelling for our vehicle, than the thick wild grass. We reached Family Bridge, on Jackall's River, and arrived at Tent-House, without either obstacle or adventure. We immediately unharnessed the animals to let them graze, while we set to work to load the sledge with the cask of butter, the cask of cheese, a small barrel of gunpowder, different instruments, some ball, some shot, and Turk's coat of mail. These exertions had so occupied our thoughts, that it was late when we first observed that our animals, attracted by the excellent quality of the grass on the other side of the river, had repassed the bridge, and wandered so far as to be out of sight. I was in hopes they would be easily found, and I directed Ernest to go with Ponto and bring them back, intending in the mean time to look for a convenient place, on the other side of Tent-House, to bathe in. In a short time I found myself at the extremity of Providence Bay, and which ended, as I now perceived, in a marsh, producing the finest bulrushes it was possible to imagine; and further on, a chain of steep rocks, advancing somewhat into the sea, and forming a kind of creek, as if expressly contrived for bathing. The juttings of the rock even seemed like little separate cabinets, where one might be concealed from one's companions. Enchanted with this discovery, I called out to Ernest to come and join me, and in the mean time, I amused myself with cutting some of the rushes, and imagining what use I could apply them to. Ernest neither replied nor came: so, after waiting a little, I resolved to go in pursuit of him, for I was unable to refrain from some uneasy sensations at his absence. Looking about in all directions, I at length discovered him at a distance, extended at his length on the ground, in the shade produced by Tent-House. I approached him with a beating heart, fearing he might have been attacked by some wild beast; and was agreeably surprised at finding him in a sound and quiet sleep, while the ass and the cow were eating the grass close to the place where he lay.

Come, come, young traveller, you must awake, cried I, shaking him: while you are sleeping here, your animals may once more make their escape. He instantly awoke starting, and was soon on his feet. Oh! but I defy them to escape across the bridge, said he, rubbing his eyes; for I have taken away some of the planks, and left a space which they will have no great inclination to jump over.

*Father.*—Since your idle fit has rendered you inventive, I forgive it with all my heart; but is it not a pity to lose in sleeping the opportunity of doing something useful? Did you not promise your mother to carry her some salt? Slothfulness is always a fault, where labour is a necessity.

*Ernest.*—But, father, my head was not idle, I assure you. I was planning something all the time.

*Father.*—Really, Ernest! Why, this is quite a novelty, for a boy of your age. Pray tell me what important and profound study it was, which made you go to sleep.

*Ernest.*—I will tell you. I was thinking, deeply, how difficult it would be to bring away from the vessel every thing which it contains.

*Father.*—And did you hit upon some method for removing the difficulty?

*Ernest.*—No, father, no great things; I fell asleep in the middle of my reflections.

*Father.*—So, this is the hard work your poor head was engaged in!—Discovering a difficulty, and finding no means for conquering it!

*Ernest.*—At this very moment an idea strikes me.—We ought to have a large raft; but the beams of the ship are too heavy for the purpose: I think it would be better to take a number of the empty casks, and nail some planks upon them to keep them all together. I have read that the savages of America fill the skins of goats with air, tie them to each other, and are thus enabled to use them as rafts upon the largest rivers.

*Father.*—This is a sound idea, and one day or other we may perhaps derive advantage from it: but for the present, my boy, we must make up for lost time: run, therefore, and fill this little bag with salt, which you will then empty into the large one that the ass is to carry; and which you will take care to fill equally on each side. During this time, I will take the refreshment of bathing; and then it will be your turn to bathe, and mine to take care of the animals. I returned to the rocks, and was not disappointed in my expectation of an enjoyment the most delicious; but I did not stay long, fearing my boy might be impatient for his share of so new a pleasure. When I had dressed myself, I returned to the place to see if his work had advanced; but he was not there, and I supposed that he had again fallen asleep in some corner. Presently, however, I heard his voice calling out, Father, father, a fish! a fish of monstrous size! Run quickly, father, I can hardly hold him! he is eating up the string of my line! I ran to the place from which the voice proceeded, and found Ernest lying along the ground on his face, upon the extremity of a point of land, and pulling in his line, to which a large fish was hanging, and beating about with all his strength. I ran hastily and snatched the rod out of his hand, for I had some apprehension that the weight and activity of the fish, would pull him into the water. I gave a certain liberty to the line, to calm the fish, and then contrived to draw him gently along, till I had got him safely into a shallow, from which he could no longer escape, and thus the animal was effectually secured. We next examined him thoroughly, and it appeared to me that it could not weigh less than fifteen pounds; so that our capture was magnificent, and would afford the greatest pleasure to our good steward of provisions at Falcon's Stream. You have now really laboured, said I to Ernest, not only with your head, but with your whole body, and I would advise you to wipe the perspiration from your face, and keep a little quiet before you venture into the water. You have procured us a dish of great excellence, which will last for several days, and have conducted yourself like a true chevalier, without fear and without reproach.

It was at least fortunate, observed he in a modest tone, that I thought of bringing my fishing-rod.

*Father.*—Certainly it was. But tell me how you came to see this large fish, and what made you think you could catch it?

*Ernest.*—I used to remark when we lived at Tent-House, that there were innumerable quantities of fish in the water, just hereabout; the recollection of this circumstance made me determine to bring my fishing-tackle with me. In my way to the place where we keep the salt, I perceived a great number of little crabs, upon which fishes feed, near the water's brink; I thought I would try to bait my hook with one of them; so I hurried my task of fetching the salt, and came to this spot, where at first I caught only about a dozen little fish, which are there in my handkerchief; but at the same time I remarked, that they were chased in the water by fishes of larger size. This gave me the idea of baiting my hook with one of the small ones; but the hook was too small, and my rod too weak. I then took one of the finest of the bulrushes you had just gathered, and put a larger hook to my line, and in a short time the large fish you see there seized upon the bait, and paid his life for his voracity. However, I must confess, that if you had not come to my assistance, I must either have let go my line, or have been dragged into the water; for the fish was stronger than I.

We now examined the smaller fishes he had caught, which for the most part appeared to me to consist of trout and herrings, while I felt certain that the large one was a salmon. I immediately cut them all open, and rubbed them in the inside with salt, that they might not be injured by the heat. While I was employed in this occupation, Ernest went to the rocks and bathed, and I had time to fill some more bags with salt, before his return. We then set about harnessing and loading our animals; after which we restored the planks which had been taken from the bridge, and then resumed the road to Falcon's Stream.

When we had proceeded about half way, Ponto, who had been walking quietly on before us, suddenly escaped, and by his barking gave us notice that he scented some game. We soon after saw him pursuing an animal, which seemed endeavouring to escape, and made the most extraordinary jumps imaginable. The dog continuing to follow, the creature in trying to avoid him, passed within gunshot of the place where I stood. I fired, but its flight was so rapid, that I did not hit. Ernest, who was at a small distance behind, hearing the report of my gun, prepared his own, and fired it off at the instant the singular animal was passing near him, in pursuit of a hiding-place among the tall herbage just by: he had fired so skilfully, that the animal fell dead at the same instant. I ran hastily, and with extreme curiosity, to ascertain what kind of quadruped it might be. We found it, in form and general appearance, the most remarkable possible to conceive. It was of the size of a sheep, with a tail resembling that of a tiger; both its snout and hair were like those of a mouse, and its teeth were like a hare's, but much larger; the fore legs resembled those of the squirrel, and were extremely short; but to make up for this, its hind legs were as long as a pair of stilts, and of a form strikingly singular. We examined the extraordinary creature for a long time in silence; I could not be sure that I had ever seen an engraving or description of it in any Natural History, or book of Travels. Ernest, after a long and close examination, interrupted our silence by an exclamation of joy: And have I really killed this extraordinary animal? said he, clapping his hands together. What will my mother and my brothers say? How astonished they will be! and how fortunate I am in securing so fine a prize! What do you think is its name, father? I would give all the world to know.

*Father.*—And so would I, my boy; but I am as ignorant as you. One thing, however, is certain, that this is your lucky day; for you have already performed two wonderful feats, by destroying two monsters, in the course of it; so that I shall be tempted to give you the name of my little Hercules. You also sometimes deserve that of my little Solomon. So let us both examine this interesting stranger with attention, that we may be certain to what family of quadrupeds it belongs: this will perhaps throw a light upon its name.

*Ernest.*—I think it can hardly be named a quadruped; for the little fore legs look much more like hands, as is the case with monkeys.

*Father.*—They are notwithstanding legs, I can assure you. Let us look for its name among the animals who give suck; on this point we cannot be mistaken. Now let us examine its teeth.

*Ernest.*—Here are the four incisory teeth, like the squirrel——.

*Father.*—Thus we see that it belongs to the order of Nibblers. Now let us look for some names of animals of this kind.

*Ernest.*—Besides squirrels, I recollect only mice, marmots, hares, beavers, porcupines, and the jumpers.

*Father.*—The jumpers! That word furnishes the necessary clue; the animal is completely formed like the gerboa or jumping hare, except that it is twice the size of those of which I have read a description . . . Wait a moment, an idea strikes me. I will lay a wager that our animal is one of the large jumpers, called kangaroo; it belongs properly to the genus Didelphis or Philander; because the female, who never bears more than one young one, carries it in a kind of purse placed between her hind legs. To the best of my knowledge, this animal has never been seen but on the coast of New Holland, where it was first observed by the celebrated navigator Captain Cook. You may then be highly flattered with your adventure, in killing an animal at once so rare and so remarkable.

*Ernest.*—You had very nearly, however, deprived me of the honour. How happened it, father, that you missed him? you, who are so much better a shot than I! I confess I should have been much mortified in your place.

*Father.*—I, on the contrary, rejoice in the circumstance.

*Ernest.*—Well, that is droll enough; and I cannot understand how any one can rejoice at having missed an animal in firing. Will you explain it to me?

*Father.*—I rejoice, because I love my son better than myself, and take a more lively interest in his pleasure, and in any little cause of exultation he may have, than if the occasion were more immediately connected with myself.—Ernest, affected by my remark, ran to embrace me. How truly I recognise in this assurance the kind temper of my ever indulgent father! cried he.— Your gratitude but increases my satisfaction, added I, embracing him in my turn; but now let us see if we shall be able to drag the animal to the sledge. Ernest requested that I would rather assist him to carry it, as he was afraid of spoiling its beautiful mouse-coloured skin, by dragging it on the ground. I therefore tied the fore legs of the kangaroo together; and by means of two canes, we with considerable trouble contrived to carry it to the sledge, upon which it was securely fastened.

Ponto, who first discovered the kangaroo, had lost the scent, and was scampering about in the tall grass, no doubt with the hope of recovering his prey. We called him to us, and loaded him with caresses and applauses: but he seemed indifferent to our most flattering addresses; he kept close to the kangaroo, and licked its wound, which was still bleeding. Having now nothing more to detain us, we continued our road towards Falcon's Stream. As we walked along, we converged on the subject of natural history, and on the necessity of studying it in our youth, that we might learn to class plants and animals according to their characteristic marks; and we observed, that to such a knowledge as this it was owing, that we had recognised the kangaroo. Ernest entreated me to tell him all I knew about the animal. It is, said I, a most singular kind of creature; and having hitherto been little observed, it furnishes but few particulars for narration. Its fore legs, as you see, have scarcely the third part of the length of the hind ones, and the most it can do, is to make them serve the purpose of walking; but the hind legs enable it to make prodigious jumps, the same as in the flea and the grasshopper. The food of the kangaroo consists of herbs and roots, which they dig up very skilfully with their fore legs. They place themselves upon their hind legs, which are doubled under them, as if on a chair, and by this means are able to look above even the tall kinds of grass; they rest too upon their tail, which is exceedingly strong, and is also of great use to them in jumping, by assisting the spring from the ground. It is said that the kangaroo, if deprived of its tail, would scarcely be able to jump at all.

We at length arrived happily, though somewhat late, at Falcon's Stream, having heard from a great distance the kind welcome of the salutations of our family. Our companions all ran to meet us: but it was now, on seeing the ludicrous style of the dress of the three boys, our turn for immoderate fits of laughter: one had on a sailor's shirt, which trained round him like the robe of a spectre; another was buried in a pair of pantaloons, which were fastened round his neck and reached to the ground; and the third had a long waistcoat which came down to the instep, and gave him the exact form of a travelling portmanteau. They all tried to jump about; but finding this impossible from the length of their garments, they next resolved to carry off the whole with an air, by strutting slowly to and fro in the manner of a great personage in a theatre. After some hearty laughing, I inquired of my wife what could be the cause of this masquerade, and whether she had assisted them in attempting to act a comedy for our amusement. She disclosed the mystery by informing me, that her three boys had also been into the water, to bathe, and that while they were thus engaged, she had washed all their clothes; but as they had not dried so soon as she expected, her little rioters had become impatient, and had fallen on the chest of sailor's clothes, and each had taken from it what article he pleased. I preferred, said she, that you should see them in this odd sort of a disguise rather than quite naked, like little savages; in which opinion, I assured her that I heartily joined.

It was now our turn to give an account of our journey: in proportion as we advanced in our narrative, we presented, one after another, casks, bulrushes, salt, fish, and lastly, with infinite triumph, our beautiful kangaroo. In a trice it was surrounded, examined, and admired by all, and such a variety of questions asked, that Ernest and I scarcely knew which to answer first. Fritz was the only one who was a little silent. I saw plainly by his countenance, what was passing in his mind. He was jealous of the good fortune of his brother Ernest; but I also saw, that he was struggling manfully against the ascendancy of so mean a passion, and was resolving to conquer it. In a short time, he had succeeded so completely, that he joined frankly and unaffectedly in our conversation and merriment, and I am persuaded, no one but myself perceived what was passing in his mind. He came near the kangaroo, and examined it with great attention; then turning to his brother, he observed to him in a kind tone, that he had had good luck, and that he must be a good shot to have killed the kangaroo with so little difficulty. But, father, said he, when you go again to Tent-House, or on any other excursion, will it not be my turn to go with you? For here at Falcon's Stream there is nothing new to amuse us; a few thrushes, and some pigeons; this is all we have from day to day, and I find it very tiresome.

I will promise you with all my heart what you desire, my dear boy, said I, for you have valiantly combated the ill humour and the jealousy which assailed your temper, on witnessing your brother's success with the kangaroo. I therefore promise, that you shall accompany me in my very next excursion, which will probably take place at no greater distance of time than tomorrow; and it will be another journey to the vessel. But in the mean time, let me observe to you, my dear Fritz, that you ought to be more flattered with the high opinion I must entertain of your prudence and judgement, in leaving you here, in charge of your mother and your brothers, than with the applause due to the event of killing a kangaroo. You have accomplished an important duty, in keeping near them all the time, and not suffering yourself to be allured by such amusements as presented themselves to your fancy; and this conduct has increased my affection and respect for you. Praise is also due to Ernest, for the moderation with which he has felt his triumph, in so extraordinary an occurrence; for he has not even told you of my humiliating failure in attempting to shoot the kangaroo. To triumph over our passions, and to have on all occasions a perfect government of our temper, is an acquisition of infinitely more value, than the showing a certain skill in firing off a gun, and killing an innocent animal. We happen, in our situation, to be forced upon the cultivation of such arts as these; but though we may practise them as necessary for our existence, we have no reason to be proud of them.

We concluded the day with our ordinary occupations; I gave some salt to each of our animals, to whom it was an acceptable treat. We next skinned our kangaroo, and put it carefully aside till the next day, when we intended to cut it to pieces, and lay such parts in salt, as we could not immediately consume. We made an excellent supper on our little fish, to which we added some potatoes, nor were our faithful companions Turk and Ponto neglected. The labours of the day had more than usually disposed us all to seek repose; we therefore said our prayers at an early hour, mounted our ladder, and were soon asleep.

## ✢ XVII ✢

# MORE STORES FROM THE WRECK

I ROSE WITH THE FIRST CROWING OF THE COCK, BEFORE THE rest of the family was awake, descended the ladder, and employed myself in carefully skinning the kangaroo, so as not to deface its beautiful mouse-coloured coat; and it was really high time to think about it. Our dogs were so well satisfied the preceding evening with their meal on the entrails of the animal, that they became partial to it, and had just sprung up in the design of making a complete breakfast of the whole carcase. Before I was at the bottom of the ladder, they had torn off the head of the kangaroo, which I had suspended at some height by the hind feet, and, half friends half foes, they were going to divide it amongst them, when my presence opportunely prevented the partition. It occurred to me, that as I had neither cellar nor safe to keep my provisions in, it behoved me to give them a slight correction: growling and barking, they took refuge under the roots, and the half-suppressed kind of howling they continued to make, awoke my wife, who, on missing me, came down alarmed to know what was the matter. For the love of God, exclaimed she, what has happened? Are the dogs run mad, or have you lost your senses?—Nothing of the kind, I answered; I was only giving our dogs a short sermon on temperance and the necessity of self-control.—Then better it would be to enforce your precepts by example, to begin by subduing anger, and not by exercising your vengeance on poor faithful animals, who are innocent, and unconscious of the mischief they are doing.

Kind-hearted creature, said I: it is well known to me how glad you would be if there were no sticks in the world! But I assure you I did not beat Turk and Ponto through anger or revenge, but from prudence and precaution; and be persuaded I have not hurt them much: they modestly intended only to eat up our kangaroo, which you promised yourself such pleasure in cooking; and unable as I was to acquaint them in the canine tongue, that it was not placed there for their use, it was proper to let them know this in such a way as to deter them in future; otherwise, as they are strongest, they would end by devouring all our stock.

My wife owned I was in the right: but I observed her from a corner of my eye hovering about the roots, and patting the dogs to console them. As to myself, I set about stripping my kangaroo, and endeavoured to remove the skin entirely without injuring it; but this gave me so much trouble, and I advanced so slowly in the business, that all my little family were assembled about me and their mother, and calling out, Famine, before I had finished my work. Having completed it, I went to the stream to wash myself thoroughly, and then to the sailor's chest to change my coat, that I might make a decent appearance at breakfast, and give my sons an example of that cleanliness which their mother was at all times eager to inculcate. Breakfast over, I ordered Fritz to prepare everything to go to Tent-House, and prepare our boat, that we might proceed to the vessel. At the moment of departure, wishing to take leave of all my family, I found that Ernest and Jack were wanting: their mother knew no more than myself what was become of them, but she thought they were gone to get some potatoes, which we wanted. I charged her to reprove them a little for this, to prevent their accustoming themselves to stray from home alone and without leave, in an unknown country; but they had taken Turk along with them this time, and I was therefore the less uneasy.

We began our journey after having taken an affectionate leave of my wife and of my little Francis. I left Ponto with her, and I entreated her not to be uneasy, and to commit herself to the care of the kind Providence who had till then so graciously watched over us, and who would again bring us back to her safe and sound, enriched with many things conducive to our welfare. But to bring her to reason on the subject of these trips to the vessel, was impracticable: I left her bathed in tears, and praying God that this might be the last.

We separated with mutual emotion, hastening our steps to make our stay the shorter, and we soon reached and crossed the bridge: at this moment, to our astonishment, we heard the shrill sounds of human voices, and almost at the same time we saw Ernest and master Jack come forth from a bush, delighted to have half alarmed us.—Ah! did not you think we were savages? said Jack;—or some of the vessel's company? continued Ernest.

Or rather, said I, two little thoughtless rogues whom I soon knew, and am much inclined to chide as they deserve, not for their little artifice, but for having left their home without permission.

*Ernest.*—Oh! father, we have such a desire to go with you to the vessel, and we were afraid you would refuse us if we asked you; but we thought that when you saw us so near to the place, you would consent to our accompanying you.

Very badly argued, my young gentleman, replied I. At Falcon's Stream I might perhaps have consented, although I have so many things to take, that it would be wrong to let you occupy a place in the boat; but as it is, I would on no account leave your poor mother in anxiety the whole day as to what is become of you, and you cannot yourselves desire it: besides, I have a commission to give you for her that I have much at heart. I then requested them to tell her that it was probable we should be forced to pass the night on board the vessel, and not return to her till the evening of the following day. I knew that was what she most feared, and I had wanted resolution to apprise her of this possibility: I was to blame for this weakness, for not to see us return at the expected time was still more painful; yet it was of essential consequence to get out of the vessel, if it yet remained afloat, all that could be saved, as every moment might complete its destruction, and all our future hopes be swallowed up with it. With this view I told my sons what they should say to their mother; I exhorted them to obey and to assist her; and that their excursion might not be useless, I made them collect some salt, and I enjoined them to be at Falcon's Stream before noon. I suffered in knowing the double anguish of my poor wife, resulting from our departure and the prolonged absence of two of her sons. To be sure of the fulfilment of this order, I requested Fritz to lend Ernest his silver watch, and told him he would find a gold one in the vessel, in which case he would allow his brother to keep the one he lent him, and that we might perhaps get another for Jack. This hope filled them with joy, and consoled them for not going on with us.

After having bid adieu to our dear boys, we got into the boat, and we left the shore to gain the current of the stream: thus we quickly cleared Safety Bay, and reached the vessel, whose open side offered us an ample space to get up it. As soon as we had got on board and our boat was securely fastened, our first care was to look out for fit materials to construct a raft. I wished to begin by executing an excellent idea suggested by my son Ernest. Our boat being built of staves had neither room nor solidity enough to carry a considerable burthen; we therefore looked about, and soon found a sufficient number of water-casks which appeared to me very proper for my intended new enterprise. We immediately emptied them, then replaced the bungs carefully, and threw the casks overboard, after securing them by means of ropes and cramps, so as to keep them together at the vessel's side: this completed, we placed a sufficient number of planks upon them to form a firm and commodious platform or deck, to which we added a gunwale of a foot in depth all round, to secure the lading. Thus we contrived to possess a very handsome raft, in which we could stow thrice as much as in our boat. This laborious task had taken up the whole day; we scarcely allowed ourselves a minute to eat a mouthful of cold meat we had provided for the expedition, that we might not lose any time in looking for the provisions on board the vessel. In the evening, Fritz and I were so weary, that it would have been impossible for us to row back to land, even if our business had not detained us; we therefore came to the necessary resolution of passing the night on board; and having taken all due precautions in case of a storm, we reposed ourselves in the captain's cabin, on a good elastic mattress essentially different from our hammocks: in fact, it so lulled us to rest, and induced such sound repose, that our prudent design to watch in turn for fear of accident quite escaped us, and we both slept heavily, side by side, till broad day-light opened our eyes, when we awoke with lively gratitude to that Providence to whom we were indebted for the quiet and comfortable night we had passed. We rose, and actively set to work to load our raft.

In the first place we completely stripped the cabin which had been occupied by my family on board the vessel, removing every thing it contained which belonged to us previous to the fatal event of the wreck: from it we proceeded to the one in which we had slept so well, and carried off the very doors and windows, with their appendages; some valuable chests of the officers were there: but this discovery and the rich lace clothes which seemed to court our grasp, were less acceptable to us than the carpenter's and gunner's chests, containing all their tools and implements: those we could remove with levers and rollers, were put entire upon the raft; and we took out of the others what rendered them too heavy. One of the captain's chests was filled with a number of costly articles, which no doubt he meant to dispose of to the opulent planters of Port Jackson, or among the savages. In the collection were several gold and silver watches, snuff boxes of all descriptions, buckles, shirt-buttons, necklaces, rings, in short an abundance of all the trifles of European luxury; there was also a strong box full of louis d'or and dollars, which attracted our notice less than another containing a very pretty table-service of fine steel, which we had substituted for the captain's that were silver, and for which my wife had shown no small regard: but the discovery that delighted me most, and for which I would readily have given the box with the louis, etc. was a chest containing some dozens of young plants of every species of European fruits, which had been carefully packed in moss for transportation. I perceived pear, plum, almond, peach, apple, apricot, chestnut trees, and vine shoots. I beheld with a feeling I cannot describe, those productions of my dear country, which once so agreeably embellished my rural dwelling, and which, if God vouchsafed to bless them, would thrive in a foreign soil. We discovered a number of bars of iron and large pigs of lead, grinding-stones, cart-wheels ready for mounting, a complete set of farrier's instruments, tongs, shovels, ploughshares, rolls of iron and copper wire, sacks full of maize, peas, oats, vetches, and even a little hand-mill. The vessel had been freighted with every thing likely to be useful in an infant colony so distant; nothing had been forgotten. We found a saw-mill, in a separated state, but each piece numbered, and so accurately fitted, that nothing was easier than to put it together for use.

I had now to consider what of all these treasures I should take or leave. It was impossible to carry with us in one trip such a quantity of goods; and to leave them in the vessel, ready to fall to pieces and threatened every moment with complete destruction, was exposing ourselves to be wholly deprived of them, while every article so lost would be a subject of regret to us.

Ah! said Fritz, let us leave, in the first place, this useless money and the chest of trinkets; except the watches we promised my brothers: all the rest can be of no service to us.

It gives me pleasure, my boy, to hear you speak thus of gold, that idol so universally adored: we will do, then, as you wish, and determine upon taking with us what is really useful, such as the powder, lead, iron, the corn and the fruit-trees, implements for gardening and agriculture; let us take as many as possible of these: if we should have any room left, we can then select a few of the objects of luxury: however, begin by taking from the chest the two watches I have promised, and keep the best of them for yourself.

We then loaded our raft, not without difficulty and hard labour; we moreover stowed away for use in a chest, a large and handsome fishing-net, quite new, and the vessel's great compass. With the net, Fritz found luckily two harpoons and a rope windlass, such as they use in the whale fishery. Fritz asked me to let him place the windlass, with the harpoons attached to the end of the rope, over the bow of our tub-boat, and thus hold all in readiness in case of seeing any large fish; and as I thought it was unusual to meet with these so near the shore, I indulged him in his innocent fancy.

It was afternoon before we had finished our lading; for not only our raft was as full as it could hold, but our boat likewise.

Having well and completely executed our undertaking, both as to construction and lading, we stepped into the tub-boat, and with some small difficulty, which a little reflection and a few experiments soon enabled us to overcome, we pushed out for the current, drawing our raft triumphantly after us with a stout rope, which we had been careful to fasten securely at its head.

# PART II

# XVIII

## THE TORTOISE HARNESSED

HE WIND WAS IN A HUMOUR FAVOURABLE TO OUR UNDERTAKING, and briskly swelled our sail; the sea was calm, and we advanced without fear at a considerable rate. Fritz had been looking steadfastly for some time at something of a large size which was floating at some distance on the water, and he now desired me to take the glass and see what it could be. I soon perceived distinctly that it was a tortoise, which, agreeably to the habits of its singular species, had fallen asleep in the sun on the surface of the water, and we observed that it did not in the least appear sensible of our approach. No sooner had Fritz gained this information, than he earnestly entreated me to steer softly within view of so extraordinary a creature, that he might examine it at his ease. I readily consented; but as his back was towards me, and the sail was between us, I did not observe what he was about, till a violent jerk of the boat, a sudden turning of the windlass, and then a second jerk, accompanied by a rapid motion of the boat, gave me the necessary explanation. For Heaven's sake what are you about, Fritz? exclaimed I. Have you a mind to destroy us with your thoughtlessness, which has put it out of my power to govern the boat?

I have caught him,—I touched him, cried Fritz, without hearing one word I had been saying.—The tortoise is ours, it cannot escape, father! Is not this then a valuable prize, for it will furnish dinners for us all for many weeks!

I soon admitted the idea that in reality the harpoon had secured the animal, which, feeling itself wounded, thus agitated the vessel in its endeavours to be disengaged, for the rope of the harpoon was necessarily fastened at the other end to the windlass. I quickly pulled down the sail, and seizing a hatchet, sprung to the boat's head to cut the rope, and let the harpoon and the tortoise go; but Fritz caught hold of my arm, conjuring me to wait a moment, there being no immediate cause for alarm, and not so hastily bring upon him the mortification of losing, at one stroke, the harpoon, the rope, and the tortoise; he proposed watching himself, with the hatchet in his hand to cut the rope suddenly should any sign of danger appear. I yielded to his entreaties, after a due exhortation to him to take good care not to upset the boat, or run her upon the rocks.

Thus then, drawn along by the tortoise, we proceeded with a hazardous rapidity, and having no small difficulty to keep the rudder in a straight direction, and so to steady the boat, as to prevent her yielding to the irregular motions of so singular a conductor. In a little time I observed that the creature was making for the sea; I therefore again hoisted the sail; and as the wind was to the land, and very brisk, the tortoise found resistance of no avail: he accordingly fell into the track we desired to take, and we soon gained the current which had always received us in our visits to and from the wreck: he drew us straight towards our usual place of landing, and by good fortune without striking upon any of the rocks which so much abound in that spot.

We, however, did not disembark without encountering one difficult adventure. I perceived that the state of the tide was such, that we should be thrown upon one of the sand-banks; and this accordingly took place: we were at this time within a gun-shot of the shore; the boat, though driven with violence, remained perfectly upright in the sand. I stepped into the water, which did not reach far above my knees, for the purpose of conferring upon our conductor his just reward for the alarm he had caused us, when he suddenly gave a plunge, and I saw him no more; following the rope, I however soon found the tortoise stretched at length at the bottom of the water, where it was so shallow that I was not long in finding means to put an end to his pain by cutting off his head with the hatchet; when he soon bled to death. Being now near Tent-House, Fritz gave a halloo, and fired a gun, to apprise our relatives that we were not only arrived, but arrived in triumph. This soon produced the desired effect: the good mother and her three young ones soon appeared, running towards us; upon which Fritz jumped out of the boat, placed the head of our sea-prize on the muzzle of his gun, and walked to shore, which I reached at the same moment; and all were once more received with the kindest salutations, and such questions as kindness best knows how to propose.

After some gentle reproaches from my wife, for leaving her and the boys for so long a time, the history of the tortoise was related in due form, and excited due interest and much meriment

PLATE 8
"He accordingly fell into the track of the current, and
drew us straight towards our usual place of landing."

in our auditors. The tender-hearted mother, after heaving a sigh for the hard fate of the creature, began to shudder at the thought of the danger we had been exposed to, and the escape we had effected. We all now fell to a new examination of the adventure, and were struck with surprise that Fritz should so exactly have hit the vulnerable part of the animal, at the first plunge of the harpoon: next that the tortoise should have gone to sleep, and left this very part exposed, contrary to his usual habit of drawing the neck within his shell; and lastly, that with the harpoon stuck in his flesh, and sunk still deeper by the act of drawing in his head to save himself, he should yet have been able to pull a heavy laden boat and a raft tied to it, along, with even an alarming degree of rapidity.

Our conversation being ended, I requested my wife to go with two of the younger boys to Falcon's Stream, and fetch the sledge and the beasts of burden, that we might not fail of seeing at least a part of our booty from the ship put safely under shelter the same evening. A tempest, or even the tide, might sweep away the whole during the night! We took every precaution in our power against the latter danger, by fixing the boat and the raft, now, at the time of its reflux, as securely as we could without an anchor. I rolled two prodigious masses of lead, with the assistance of levers, from the raft upon the shore, and then tied a rope to each, the other ends of which were fastened, one to the raft, and the other to the boat, and thus satisfied myself that they could not easily be forced away.

While we were employed on this scheme, the sledge arrived, and we immediately placed the tortoise upon it, and also some other articles of light weight, such as mattresses, pieces of linen, etc.; for I reckoned that the animal itself weighed at least three quintals. The strength of our whole party was found necessary to move it from the raft to the sledge: we therefore all set out together to unload it again at Falcon's Stream. We pursued our way thither with the utmost gaiety of heart, and found the time pass both agreeably and quickly, in answering the numerous questions with which the three youngest boys assailed us, as to the nature and amount of the treasures we had brought from the vessel. The chest containing the articles in silver, and another filled with trinkets and utensils made of different kinds of metals, the most powerfully excited their interest; for Fritz had dropped a hint of what was in them, and nothing could exceed the measure of their curiosity.—Are they left on the raft or in the boat? asked Ernest. We will open them to-morrow, and I shall have my watch.

*Jack.*—I assure you, I shall not be content with only a watch; I must have, since I hear there are so many, a snuff-box also.

*Francis.*—And I shall ask for a pretty purse filled with louis.

*Father.*—Vastly well imagined, my young ones.—Jack intends then, I presume, to take now and then a pinch of the snuff he has not got, and Francis perhaps means to sow his louis that they may produce him a crop.

*Jack.*—Now, father, you are for this once mistaken; I have no liking for snuff, and know very well we have not any: what I want the box for is, to preserve in it the seeds I mean to collect from all the charming plants that we see around us, as, should we ever return to Europe, I could then have them in our garden. I have also found some chaffers, and different kinds of flies, which I should also be glad to keep,

*Francis.*—And I should keep my money to buy some of the nice cakes mamma used to give us. If we stay here long, I dare say there will be a fair; and then I will buy as many as will last us all a very long time, for I like sweet cakes better than the hard biscuits mamma gives us now.

*Father.*—You will wait for a fair long enough to tire the patience of a little boy like you, Francis; but if you are so fond of sweet cakes, I should advise you to make them yourself, with some of the honey you get so cleverly.—The poor child blushed like scarlet; he, a few days before, had discovered a swarm of bees and some fine honey-combs in a tree, and had attempted to beat down a little of them with a stick:—the whole swarm rushed out enraged, and lighted on him, so that his face and hands were severely stung: he thus paid dear for his discovery, which might, however, at some time or other, prove a useful acquisition to us.

In this trifling kind of prate we beguiled the time, till we reached the foot of our castle. Our first concern, now, was the tortoise, which we immediately turned on his back, that we might strip off the shell, and make use of some of the flesh while it was fresh. My wife expressed her fear that we should fail in our attempt; but taking my hatchet, I separated the upper and under shell all round, which were joined together by cartilages. The upper shell of the tortoise is extremely convex; the under, on the contrary, is nearly flat. Having succeeded in dividing them, I cut away as much of the flesh of the animal as was sufficient for a meal, and then laid the remaining mass carefully and neatly on the under shell, which served as a dish, recommending to my wife to cook what I had cut off, on the other shell, with no other seasoning than a little salt, and pledged myself that she would by this means produce a most luxurious food.

My wife asked leave, however, to take away the *green-coloured* part of the flesh, which she said she could not even look at without distaste.—I answered that she was wrong in this; that it was not unusual, for a thing that displeased the eye, to be agreeable to the taste: I informed her that the green was the fat of the animal, and would add to the fine flavour and general moisture of the dish: but, added I, if you think it is too abundant, you can take a part and preserve it, by melting, for future use. We will then, said I, put what we mean to keep in salt, and distribute the head, the entrails, and the feet to the dogs; for all, you know, must live.

Oh dear papa, cried Francis, do give me the shell, it will be such a pretty plaything!

No, no, bawled out another: and one and all contended for the preference. I imposed silence, declaring that the right was entirely in Fritz, since it was he who had harpooned the animal, who, but for his dexterity and skill, would be at this moment existing in the sea.—But, continued I, it may be well to ask what each of you thought of doing with the shell, if he had obtained it?

*Ernest.*—I should turn it into a shield to defend myself with, if the savages should come upon us.

*Father.*—Ah, there is my egotist again; this is as I expected; but let us see in what way you would use it? You would fling it across your shoulders no doubt, and take to your heels manfully.— I fancy I have guessed right, my poor Ernest, have I not?—And you, Jack, what have you to say?

*Jack.*—I should make a nice little boat of it, which would help to amuse us all. I was thinking how cleverly we could fill it with potatoes, or the other things we want to take from Tent-

House to Falcon's Nest; it would glide along so nicely with the stream, and we should be saved all the fatigue we now have in carrying them.

*Father*.—Your scheme, I grant, is not ill-imagined; but a small raft or an old chest would do just as well for your purpose.— And now for my little Francis; I wonder what pretty plan he had thought of?

*Francis*.—I thought I should build a little house, papa, and the shell would make such a nice roof to it!

*Father*.—Vastly well, my lads, if we had only our amusement or our ease to think of; but I want you all to form the habit of thinking and acting for the general good, rather than of what will most gratify or accommodate his single self.—Now, then, let me ask to what use Fritz, the only rightful claimant to the shell, had intended to apply it?

*Fritz*.—I thought, father, of cleaning it thoroughly and fixing it by the side of our river, and keeping it always full of pure water for my mother's use, when she has to wash the linen or cook our victuals.

*Father*.—Excellent, excellent, my boy! all honour to the founder of the *pure water-tub*! This is what I call *thinking for the general good*. And we will take care to execute the idea as soon as we can prepare some clay, as a solid foundation for its bottom.

*Jack*.—Hah, hah! Now then it is my turn; for I have got some clay, which I have put by to keep for use, behind those old roots yonder.

*Father*.—And where did you get it, boy?

*Mother*.—Oh, you may apply to me for this part of the information; to my cost I know where the clay was got.—This morning early, my young hero falls to digging and scrambling on the hill you see to the right, and home he comes with the news that he has found a bed of clay; but in so dirty a condition himself, that we were obliged to think next of the washing-tub.

*Jack.*—And if I had minded a little dirt, mother, I should not have discovered this bed of clay, which you will see will be of great use to us. As I was returning from looking for potatoes, I thought I would take the high path along the river, just to see how rapidly it runs and forms those nice cascades: by and by I came to a large slope, watered by the river; it was so slippery that I could not keep upon my legs: so I fell, and dirtied myself all over: on looking, I saw that the ground was all of clay, and almost liquid, so I made some of it into balls, and brought them home.

*Mother.*—And boasted of your discovery as if you had made it in consequence of the most earnest desire to be of use, while the benefit was the result of chance alone. But I will not put you further to the blush, my boy; you at last confess the truth, and for this deserve our praise.

*Ernest.*—When the water-tub is complete, I will put the roots I have found to soak a little in it, for they are now extremely dry. I do not exactly know what they are; they look something like the radish or horseradish, but the plant from which I took them was almost the size of a bush: being ignorant, however, of its name or nature, I have not yet ventured to taste the roots, though I saw our sow eat heartily of them.

*Father.*—It was quite right to be cautious, my son: but let me look at these roots. I am always glad to hear that you observe and reflect upon all the objects which fall in your way. How did you first discover them?

*Ernest.*—I was rambling about, father, and met with the sow, who with her snout was turning up the earth under the plant I have been speaking of, and stopped only to chew and swallow greedily something she seemed to find there. I drove her away; and on looking into the place, I found a knot of roots, which I tore out and brought home.

*Father.*—If my suspicion is right, you have made a beneficial discovery, which with the assistance of our potatoes may furnish us the means of existence as long as we may remain in this island! I am tolerably certain that these roots are *manioc*, of which the natives of the West Indies make a sort of bread or cake which they call *cassave*. But if we would make this use of it, we must first carry it through a certain preparation, without which these roots possess pernicious properties. If you are sure of finding the same place, or we can collect enough in any other, we will secure a sufficiently large quantity for our first experiment, which I have great confidence will succeed.

By the time of ending this discourse, we had also finished unloading the sledge, and I bade the three eldest boys accompany me to fetch another load before it should be dark. We left Francis and his mother busy in preparing what we indeed stood much in need of after a day of such fatigue, a refreshing meal for supper, the tortoise having presented itself most opportunely for this effect. I promise you, cried my wife, as we were moving off, you shall not at your return find reason to complain.

As we walked along, Fritz asked me if this handsome shell was of the kind so much valued in Europe for making into boxes, combs, etc.? and if it was not a pity to use it for a water-tub?

I replied, that in our deserted situation the utility of a thing formed its greatest, and indeed only value. According to this way of reasoning then, were your water-tub of diamonds, it would be of no more worth to us than the rudest stone, if in such a form as to be able to contain water. However, dear boy, I shall inform you, for your consolation, that our tortoise, which makes such excellent food, is not of the species, the shells of which are so much esteemed for the uses you have mentioned. This latter kind, which is called *caret*, does not furnish a wholesome food, its flesh being no less remarkable for its bad and unpalatable properties, than those of our tortoise for savouriness and nourishment. The shell of the caret tortoise is prepared for use by the action of heat, which separates the layer that from its colour and transparency is so attractive, from the inferior and useless parts. It is usual to preserve even the clippings of the real tortoise shell and unite them by heat for making articles of small price; but these are much more liable to break than the former, and of course possess very little of their beauty.

We now reached the raft, and took from it as many effects as the sledge could hold, or the animals draw along. The first object of my attention was to secure two chests which contained the clothes of my family, which I well knew would afford the highest gratification to my exemplary wife, who had frequently lamented that they were all compelled to wear clothes that were not their own; reminding her at every moment, she said, how much they might be wanted by their proper claimants. I reckoned also on finding in one of the chests some books on interesting subjects, and principally a large handsomely printed Bible. I added to these, four cart-wheels and a hand-mill for grinding; which, now that we had discovered the manioc, I considered of signal importance. These and a few other articles completed our present load.

On our return to Falcon's Nest, we found my wife looking anxiously for our arrival, and ready with the welcome she had promised, of an ample and agreeable repast; nor was her kind humour diminished by the view of the acquisitions we now added to her store of necessaries. Before she had well examined them, she drew me, with one of her sweetest smiles, by the arm— Step this way, said she, and I too will produce something that will both refresh and please you. And leading to the shade of a tree—This, continued she, is the work I performed in your absence, pointing to a cask of tolerable size, half-sunk into the ground, and the rest covered over with branches of trees. She then applied a small cork-screw to the side, and filling the shell of a cocoa-nut with the contents, presented it to me. I found the liquor equal to the best Canary I had ever tasted.—How then, said I, have you performed this new miracle? I cannot believe the enchanted bag produced it.—Not exactly, replied she; for this time it was an obliging white wave which threw on shore the agreeable liquid with which I have now the pleasure to regale you. I took a little ramble in your absence yesterday, to see what I could find, and behold how well my trouble was rewarded! The boys ran for the sledge, and had but little difficulty in getting it to Falcon's Stream, where our next care was to dig a place in the earth, to receive and keep it cool. We guessed it must contain some sort of wine; but to be quite sure, Ernest and Jack bored a small hole in the side, and inserting a hollow reed, they contrived to taste it, and assured me the cask was filled with a most delicious beverage. I now thought it was high time to forbid their proceeding any further with the tasting, fearing for the effect on their poor heads; and I closed up the hole with a small piece of wood. I have nothing more to relate, but that the boys kept the secret, as I desired them.

My wife and I agreed that we would now recompense them, by giving each a small glass of the precious liquor; but the young creatures took such a fancy to it, that they obtained again and again a little more, till at last we perceived their spirits so much raised, that we were obliged to refuse their further entreaties with gravity and firmness; observing to them, that man is required to restrain his appetite, and not to abuse, by excesses, the good things a bountiful Providence allows us for the purpose of rejoicing our hearts and strengthening our bodies when used with moderation.

By means of this little lecture I succeeded in appeasing their turbulence, and in drawing them from the dangerous vicinity of the cask. For my own part, the generous character of the wine had so invigorated me, that I found myself able to complete my day's work, by drawing up the mattresses we had brought from the ship, to our chamber in the tree, by means of a pulley. When I had laid them along to advantage, they looked so inviting, that I could scarcely resist my desire of at once committing myself to the kind relief they seemed to offer to my exhausted strength.

But now the tortoise, through the voice of my wife, laid claim to my attention. The savoury smell ascended to our castle; I hastened down, and we all partook heartily of the luxurious treat. We returned thanks to God, and speedily retired to taste the blessing of sweet and sound repose upon our mattresses.

# XIX

# ANOTHER TRIP TO THE WRECK

ROSE BEFORE DAY TO GO TO THE SEA-SIDE AND INSPECT OUR two vessels. My family did not hear me depart, and I was unwilling to disturb their balmy sleep, that sweet restorative of strength, so requisite for children. I therefore gently descended the ladder. Above, the scene was all repose; below, I found every thing in life and motion. The dogs jumped about me for joy, perceiving I was going out; the cock and the hens flapped their wings and chuckled, and our goats shook their long beards as they browsed; but the ass, the only creature amongst them I was likely to want at that time, still lay stretched at full length on the grass, and discovered no inclination for the morning jaunt I designed for him. Taking less of the creature's feelings into the account than my own occasion for his services, I quickly roused and harnessed him singly for the sledge, not wishing to yoke the cow to it before she had been milked. It was unnecessary to call the dogs after me. As I walked towards the shore, animated at different moments by hope and fear, with pleasure I saw there,

that, with the help of my lead and iron bars used as anchors, the boat and raft had resisted the tide, though it had partially heaved them up. I got quickly on the raft, where I took a small loading, and returned to Falcon's Stream in time for breakfast. Judge of my surprise when arrived, that I neither saw nor heard a single creature of its inhabitants, though the sun had climbed high above the horizon.—Thinking it time for our fellow-labourers to be stirring, I gave a shout as loud as a war-whoop. My wife awoke first, and wondered to see the day so far advanced. Really, my dear, said she, I think it must be the magic charm of the good mattress you brought home yesterday that has lulled me into such a long sound sleep, and that appears to be still exerting its influence upon our boys. In fact, though they rubbed their eyes, they could scarcely keep them open: they yawned, stretched, turned round, and turned back again. Come come, up, my lads, exclaimed I, once again; the more we venture to parley with sloth, the longer she holds us in her chains; brave youths like you, ought to awake at the first call, and leap quick and gaily out of bed. Fritz, ashamed to have slept so long, was dressed first; Jack soon after him, and Francis next; the ever-slothful Ernest was the last.

Is it possible, dear boy, said I to him, that at your age you allow even little Francis to get the start of you?

Oh! father, answered he, it is so delightful to lose oneself again after having been awakened! one feels sleep come on afresh so gently, ideas vanish so agreeably! I should be glad to be awakened thus every morning, that I might have the pleasure of falling into a new slumber.

I answer, Ernest, that this is a refinement in slothfulness I never heard of till now! It is my duty to tell you, and that gravely, if you acquire this habit, you will become an effeminate useless character. A man, though not like us, in a desert, is bound to provide for his existence, and avoid being a burthen to society; he should do what is right with courage and promptness, without consulting convenience or pleasure. He who indulges himself in all that flatters his senses, will end by falling a victim to them. Nature produces, too, certain poisons, which are grateful to the palate; yet the persons who unguardedly taste them, fail not to suffer the death they conceal.

After this short admonition, we all came down; and prayers and breakfast being over, we returned to the sea-side to complete the unloading of the raft, that it might be ready for sea on the ebbing of the tide. I was not long, with the additional assistance I had, in taking two cargoes to Falcon's Stream. At our last trip the tide was nearly up to our craft. I immediately sent back my wife and three children, and remained with Fritz waiting till we were quite afloat; when observing Jack hovering round us and dilatory in following his mother, I perceived his wish and assented to his embarking with us. Shortly after, the tide was high enough for us to row off. Instead of steering for Safety Bay to moor our vessels there securely, I was tempted by the fineness of the weather to go out again to the wreck, which it was with considerable difficulty we got up to, though aided by a very fresh sea breeze. On our getting along-side, it was too late to undertake much, and I was unwilling to cause my dear partner uneasiness by passing another night on board; I therefore determined to bring away only what could be obtained with ease and speed: in this resolution we searched hastily through the ship for any trifling articles that might be readily removed. Jack was up and down, every where, at a loss, what to select; and when I saw him again, he drew a wheel-barrow after him, shouting and rejoicing at having found such a vehicle for the convenient carriage of our potatoes. But Fritz next disclosed still better news, which was that he had discovered behind the bulk-head amid-ship, a pinnace (*i.e.* a small craft, the forepart of which is square) taken to pieces, with all its appurtenances, and even two small guns for its defence. This intelligence so delighted me, that I quitted every thing else to run to the bulk-head, when I was convinced of the truth of the lad's assertion: but I instantly perceived, that to put it together and launch it into the sea, would be an Herculean task, which I relinquished for the present. I then collected some house utensils and whatever else I thought most useful; such as a large copper boiler, some plates of iron, tobacco graters, two grinding-stones, a small barrel of gunpowder, and another full of flints, which I much valued. Jack's barrow was not forgotten; two more were afterwards found and added, with straps belonging to them. All these articles were hurried into the boat, without our stopping to eat, or in any manner refresh ourselves, and we re-embarked with speed, to avoid meeting the land wind that invariably rises in the evening. As we were safely and happily drawing near to shore, we were struck with the appearance of an assemblage of small figures ranged in a long line on the strand, and that seemed to be viewing us attentively: they were dressed in black, and all uniform, with white waistcoats and full cravats: the arms of these beings hung down carelessly; now and then, however, they seemed to extend them tenderly, as if they wished to embrace or offer us a token of friendship.

I really think, said I to the boys, who were steadfastly gazing at so novel a spectacle, that we are in the country of the pygmies, and that, having discovered us, they wish to form a friendly alliance.

*Jack.*—Oh, no! father, they are certainly Lilliputians, though somewhat bigger than those of whom I read the description in *Gulliver's Travels.*

You, then, child, said I, consider those travels as true; that there is an island of Lilliput, and inhabited by dwarfs?

*Jack.*—Gulliver says so. He met also with men of an immense stature, besides an island inhabited by horses. . . .

And yet I must tell you that the only reality in all his discoveries is the rich imagination of the author, whose taste and feeling led him to resort to allegory for the purpose of revealing grand truths. Do you know, Jack, what an allegory is?

It somewhat resembles a parable, I presume.

Right, one is very similar to the other,

*Jack.*—And the pygmies you mentioned, are any to be found?

No more than there are Lilliputians; they exist only in poetical fiction, or in the erroneous account of some ancient navigator, in which a group of monkeys has been fallaciously described as diminutive men.

*Fritz.*—Such probably are the mannikins that we see now stretching out their arms towards us. Ah, now I begin to perceive that they have beaks, and that their arms are short drooping wings;—what strange birds!

You are right, son, they are penguins or ruffs. They are of the *stupid* species; Ernest killed one soon after our arrival. They are excellent swimmers, but cannot fly; and so confused are they when on land, that they run in the silliest way into danger; catching such birds as these, is a fit sport for none but the indolent.

While we were talking I steered gently towards shore, to enjoy the uncommon sight the longer; but the very moment we got into shallow water, my giddy boy Jack leaped out of his cask up to his waist into it, and was quickly on land battering with his stick among the penguins before they were aware of his approach, so that half a dozen of them were immediately laid flat; they were not dead, but only stunned: the remainder, seeing they were so roughly accosted, plunged into the sea, dived, and disappeared.

Fritz murmured audibly at his brother for having frightened them away before he could fire. I could not help laughing at this perpetual shooter of guns, who was so disposed to waste his powder on animals which were to be taken with the hand without resistance: I also taunted Jack a little for having jumped into the water at the risk of being drowned. While I was making these observations, the birds, that had been merely stunned, gradually recovered, rose upon their legs and began a tottering sort of march with a gravity which irresistibly excited our laughter. I did not allow Jack's game to escape; I took hold of them, tied their legs together with reeds, without hurting them, and laid them on the beach while we were landing our treasures. But as the sun declined, and we despaired of finishing before night set in, each of us filled a barrow in order to take home something. I requested that the tobacco-graters and iron plates might be in the first load; to these we added the penguins living and dead, and then set out. As we drew near Falcon's Stream I heard with pleasure the watchful dogs proclaim our approach with loud barking: they no sooner saw us than they ran up with lively demonstrations of joy, and in the midst of their rough greetings completely overset poor Jack, who was wheeling along his barrow with difficulty and some ill-humour, and to this he gave vent by two or three lusty cuffs of his fist, which were divided between his friends Turk and Ponto, who so little thought of resenting them, that they sprang upon him as often as he took his barrow, and thus renewed the contest to the no small amusement of his brothers, who ran up to disengage him. My wife was highly pleased with the wheel-barrows and for the most part with their contents, but she had no partiality for the tobacco-graters.—In the name of Heaven, said she, what is the use of these graters? Are our four sons to become snuff-takers? Luckily for my fears, said she, the article is not to be obtained in our island.

No, dear wife, I replied; and pray do not be uneasy about them; these graters are not for the gratification of our noses; I am too happy in having myself abandoned the bad and filthy habit of snuff-taking, to permit my sons to use it. Come, children, said I, pointing to the penguins, look after the newcomers to the poultry-yard. I then directed them to fasten the birds one by one to a goose or a duck, as a means of taming and inuring them to the society of their companions. This essay, however, was tedious and inconvenient to our feathered animals, who were but slowly reconciled to their singular companions. My wife now showed me a good store of potatoes which she had got in during our absence, and a quantity of the roots I had taken for manioc, and in which I was not mistaken: I much applauded her diligence and foresight, and gave Ernest and little Francis their share of approbation.

Papa, we have worked very hard indeed, said the latter; what will you say when we have a fine crop of maize, melons, dates, and gourds? Mamma has planted all these in the potatoe holes.

I must tell you, master Francis, exclaimed his mother, you are a little thoughtless babbler. Why did you tell my secret? you have spoiled all the pleasure I promised myself in surprising your father with my new plantation.

*Father.*—I am sorry for this, my dear; but be assured I am not the less gratified for hearing of your kindness in this unexpected manner. But tell me, I beseech you, where did you procure all these seeds and grains, and how came you to think of so extraordinary a plan?

*Mother.*—I took the grain and seeds from the bottom of my enchanted bag, and your thirst after fresh booty and your endless trips to the wreck are the sources of the resolution I formed to increase the number of your comforts at home, and thus render them the less necessary. I determined then during the fine season to fit up a kitchen-garden, and to sow as much of it with seed as I was able to dig and put in order; at the same time taking particular care to leave all the smallest-sized potatoes in the ground, that they might produce us a full and abundant crop.

*Father.*—This was well thought, my love; but we must not despise the trips to the vessel neither; this very day we unexpectedly discovered in her a new and handsome little pinnace, which at some time or other may be of the greatest service to us.

*Mother.*—I cannot say that this discovery gives me very much pleasure; I have no desire to trust myself again on the sea; but should it at any time be absolutely necessary, I must confess I should prefer a well made solid vessel to our miserable raft composed of tubs.

*Father.*—Well, this you shall possess, if you will consent to my returning once more to the wreck; in the mean while, let us have some supper, and then we will retire to rest; and if my little workmen should be industriously inclined to-morrow, I shall reward them with what to children is always a source of pleasure—the novelty of a new trade to be learnt. This did not fail to excite the curiosity of all; but I kept my word, and made them wait till the following day for the explanation I had to give.

# XX

# THE BAKE-HOUSE

**I** WAKED THE BOYS VERY EARLY, REMINDING THEM THAT I HAD promised to teach them a new trade. What is it? What is it? exclaimed they all at once, springing suddenly out of bed and hurrying on their clothes.

*Father.*—It is the art of baking, my boys, which at present I am no more acquainted with than yourselves; but we will learn it together, and I am much mistaken if we shall not be able to produce an excellent batch of bread, which will be the greater luxury, from our having been altogether deprived of it during our residence in this island. Hand me those iron plates that we brought yesterday from the vessel, and the tobacco-graters also.

*Mother.*—I really cannot understand what tobacco-graters and iron plates can have to do with making bread; a good oven would afford me much better hopes, and this, unfortunately, we do not possess.

*Father.*—These very iron plates, the same you looked so disdainfully upon no longer since than yesterday, will serve the purpose of the things you are now wishing to have.—I cannot, it is true, promise, in this early attempt, to produce you light and handsome-looking bread; but I can answer that you shall have some excellent-tasted cakes, though they should be a little flat and heavy;—we will immediately make our experiment. Ernest, bring hither the roots found underground: but first, my dear, I must request you to make me a small bag of a piece of the strongest wrapper linen.

My wife set instantly to work to oblige me; but having no great confidence in my talents for making cakes, she first filled with potatoes the large copper boiler we had brought from the ship, and put it on the fire, that we might not find ourselves without something to eat at the time of dinner: in the meanwhile I spread a large piece of coarse linen on the ground, and assembled my young ones round me to begin our undertaking; I gave each of the boys a grater, and showed him at the same time how to rest it on the linen, and then to grate the roots of manioc; so that in a short time each had produced a considerable heap of a substance somewhat resembling pollard. The occupation, as is always the case with novelties, proved infinitely amusing to them all, and they looked no further into the matter; one showed the other his heap, saying in a bantering tone: Will you eat a bit of nice cake, made of grated radishes?

*Father.*—Make as merry as you please, young gentlemen, on the subject of this excellent production of nature, which ere long you will acknowledge to have yielded you a most palatable kind of food; a food which is known to be the principal sustenance of whole nations of the continent of America, and which the Europeans who inhabit those countries even prefer to our wheaten bread. I must tell you, there are many kinds of manioc; one of these shoots rapidly, and its roots become mature in a short time; a second sort is of more tardy growth; and there is another, the roots of which require the space of two years to be fit for use. The first two kinds have pernicious or unwholesome qualities when eaten raw, but the third may be eaten without fear: for all this, the two first are generally preferred, as being more productive, and requiring a shorter time for being fit for use.

*Jack.*—One would think only madmen could prefer those that are pernicious: we cannot to be sure but be overwhelmed with gratitude for some cake that is to kill us (and the young rogue threw his grater from him as he spoke)! who shall tell us that our fine roots here are not of the same pernicious kind.

*Father.*—At all events we shall not eat them raw; as nearly as I recollect, the tardy kind, like these we have procured, grow in the form of a bush; while the other two are creeping plants. However, to be quite sure, the first thing we will do, shall be to press the pollard.

*Ernest.*—For what end, father, shall we press it?

*Father.*—Because, even in the pernicious kind it is only the sap which is hurtful; the more substantial part being when dried extremely wholesome and even nourishing. But that we may act with the greatest possible prudence, we will give some of our cakes to the fowls and to the monkey, before we venture to eat of them ourselves; if they do them no harm, we may then proceed to feast on them with safety.

*Jack.*—Thank you, father; but I have no fancy to let my monkey be poisoned.

*Father.*—You may be perfectly easy, Jack, for the preservative instinct of your monkey is such, that he would not touch it if it were poisonous; animals are in this respect better treated than man, who is called upon to use his reason in supplying the deficiency: at all events, however, we will give him so little that no harm can possibly ensue.

Upon this Jack picked up his grater, and with the others began to grate the roots with new alertness: dread of the poison had for an instant palsied every arm; but a very short time was now sufficient for producing a considerable quantity of ground manioc. By this time my wife had completed the bag . . . had it well filled with what we called our pollard, and she closed it effectually by sewing up the end. I was now to contrive a kind of press: I cut a long, straight, well-formed branch, of considerable strength, from a neighbouring tree, and stripped it of the bark; I then placed a plank across the table we had fixed between the arched roots of our tree, and which was exactly the right height for my purpose, and on this I laid the bag; I put other planks again upon the bag, and then covered all with the large branch, the thickest extremity of which I inserted under an arch, while to the other, which projected beyond the planks, I suspended all sorts of heavy substances, such as lead, our largest hammers and bars of iron, which, acting with great force as a press on the bag of manioc, caused the sap it contained to issue in streams, which flowed plentifully on the ground.

*Fritz.*—This machine of yours, father, though simple, is as effectual as can be desired.

*Father.*—Certainly. It is the simplest lever that the art of mechanism can furnish, and may be made extremely useful.

*Ernest.*—I thought that levers were never used but for raising heavy masses, such as blocks of stone, and things of that degree of weight; I had no notion that they were used for pressing.

*Father.*—But, my dear boy, you see that the point at which the lever rests on the planks, must always be the point of rest or compression; the point at which its extremity touches the roots of the tree would no doubt be that of the raising power, if the root was not too strong to yield to the point of the lever; but then the resistance at the point of compression or rest is still stronger, and presses effectually, as you see, the contents of the bag. The Negroes, however, have another manner of proceeding; but it would have been much too tedious in the process for us to imitate. They make tresses of the bark of a tree, and with it form a kind of basket of tolerable size; they fill it with manioc, and press it so tightly that the baskets become shorter, and increase in breadth; they then hang the baskets to the strongest branches of trees, and fasten large stones to them, which draw the baskets again lengthways; by which action upon the manioc, the sap runs out at the openings left by the tresses.

*Mother.*—Can one make no use of this sap?

*Father.*—Certainly, we may: the same Negroes use it as food, after mixing with it a considerable quantity of pepper; and, when they can procure them, some sea crabs. The Europeans, on the other hand, leave it to settle in vessels till it has formed a sediment; they then pour off the liquid part, wash the sediment with fresh water, and place it to dry in the sun: in this manner they obtain from it an excellent sort of starch, which is used for clearing linen. I must tell you that the potatoe also contains the same sort of substance, which may be put to the same use: for the rest, the latter is less nourishing than the manioc.

*Mother.*—But pray tell me, are we to prepare the whole of this manioc at once? If so, we have at least a whole day's work, and a great part must be spoiled at last.

*Father.*—Not so, my, dear; when the pollard is perfectly dry, it may be placed in casks, and being shut closely down, it will keep for years; but you will see that the whole of this large heap will be so reduced in quantity by the operation we are going to apply of baking, that there will be no cause for your apprehension.

*Fritz.*—Father, it no longer runs a single drop; may we not now set about making the dough?

*Father.*—I have no objection; but it would be more prudent to make only a small cake, at first, by way of experiment, which as I said before we will give to the monkey and the fowls, and wait to see the effect, instead of exhausting our whole store at once.

We now opened the bag, and took out a small quantity of the pollard, which already was sufficiently dry; we stirred the rest about with a stick, and then replaced it under the press. The next thing was to fix one of our iron plates, which was of a round form, and rather convex, so as to rest upon two blocks of stone at a distance from each other; under this we lighted a large fire, and when the iron plate was completely heated, we placed a portion of the dough upon it with a wooden spade. As soon as the cake began to be brown underneath, it was turned, that the other side might be baked also.

*Ernest.*—O how nicely it smells! what a pity that we may not eat some of it immediately!

*Jack.*—And why not? I would eat some without the least fear; and would not you, Francis?

*Father.*—Hah, hah! What is then become of our terrible fear of being poisoned, which made you even throw your grater from you? Ah, I see how it is; the passion of gluttony is stronger than your fear.—However, I certainly believe that in this case it might be gratified without doing you an injury; nevertheless it is better perhaps to wait till the evening, and not run a greater risk than the loss of one or two of our fowls and of the monkey; and we may say this trial of the cake will be the first service he has rendered us.

As soon as the cake was cold, we broke some of it into crumbs, and gave it to two of the fowls, and a larger piece to the monkey, who nibbled it with a perfect relish, making all the time a thousand grimaces to testify his content, while the boys stood by envying the preference he enjoyed.

*Fritz.*—Now tell me, father, how the savages manage to grate their manioc, for surely they have not, like us, an instrument fitted for the operation:—and tell me also, if they call their composition by the name of cake or bread, as we do?

*Father.*—The savages having no such article as bread in their bill of fare, have consequently no word in their language to express it. At the Antilles, the bread from the manioc is called *cassave*; the savages make a kind of grater with sharp stones, or shells; or when they can get nails, on which they set a high value, they drive them into the end of a plank, and rub the manioc upon it. But now, I pray you, good wife, give us quickly some dinner, and we will afterwards resume the baking trade, provided our tasters show no signs of the colic or swimming in the head.

*Fritz.*—Are these, then, the only effects of poison, father?

*Father.*—At least they are the most ordinary ones: there are poisons which paralyse and induce a heavy sleep; such are opium, if taken in too large a quantity; hemlock, etc. etc. Others are sharp and corrosive, attacking the stomach and intestines: of this class are arsenic, sublimate, and the pernicious sorts of mushrooms. If, when either of these has been swallowed, there be not immediate assistance procured, the human machine stops, becomes disorganized, and the patient dies.—I will take this occasion, my dear children, to caution you against a kind of fruit extremely dangerous in its nature, and the more so from the remarkable attraction of its external appearance. This fruit is frequently found in America on the banks of rivers or in marshes, and you may perhaps meet with it in this island. Its aspect is agreeable to the eye, resembling a handsome kind of yellow apple with red spots. It is, however, one of the strongest poisons in the world: it is even said to be dangerous to sleep under the shade of the tree which produces it. Be very careful, therefore, should you happen to meet with it: it is known by the name of *mancenilla*. Indeed I cannot too seriously exhort you not to venture on eating any thing you may find, however alluring in appearance, till you have first consulted me. Promise me this, children, one and all of you.

*Jack.*—I promise you heartily, father; and still further, I will keep my word more faithfully than Adam did towards God, who had forbidden him to eat of a certain apple.

*Father.*—You will do well in this; but do not so presumptuously and so readily blame that in another which under the same circumstances you would have done yourself; I would lay a wager that you would be the first to be led away by any worthless knave who should come and tell you that I had been laughing at you all the while, that the mancenilla is the finest apple in the world, and that by eating it you would be rendered as strong as a lion; that ready appetite of yours, and that little vanity we now and then discover in you, would make you, I fear, forget my advice, and greedily devour the apple.—But this is enough on the subject; instead of thinking more of poisons, let us resort with confidence to our plentiful dish of boiled potatoes; perhaps, dear wife, you have some little relish to add to them to-day:—what, I pray you, may there be in that boiling vessel yonder?

*Mother.*—It is the penguin that Jack killed and brought home.

To say the truth, we did not take a fancy to the dish, the bird being of a strong and fishy flavour. Jack, however, was of a different opinion, and he was left at full liberty to regale himself to his appetite's content.

The first thing we did after dinner was to visit our fowls. Those among them which had eaten the manioc, were in excellent condition, and no less so the monkey, who gave us sufficient proofs of life and health in the multitude of gambols and grimaces he exhibited. Now then to the bake-house, young ones, said I— to the bake-house as fast as you can scamper. The grated manioc was soon emptied out of the bag, a large fire was quickly lighted, and when sufficiently fervent, I placed the boys where a flat surface had been prepared for them, and gave to each a plate of iron and the quantity of a cocoa-nut full for them to make a cake apiece, and they were to try who could succeed the best. They were ranged in a half circle round the place, where I stood myself, that they might the better be enabled to observe how I proceeded, and adopt the same method for themselves. The result was not discouraging for a first experiment, though it must be confessed we were now and then so unlucky as to burn a cake; but there was not a greater number of these than served to feed the pigeons and the fowls, which hovered round us to claim their share of the treat. My little rogues could not resist the pleasure of frequently tasting their cake, a little bit at a time, as they went on. At length the undertaking was complete; the cakes were put in a

partner. The boys, on the contrary, were gay and on the alert, in the expectation of the pleasure that awaited them; particularly Ernest, who had not yet made a single voyage with us to the vessel. We took with us an ample provision of boiled potatoes and cassave; and in addition, arms and weapons of every kind. We embarked and reached Safety Bay without the occurrence of any remarkable event: here we thought it prudent to put on our cork jackets; we then scattered some food for the geese and ducks which had taken up their abode there, and soon after stepped gaily into our tub-raft, at the same time fastening the new boat by a rope to her stern, so that she could be drawn along. We put out for the current, though not without considerable fear of finding that the wreck had entirely disappeared. We soon, however, perceived that she still remained firm between the rocks. Having got on board, our first care was to load our craft with different stores, that we might not return without some acquisition of comfort for our establishment; and then all on the wings of curiosity and ardour we repaired to that part of the vessel called the bulk-head, which contained the enviable prize, the pinnace. On further observation, it appeared to me that the plan we had formed was subject to at least two alarming and perhaps insurmountable difficulties: the one was the situation of the pinnace in the ship; and the other was the size and weight it would necessarily acquire when put together. The inclosure in which she lay in pieces was far back in the interior of the ship, and close upon the side which was in the water, immediately under the officers' cabin. Several inner timbers of prodigious bulk and weight separated this inclosure from the breach at which only we had been able to get on board, and in this part of the deck there was not sufficient space for us to work at putting the pinnace together, or to give her room should we succeed in completing our business. The breach also was too narrow and too irregular to admit of her being launched from this place, as we had done with our tub-raft. In short, the separate pieces of the pinnace were too heavy for the possibility of our removing them even with the assistance of our united strength. What therefore was to be done? and how could we meet so formidable a difficulty? I stood on the spot absorbed in deep reflection, while the boys were running from place to place, conveying every thing portable they could find on board the raft.

The cabinet which contained the pinnace was lighted by several small fissures in the timbers, which after standing in the place a few minutes to accustom the eye, enabled one to see sufficiently to distinguish objects. I discovered with pleasure that all the pieces of which she was composed were so accurately arranged and numbered, that without too much presumption, I might flatter myself with the hope of being able effectually to collect and put them together, if I could be allowed the necessary time, and could procure a convenient place. I therefore, in spite of every disadvantage, decided on the undertaking; and we immediately set about it. We proceeded, it must be confessed, at first so slowly as to produce discouragement, if the desire of possessing so admirable a little vessel, quite new, perfectly safe, easy to conduct, and which might at some future day be the means of our deliverance, had not at every moment inspired us with new strength and ardour.

Evening, however, was fast approaching, and we had made but small progress; we were obliged to think of our promise to my wife; and though with reluctance, we left our occupation and re-embarked. On reaching Safety Bay, we had the satisfaction of finding there our kind steward and little Francis; they had been, during the day, employed in some necessary arrangements for our living at Tent-House as long as we should have occasion to continue the excursions to the vessel: this she did to shorten the length of the voyage, and that we might be always in sight of each other. This new proof of her kind attention affected me in a lively manner, and I could not sufficiently express the gratitude which I felt, particularly as I knew the dislike she had conceived to living in this spot. I presented her with the valuable cargo we brought, which I knew would give her pleasure, and regretted that I had no better recompense to offer for the voluntary sacrifice she had made to my accommodation. I made the best display I could of two casks of salted butter, three of flour, some small bags of millet-seed and of rice, and a multitude of other articles of utility and comfort for our establishment. My wife rewarded me by the expression of her perfect satisfaction, and the whole was removed to our storehouse at the rocks. We passed an entire week in this arduous undertaking of the pinnace. I embarked regularly every morning with my three sons, and returned every evening, and never without some small addition to our stores. We were now so accustomed to this manner of proceeding, that my wife bade us good bye without concern, and we, on our parts, left Tent-House without anxiety; she even had the courage to go several times, with no companion but her little Francis, to Falcon's Stream, to feed and take care of the poultry and to bring back potatoes for our use. As night successively returned, we had a thousand interesting things to tell each other, and the pleasure of being together was much increased by these short separations: we even enjoyed with a better appetite the excellent supper our kind hostess at all times took care to prepare for us.

At length the pinnace was completed, and in a condition to be launched: the question now was, how to manage this remaining difficulty. She was an elegant little vessel, perfect in every part: she had a small neat deck; and her mast and sails were no less exact and perfect than those of a little brig. It was probable she would sail well, from the lightness of her construction, and in consequence, drawing but little water. We had pitched and towed all the seams, that nothing might be wanting for her complete appearance: we had even taken the superfluous pains of further embellishing by mounting her with two small cannon of about a pound weight; and, in imitation of larger vessels, had fastened them to the deck with chains. But in spite of the delight we felt in contemplating a commodious little vessel, formed for usefulness in all its parts, and the work, as it were, of our own industry, yet the great difficulty still remained: the said commodious, charming little vessel still stood fast, inclosed within four walls; nor could I conceive of a means of getting her out. To support the idea of so much time and labour bestowed for no end or advantage, was absolutely impossible; to effect a passage through the outer side of the vessel, by means of our united industry in the use of all the utensils we had secured, seemed to present a prospect of exertions beyond the reach of man, even if not attended with dangers the most threatening and alarming. We now examined if it might be practicable to cut away all intervening timbers, to which, from the nature of the breach, we had easier access; but should we even succeed in this attempt, the upper timbers being, in consequence of the inclined position of the ship, on a level with the water, our labour would be unavailing: besides, we had neither strength nor time for such a proceeding; from one moment to another, a storm might arise and engulf the ship, timber, pinnace, ourselves, and all. Despairing, then, of being able to find a means consistent with the sober rules of art, my impatient fancy inspired the thought of a project, which, if subjected to the experiment, must necessarily be attended with hazards and dangers of a tremendous nature.

I had found on board, a strong iron mortar, such as is used in kitchens. I took a thick oak plank, and nailed to a certain part of it some large iron hooks: with a knife I cut a groove along the middle of the plank. I sent the boys to fetch some match-wood from the hold, and I cut a piece sufficiently long to continue burning at least two hours. I placed this train in the groove of my plank: I filled the mortar with gunpowder, and then laid the plank, thus furnished, upon it, having previously pitched the mortar all round; and, lastly, I made the whole fast to the spot with strong chains crossed by means of the hooks in every direction. Thus I accomplished a sort of cracker, from which I expected to effect a happy conclusion. I hung this infernally contrived machine against the side of the bulk-head next the sea, having taken previous care to choose a spot in which its action could not affect the pinnace. When the whole was arranged, I set fire to the match, the end of which projected far enough beyond the plank to allow us sufficient time to escape. I now hurried on board the raft, into which I had previously sent the boys before applying a light to the match; and who, though they had assisted in forming the cracker, had no suspicion of the use for which it was intended, and believing all the while it concealed some subject of amusement for their next trip to the vessel. I confess I had purposely avoided giving them the true explanation, from the fear of the entire failure of my project, or that the vessel, pinnace, and all that it contained, might in consequence be blown up in a moment. I had naturally, therefore, some reluctance to announce myself before the time, as the author of so many disasters.

On our arrival at Tent-House, I immediately put the raft in a certain order, that she might be in readiness to return speedily to the wreck, when the noise produced by the cracker should have informed me that my scheme had taken effect. We set busily to work in emptying her; and during the occupation, our ears were assailed with the noise of an explosion of such violence, that my wife and the boys, who were ignorant of the cause, were so dreadfully alarmed as instantly to abandon their employment. What can it be?—what is the matter?—what can have happened? cried all at once. It must be cannon. It is perhaps the captain and the ship's company who have found their way hither! Or can it be some vessel in distress? Can we go to its relief?

*Mother.*—The sound appeared to come in the direction of the wreck; perhaps she has blown up. Were you careful of not leaving any light which could communicate with gunpowder?—From the bottom of her heart she made this last suggestion, for she desired nothing more earnestly than that the vessel should be annihilated, and thus an end be put to our repeated visits.

*Father.*—If this is the case, said I, we had better return immediately, and convince ourselves of the fact.—Who will be of the party?

I, I, I, cried the boys; and the three young rogues lost not a moment in jumping into their tubs, whither I soon followed them, after having whispered a few words to my wife, somewhat tending to explain, but still more to tranquillise her mind during the trip we had now to engage in.

We rowed out of the bay with more rapidity than on any former occasion; curiosity gave strength to our arms. When the vessel was in sight, I observed with pleasure that no change had taken place in the part of her which faced Tent-House; and that no sign of smoke appeared: we advanced, therefore, in excellent spirits; but instead of rowing, as usual, straight to the breach, we proceeded round to the side, on the inside of which we had placed the cracker. The horrible scene of devastation we had caused now broke upon our sight. The greater part of the ship's side was shivered to pieces; innumerable splinters covered the surface of the water; the whole exhibited a scene of terrible destruction, in the midst of which presented itself our elegant pinnace, entirely free from injury! I could not refrain from the liveliest exclamations of joy, which excited the surprise of the boys, who had felt the disposition such a spectacle naturally inspired, of being dejected at the sight of so melancholy an event. They fixed their eyes upon me with the utmost astonishment.—Now then she is ours, cried I—the elegant little pinnace is ours! for nothing is now more easy than to launch her. Come, boys, jump upon her deck, and let us see how quickly we can get her down upon the water.

*Fritz.*—Ah! now I understand you, father, you have yourself blown up the side of the ship with that machine you contrived in our last visit, that we might be able to get out the pinnace; but how does it happen that so much of the ship is blown away?

*Father.*—I will explain all this to you when I have convinced myself that the pinnace is not injured, and that there is no danger of any of the fire remaining on board: let us well examine. We entered by the new breach, and had soon reason to be satisfied that the pinnace had wholly escaped from injury, and that the fire was entirely extinguished. The mortar, however, and pieces of the chain, had been driven forcibly into the opposite side of the inclosure. Having now every reason to be satisfied and tranquil, I explained to the boys the nature of a cracker, the manner of its operation, and the important service for which I was indebted to the old mortar.

I now attentively examined the breach we had thus effected, and next the pinnace, I perceived that it would be easy, with the help of the crow and the lever, to lower her into the water. In putting her together, I had used the precaution of placing the keel on rollers, that we might not experience the same difficulty as we had formerly done in launching our tub-raft. Before letting her go, however, I fastened the end of a long thick rope to her head, and the other end to the most solid part of the wreck, for fear of her being carried out too far. We put our whole ingenuity and strength to this undertaking, and soon enjoyed the pleasure of seeing our pretty pinnace descend gracefully into the sea; the rope keeping her sufficiently near, and enabling us to draw her close to the spot where I was loading the tub-boat, and where for that purpose I had lodged a pulley on a projecting beam, from which I was enabled also to advance with the completing of the necessary masts and sails for our new barge. I endeavoured to recollect minutely all the information I had ever possessed on the art of equipping a vessel; and our pinnace was shortly in a condition to set sail.

On this occasion a spirit of military affairs was awakened in the minds of my young flock, which was never after extinguished.

We were masters of a vessel mounted with two cannon, and furnished amply with guns and pistols! This was at once to be invincible, and in a condition for resisting and destroying the largest fleet the savages could bring upon us! In the height of exultation it was even almost wished they might assail us! For my own part, I answered their young enthusiasm with pious prayers that we might ever escape such a calamity as the being compelled to use our fire-arms. Night surprised us before we had finished our work, and we accordingly prepared for our return to Tent-House, after drawing the pinnace close under the vessel's side. We arrived in safety, and took great care, as had been previously agreed on, not to mention our new and invaluable booty to the good mother, till we could surprise her with the sight of it in a state of entire completeness. In answer, therefore, to her inquiries as to the noise she heard, we told her that a barrel of gunpowder had taken fire, and had shivered to pieces a small part of the ship. We relied that no suspicion of the secret would occur to her mind, should she even have the fancy of looking at the vessel through the glass, as she sometimes did; for the pinnace lay so as to be concealed by the immense bulk of the ship's body.

Two whole days more were spent in completely equipping and loading the beautiful little barge we had now secured. When she was ready for sailing, I found it impossible to resist the earnest importunity of the boys, who, as a recompense for the industry and discretion they had employed, claimed my permission to salute their mother, on their approach to Tent-House, with two discharges of cannon. These accordingly were loaded, and the two youngest placed themselves, with a lighted match in hand, close to the touch holes, to be in readiness. Fritz stood at the mast to manage the ropes and cables, while I took my station at the rudder. These matters being adjusted, we put off with sensations of lively joy, which was demonstrated by loud huzzas and suitable gesticulation. The wind was favourable; and so brisk, that we glided with the rapidity of a bird along the mirror of the waters: and while my young ones were transported with pleasure by the velocity of the motion, I could not myself refrain from shuddering at the thought of some possible disaster.

Our old friend the tub-raft had been deeply loaded and fastened to the pinnace, and it now followed as an accompanying boat to a superior vessel. We took down our large sail as soon as we found ourselves at the entrance of the Bay of Safety, to have the greater command in directing the barge; and soon, the smaller ones were lowered one by one, that we might the more securely avoid being thrown with violence upon the rocks so prevalent along the coast: thus, proceeding at a slower rate, we had greater facilities for managing the important affair of the discharge of the cannon. Arrived within a certain distance—"*Fire*"—cried commander Fritz. The rocks behind Tent-House returned the sound.—"*Fire*"—said Fritz again.—Ernest and Jack obeyed, and the echoes again majestically replied. Fritz at the same moment had discharged his two pistols, and all joined instantly in three loud huzzas.

Welcome! welcome! dear ones, was the answer from the anxious mother, almost breathless with astonishment and joy! Welcome, cried also little Francis with his feeble voice, as he stood clinging to her side, and not well knowing whether he was to be sad or merry! We now tried to push to shore with our oars in a particular direction, that we might have the protection of a projecting mass of rocks, and my wife and little Francis hastened to the spot to receive us: Ah, dear deceitful ones! cried she, throwing herself upon my neck and heartily embracing me, what a fright have you, and your cannon, and your little ship thrown me into! I saw it advancing rapidly towards us, and was unable to conceive from whence it could come, or what it might have on board: I stole with Francis behind the rocks, and when I heard the firing, I was near sinking to the ground with terror; if I had not the moment after heard your voices, God knows where we should have run to—but come, the cruel moment is now over, and thanks to Heaven I have you once again in safety! But tell me where you got so unhoped-for a prize as this neat charming little vessel? In good truth it would really almost tempt me to venture once more on a sea voyage, especially if she would promise to convey us back to our dear country! I foresee of what use she will be to us, and for her sake I think that I must try to forgive the many sins of absence you have committed against me.

Fritz now invited his mother to get on board, and gave her his assistance. When they had all stepped upon the deck, they entreated for permission to salute, by again discharging the cannon, and at the same moment to confer on the pinnace the name of their mother—*The Elizabeth.*

My wife was particularly gratified by these our late adventures; she applauded our skill and perseverance: but do not, said she, imagine that I bestow so much commendation without the hope of some return in kind: on the contrary, it is now my turn to claim from you, for myself and little Francis, the same sort of agreeable recompense; for we have not, I assure you, remained idle while the rest were so actively employed for the common benefit.—No, not so; little Francis and his mother found means to be doing something also, though not at this moment prepared to furnish such unquestionable proofs as you, by your salutations of cannon, etc.: but wait a little, good friends, and our proofs shall hereafter be apparent in some dishes of excellent vegetables which we shall be able to regale you with.—It depends, to say the truth, only on yourselves, dear ones, to go with me and see what we have done.

We did not hesitate to comply, and jumped briskly out of the pinnace for the purpose. Taking her little coadjutor Francis by the hand, she led the way, and we followed in the gayest mood imaginable. She conducted us up an ascent of one of our rocks, and stopping at the spot where the cascade is formed from Jackall's River, she displayed to our astonished eyes a handsome and commodious kitchen garden, laid out properly in beds and walks, and, as she told us, every where sowed with the seed of useful plants.

This, said she, is the pretty exploit we have been engaged in, if you will kindly think so of it. In this spot the earth is so light, being principally composed of decayed leaves, that Francis and I had no difficulty in working it, and then dividing it into different compartments; one for potatoes, one for manioc, and other smaller shares for lettuces of various kinds, not forgetting to leave a due proportion to receive some plants of the sugar-cane. You, dear husband, and Fritz, will easily find means to conduct sufficient water hither from the cascade, by means of pipes of bamboo, to keep the whole in health and vigour; and we shall have a double source of pleasure from the general prosperity, for both the eyes and the palate will be gratified. But you have not yet seen all: there, on the slope of the rock, I have transplanted some plants of the ananas. Between these, I have sowed some melon seeds, which cannot fail to succeed, thus securely sheltered and in so warm a soil: here is a plot allotted to peas and beans, and this other for all sorts of cabbage. Round each bed or plot I have sowed seeds of maize, on account of its tall and bushy form, to serve as a border, which at the same time will protect my young plants from the scorching heat of the sun.

I stood transported in the midst of so perfect an exhibition of the kind zeal and persevering industry of this most amiable of women! I could only exclaim, that I should never have believed in the possibility of such a labour in so short a time, and particularly with so much privacy as to leave me wholly unsuspicious of the existence of such a project

*Mother*.—To confess the truth, I did not myself at first expect to succeed, for which reason I resolved to say nothing of the matter to any one, that I might not be put to the blush for my presumption. But as I found my little calculations answer better than I expected, I was encouraged, and the hope of surprising you so agreeably, gave me new strength and activity. I, on my part, however, had my suspicions that your daily visits to the wreck were connected with some great mystery, which at a certain time you would be prepared to unfold—So, mystery for mystery, thought I; and thus, my love, it has turned out. Though acting in different directions, one only object has been our mutual aim—the substantial good of our beloved companions of the desert!

After a few jocose remarks with which we closed this conversation, we moved towards Tent-House. This was one of our happiest days, for we were all satisfied with ourselves and with each other; we had conferred and received benefits, and I led my children to observe the goodness of Providence, who renders even labour a source of enjoyment, and makes our own happiness result from that of the objects of our affection, and our pride to arise from the commendations of which those objects may be deserving.

I had almost forgot though, said my wife, after a short pause, one little reproach I had to make you: your trips to the vessel have made you neglect the bundle of valuable fruit saplings we laid together in mould at Falcon's Stream; I fear they by this time must be dying for want of being planted, though I took care to water and cover them with branches. Let us go, my love, and see about them.

I readily consented to so reasonable a proposal. I should have been no less grieved than my wife, to see this charming acquisition perish for want of care. We had reason on many accounts to return quickly to Falcon's Stream, where different matters required our presence. We had now in possession the greater part of the cargo of the vessel; but almost the whole of these treasures were at present in the open air, and liable to injury from both sun and rain.

My wife prepared with alertness for our walk; and the rather from the aversion she had ever entertained, on account of the intense heat, for Tent-House. We hastened to unload the boat, and to place the cargo safely under shelter along with our other stores.

The pinnace was anchored on the shore, and fastened with a rope, by her head, to a stake. When all our stores were thus disposed of, we began our journey to Falcon's Stream, but not empty-handed; we took with us every thing that seemed to be absolutely wanted for comfort; and when brought together, it was really so much, that both ourselves and our beasts of burthen had no easy task to perform.

# XXII

# GYMNASTIC EXERCISES;—VARIOUS DISCOVERIES; SINGULAR ANIMALS, ETC.

EITHER OUR VOYAGES TO THE WRECK, NOR THE LABORIOUSNESS of our occupations at Tent-House had made us forget the regular observance of our duties on the sabbath-day, which now again occurred the day after our return to Falcon's Stream; and we accordingly distinguished it by consecrating the forenoon to reading the church prayers, some chapters in the Bible, singing psalms, and lastly, the recital of a new parable I had invented, and which I had named the *Arabian Travellers*. I reminded my children in it, by the help of imagery and fictitious names, of all the aid and all the benefits bestowed upon us by an all-beneficent Providence, from the moment of our being cast upon our present abode;— that it was his compassion for our situation which had endued us with sagacity and perseverance in the discovery of so many things necessary for our existence; and one treasure, valuable above all the rest—a talisman, bestowed by the good genius who watched over poor defenceless wanderers. This talisman was such as to inspire them on every occasion with the knowledge of what was best for their happiness, and that by listening to these inspirations, they might be sure of always keeping in the right path, and finding every want supplied. I need not explain that by the good genius I alluded to the ever-watchful care or the exemplary wife and mother; and by the talisman, the sacred volume she had so miraculously preserved and concealed in her enchanted bag. I was well understood by my hearers; and as I finished my discourse, the children all ran spontaneously at once to embrace their mother, addressing her by the term *Good Genius*, and thanking her for having been the means of securing the Bible, to which we might all resort for consolation and instruction.

After dinner I again addressed my family with a short moral discourse, and then allowed them to use whatever kind of recreation they pleased; one feature of my system being, not to tire them with the subjects I wished them to feel an attachment for. I recommended to them, for the sake of uniting usefulness with their amusement, to resume the exercise we began upon the first Sunday of our abode in these regions, the shooting of arrows; for I had an extreme solicitude about their preserving and increasing their bodily strength and agility, which in a situation like ours, might prove of such critical importance. Nothing tends more to the extinction of personal courage in a human being, than the consciousness of wanting that strength of limb, or that address, which may be necessary to aid us in defending ourselves, or in escaping from dangers. On this occasion, I added the exercises of running, jumping, getting up trees, both by means of climbing by the trunk, or by a suspended rope, as sailors are obliged to do to get to the mast-head. We began at first by making knots in the rope at a foot distance from each other; then we reduced the number of knots, and before we left off, we contrived to succeed without any. I next taught them an exercise of a different nature, with which they were unacquainted, and which was to be effected by means of two balls made of lead, fastened one to each end of a string about a fathom in length. While I was preparing this machinery, all eyes were fixed upon me.—What can it be intended for? cried one: How can we use it? asked another: Will it soon be ready? continued a third.

*Father.*—Have a little patience, boys, if it be not quite impossible for you to practise this precious virtue; for though the thing I am endeavouring to make for you may turn out extremely useful, yet this said virtue of patience is much more likely to be a constant, steady, and efficient friend.—But now for the object of your curiosity. It is nothing less than an imitation of the arms used by a valiant nation remarkable for their skill in the chase, and whom you all must have heard of: I mean the Patagonians, inhabitants of the most southern point of America; but instead of balls, which they are not able to procure, they tie two heavy stones, one at each end of a cord, but considerably longer than the one I am working with: every Patagonian is armed with this simple instrument, which they use with singular dexterity. If they desire to kill or wound an enemy or an animal, they fling one of the ends of this cord at him, and begin instantly to draw it back by the other, which they keep carefully in their hand, to be ready for another throw if necessary: but if they wish to take an animal alive, and without hurting it, they possess the singular art of throwing it in such a way as to make it run several times round the neck of the prey, occasioning a perplexing tightness; they then throw the second stone, and with so certain an aim, that they scarcely ever miss their object: the operation of the second is, the so twisting itself about the animal as to impede his progress, even though he were at a full gallop. The stones continue turning, and carrying with them the cord: the poor animal is at length so entangled, that he can neither advance nor retire, and thus falls a prey to the enemy.

This description of the field sports of the Patagonians was heard with much interest by the boys, who now all entreated I would that instant try the effect of my own instrument upon a small trunk of a tree which we saw at a certain distance. My throws entirely succeeded; and the string with the balls at the ends so completely surrounded the tree, that the skill of the Patagonian huntsmen required no further illustration. Each of the boys must then needs have a similar instrument; and in a short time Fritz became quite expert in the art, as indeed he was in every kind of exercise that required strength or address: he was not only the most alert of my children, but being the eldest, his muscles were more formed, and his intelligence was more developed, than could yet be expected in the other three.

The next morning, as I was dressing, I remarked from my window in the tree that the sea was violently agitated, and the waves swelled with the wind. I rejoiced to find myself in safety in my home, and that the day had not been destined for out-of-door occupation. Though such a wind was in reality quite harmless for skilful sailors, for us it might be truly dangerous, from our igno-rance in these matters, I observed then to my wife that I should not leave her the whole day, and should therefore hold myself ready to execute any little concerns she found wanting in our domestic arrangement. We now fell to a more minute examination than I had hitherto had time for, of all our various possessions at Falcon's Stream. She showed me many things she had herself found means to add to them during my repeated absences from home: among these was a large barrel filled with small birds half-roasted and stowed away in butter to preserve them fresh: this she called her *game*, which she had found means to ensnare with birdlime in the branches of the neighbouring bushes. Next she showed me a pair of young pigeons which had been lately hatched, and were already beginning to try their wings, while their mother was again sitting on her eggs. From these we passed to the fruit-trees we had laid in earth to be planted, and which were in real need of our assistance, being almost in a decaying state. I immediately set myself to prevent so important an injury. I had promised the boys, the evening before, to go all together to the wood of gourds, for the purpose of providing ourselves with vessels of different sizes to keep our provisions in: they were enchanted with the idea, but I bargained that they must first assist me to plant all the young trees; which was no sooner said than executed, excited as we were by our eager desire for the promised excursion.

When we had finished, a little disappointment however occurred; the evening, I thought, seemed too far advanced for so long a walk, especially as my wife and little Francis were to be of the party. By the time that all were ready, it was too late to think of setting out, and we accordingly postponed the expected pleasure till the following day, when we made the necessary preparations for leaving Falcon's Stream very early in the morning. By sunrise all were on foot; for nothing can exceed the alertness of young persons who act in expectation of a pleasurable change of scene. The ass, harnessed to the sledge, played on this occasion the principal character; his office was to be the drawing home the empty gourds for the service of our kitchen and the table, and in addition, little Francis, if he should be tired: in the journey out, he carried our dinner, a bottle of the Canary wine, and some powder and shot. Turk, according to custom, led the way as our advanced guard; next followed the three eldest boys, equipped for sporting; after them, their amiable mother, leading the little one; and Ponto brought up the rear with the monkey on his back, to which the boys had given the name of Knips. On this occasion I took with me a double-barreled gun, loaded on one side with shot for game, and on the other with ball, in case of meeting with an enemy.

In this manner we set out, full of good humour and high spirits, from Falcon's Stream. Turning round Flamingo Marsh, we soon reached the pleasant spot which before had so delighted us. My wife, who now beheld for the first time its various beauties, was never tired of praising and admiring it. Fritz, who longed to be engaged in some sporting adventure, took a direction a little further from the sea-shore; and sending Turk into the tall grass, he followed himself, and both disappeared. Soon, however, we heard Turk barking loud, a large bird sprang up, and almost at the same moment a shot from Fritz brought it down: but the bird though wounded was not killed; it raised itself and got off with incredible swiftness, not by flying, but by running. Turk pursued with the eagerness of an animal enraged; Fritz, bawling out like a mad creature, followed; and Ponto, seeing what was going on, threw the monkey off his back, and fell speedily into the same track. It was Ponto that seized the bird, and held it fast till Fritz came up. But now a different sort of scene succeeded from that which took place at the capture of the flamingo. The legs of that

bird are long and weak, and it was able to make but a poor resistance. The present captive was large in size, and proportionately
strong; it struck the dogs, or whoever came near, with its legs,
with so much force, that Fritz, who had received a blow or two,
retired from the field of battle, and dared not again approach this
feathered antagonist. Turk, who had gallantly assailed the bird,
was also discouraged by some severities applied to his head by the
sturdy combatant, and yielded the contest. The brave Ponto alone
withstood the animal's attacks; he seized one of its wings, and did
not let it go till I reached the spot, which I was long in doing on
account of the height of the grass and the great weight of my gun;
but when I was near enough to distinguish the bird as it lay on
the ground, I was overjoyed to see that it was a female bustard
of the largest size. I had long wished to possess and to tame a
bird of this species for our poultry-yard, though I foresaw that it
would be somewhat difficult.

To effect the complete capture of the bird without injuring
it, I took out my pocket-handkerchief, and seizing a favourable
moment, I threw it over the head of the bustard; it could not disengage itself, and its efforts only served to entangle it the more.
As in this situation it could not see me, I got sufficiently near
to pass a string with a running knot over its legs, which, for the
present, I drew tight, to prevent further mischief from such powerful weapons. I gently released its wing, which was still in the
possession of Ponto, and tied that and its fellow close to the bird's
body. In short, the bustard was at length vanquished, though not
till each and all of us had felt the powerful blows it was capable
of inflicting.—But it was our own, and that in a condition to
promise its preservation when we should once have conveyed it

to Falcon's Stream, and could administer abundance of care and kindness to compensate for the rough treatment it had experienced at our hands.

Without further delay we removed the prisoner to the spot on the shore where some of our companions had been waiting our return. On seeing us, Ernest and Jack ran briskly forward, bawling out, Oh what a handsome bird! And what a size! What beautiful feathers!—I will lay a wager that it is a female bustard, said Ernest, the instant he had cast his eyes upon it. And you would win, my boy, answered I; it is a female bustard; its flesh is excellent, having somewhat of the flavour of the turkey, to which it also in some other respects has a resemblance. The male spreads its tail in the form of a wheel, as is said, to please its female. Let us endeavour to tame and preserve it by all means.

*Mother.*—If I had the choice, I would give it back its liberty: most likely it has young ones which stand in need of its assistance.

*Father.*—For this once, my dear, the kindness of your heart misleads you; the poor bird, being wounded, would perish if set at liberty, for want of care. If, when I have examined its wound, I find it too serious to admit of cure, I shall kill it, and thus secure an excellent dish. But if the wound is slight, we shall have gained for our poultry-yard a bird of rare value on account of its size, and which will, it may be hoped, attract its mate, and thus furnish us with a brood of its species: should it even happen that it has at this time a young brood, it is not improbable that they will find the way to take care of themselves, for no doubt, like chickens, they were able to run as soon as they came out of the egg.

While conversing on this subject I had been fixing the bustard on the sledge, taking care to place it in such a posture as to be the least painful, and to avoid exciting it to struggle against its fetters. We then pursued our way towards the wood where Fritz and I had seen such troops of monkeys, who in their spite thought to beat us from the field by assailing us with showers of cocoa-nuts. Fritz now again repeated the adventure with much humour to his mother. During this recital, Ernest was employed in going a little from us in every direction, in admiration of the height and beauty of the trees: he stopped in ecstasy at the sight of one in particular which stood alone, gazing with rapturous wonder at the prodigious distance from the root to the nearest bunches of cocoa-nuts, which he saw hanging in clusters under their crown of leaves, and which excited an eager desire to possess some of them. I glided behind him without his perceiving me, and was highly amused with the expression of his features: at length he drew a deep sigh and uttered these words:—Heavens! What a height!

*Father.*—Yes, my Ernest, they are indeed at a most unaccommodating height, and not a monkey in the way to throw them down to you! Even were I to set Knips at liberty, besides that he is not in the habit of giving away what he might keep for himself, he would perhaps take it into his head to stay in the tree when once there, so fond is every creature that lives of liberty! It is really a pity, and I am sure you are of my opinion, that those fine cocoa-nuts cannot find a way to drop down into your mouth.

*Ernest.*—No indeed, father, this is not the case; I have no great mind to them, I assure you; they are too hard, and would fall from too great a height: I should expect to have a tooth or two knocked out at least.

Scarcely had he ended his sentence, when a nut of the very largest size fell down. Ernest, alarmed, stepped aside, and looked up at the tree: another fell, and almost near enough to touch me; so that I was no less surprised than he, not being able to imagine the cause of the phenomenon. Not the smallest sign of a living creature appeared, and I was certain that cocoa-nuts never fall of themselves, but when in a state of over-ripeness, while those were absolutely hard and immature.

*Ernest.*—This is somewhat like the adventures of Fairy-land, father, I think—No sooner do the personages form a wish, than it is granted.

*Father.*—I begin indeed to think so. However, it may be that the magician who is so ready to oblige us, may lie concealed behind some of the leaves in the tree in the form of a wicked little monkey, which all the time may not intend so much to do us a favour, as to drive us from the place.

Ernest now ventured to take up the nuts. We found them even too unripe to be made use of, and were more than ever at a loss to account for their falling from the tree, round which we continually paced, endeavouring to explain the mystery. In vain, however, we strained our eyes; we saw nothing, but now and then a slight motion of the leaves: but neither bird nor beast appeared; and not a breath of wind was stirring.

Fritz had by this time concluded his narration to his mother; and observing that Ernest and I seemed occupied by something of a perplexing kind, and looked up repeatedly at one tree, he supposed we must have discovered some animal in it, and ran to have his share of the adventure, bringing also his younger brothers. We told him what had passed:—he shewed us that he had the eyes of a lynx. I shall soon, said he, see what it all means, raising his face to gaze at the tree; if one would but fall at this moment, I would soon tell you who threw it.—At the very instant two nuts fell, and so near to the speaker as to bruise his lip and his chin. Ernest could not refrain from laughing heartily. The magician is at least polite, said he; he conducts his gifts to your very mouth; and it is no fault of his if the dimensions of yours are not large enough to receive it:—but look, look, there are two more falling close to our mother and Francis. How well-behaved this magician shows himself;—In proportion as the guests increase, he takes care to send one for each. Let us quickly open one of them and refresh ourselves with the liquor it contains, in drinking to the health of our unknown friend. We did so; and each obtained a small quantity of the milk, in the fragments of the shell; and all called out together as they drank it, looking up at the tree, Long life and thanks to the good magician!—Ah, ah, I see him; there he is, exclaimed Jack. Oh, heavens! what a hideous creature! what an ugly shape he has! he is as large as my hat, and has two monstrous pincer claws.

Where is he then? said I, for I do not see him.—There, that is he, father, crawling slowly down the tree; do you see him now?— It was a land crab, an animal that, to say the truth, deserved Jack's description of him. The land crab resembles the sea crab, but is ten times more hideous: some kinds of them are excellent food, and are the principal subsistence of the natives where they are found. The one we now met with was of the kind called cocoa crab, on account of its fondness for that fruit. It crawls with great difficulty and slowly, up the trunk of the tree; when it has reached the clumps of leaves, it conceals itself in them, and falls to pinching off the bunches of cocoa-nuts at the stalks; he separates and then throws them down one by one, which often bruises them considerably. The crab then descends, and finds below a plentiful regale. It is said by some that their claws are strong enough to break the shell of the nut; but for myself, I doubt this, having always believed rather that they suck the milk by means of the small hole found in the fruit near the stalk. The land crab is not dangerous unless you are within reach of its claws, or, which is rarely the case, when they are found together in great numbers. Little Francis on seeing the animal was terribly frightened, and hid himself behind his mother; even Ernest drew back, and looked for a place of refuge: Jack, with a menacing air, raised the end of his gun; and we all cast some looks of curiosity as the creature slowly descended the tree. The moment he was on the ground, the intrepid Jack aimed a blow at him with his gun, which missed him. The crab, finding himself attacked, turned round and advanced with his claws stretched open towards his enemy. My little ruffian defended himself valiantly; he did not retreat a single step, but his attempts to strike, entirely failed, for the crab was perfect in the art of evading every blow. I however determined not to interfere: I saw that there could be no danger to the boy, and that the scene would conclude by his subduing the animal, if he conducted the affair with prudence and address. I must observe that nothing could be more amusing than this exhibition of a fight between a little boy and a crab.

After some time, being tired out with so many fruitless attempts, and perhaps recollecting that the pinches he might get from the animal's claws would not be very agreeable, and finding himself likely to be brought to close quarters with him, suddenly gave him the slip and ran off. The other boys now burst into peals of laughter, bawling out: So the magician has conquered you! he has made you run away! poor Jack! but why did you engage with a magician, Jack? On this, the lad piqued by their jeers, stopped short, threw his gun and his game-bag on the ground, stripped off his coat, spread it before him, and made a stand at his adversary, who was making up to him with his claws stretched out in a menacing sort of motion. Jack, without a moment's hesitation, threw his coat upon the creature, and wrapped him round in it; then tapping on the outside upon his shell: Wicked magician, cried he, I have you at last! I will teach you to brandish your horns another time.

I laughed so heartily at this scene, that I had not the power to give him any assistance. I saw by the motion under the coat that the crab was still alert and angry. I therefore took my hatchet and applied two or three powerful blows with it on the coat, which I took for granted would finish the affair at once. I lifted up the coat; and, as I expected, the terrible animal was dead, but still preserved a menacing posture.

What an ugly monster! cried Jack, as he stood over him: but far from being terrified by his ugliness, it only served to quicken my ardour:—one must always be glad to deliver the earth of such a monster.

You would have something to do, my young Hercules, said I, tapping him on the shoulder; no animal is so common as the crab on the shores of the sea: they are of numerous kinds, and may be seen by millions, all equally ugly. This, if I mistake not, is distinguished by the name of *the poet's crab*. What say you, Jack, to a thought just come into my head, of creating an order of knighthood for you, in which you shall be dubbed—*Sir Crab?* This is the second time that you have engaged in combat with these pincer-clawed animals. We will say nothing of the first, in which you got a bite by the leg; but this time you have evinced considerable courage and presence of mind. The thought of throwing your coat over the creature was well imagined; I doubt if you would have subdued him by any other means. It must be an animal of prodigious strength for its size, to be able to open a cocoa-nut, so that it was no inconsiderable enemy you were engaged with: but human prudence and reason give man the advantage over even the most formidable of the brute creation.

*Jack*.—May we eat crabs, father?—they are so very ugly!

*Father*.—Use makes all things easy. Many ugly things find their way to the most delicately served tables. For our crab, it is the favourite food of the negro slaves of the Antilles, and frequently of their masters also. I should think its flesh must be hard and indigestible; but we will make trial of it for dinner.

I put the famous animal along with the cocoa-nuts it had been the means of procuring us, together on the sledge, and we resumed our march. As we advanced, the wood became thicker and more difficult to pass; I was frequently obliged to use the hatchet to make a free passage for the ass. The heat also increased, and we were all complaining of thirst, when Ernest, whose discoveries were generally of a kind to be of use, made one at this moment of a most agreeable nature. He has already been described as a great lover of natural history, and now he was continually gathering, as he proceeded, such plants as he met with, and examining them with care, with the view of adding to his stock of knowledge. He found a kind of hollow stalk of a tolerable height, which grew at the foot of the trees, and frequently entangled our feet in walking. He cut some of the plants with his knife, and was much surprised in about a minute to see a drop of pure fresh water issue from them at the place where the knife had been applied: he showed it to us, put it to his lips, and found it perfectly agreeable, and felt much regret that there was no more. I then fell to examining the phenomenon myself, and soon perceived that the want of air prevented a more considerable issue of water. I made some more incisions, and presently water flowed out as if from a small conduit. Ernest, and after him the other boys, refreshed themselves and quenched their thirst at this new fountain, in the completest manner. For my own part, touched with deep gratitude for the goodness of God towards me and my beloved family, I raised my eyes to heaven: See, children, said I, what a blessing is sent us by Providence in these beneficial plants, the name of which I am much concerned to be unacquainted with. What would become of poor travellers in this burning climate, in crossing such immense forests far from the relief of water-springs! they must inevitably perish with heat and thirst, if the Almighty did not extend his goodness to the providing these necessary benefits.

I tried the experiment of dividing the plants longways, and they soon gave out water enough to supply even the ass, the monkey, and the wounded bustard. We were still compelled to fight our way through thick bushes, till at length we arrived at the wood of gourds, which was the object of our excursion, and we were not long in finding the spot where Fritz and I had once before enjoyed so agreeable a repose. Our companions had not soon done admiring and wondering at the magnificence of the trees they now beheld, and the prodigious size of the fruit which grew in so singular a manner upon the trunk. Fritz, who was already acquainted with particulars respecting them, now performed the

JOHANN DAVID WYSS

office of lecturer to the rest, as I before had done to him. I was glad to observe that he had not forgot any part of the detail he received from me during our first visit; and while he was talking, I strolled about the wood, choosing among the numerous sizes of the gourds, such as were particularly suited for our necessities, and marking the places in my mind's eye. I sought also to discover whether the malicious horde of monkeys were not still in the same neighbourhood, for I a little apprehended being molested by them during our occupation. I, however, to my great satisfaction, discovered no trace of them, and I returned to my companions.

I found Jack and Ernest actively employed in collecting dried branches and flints, while their mother was occupied in attending to the poor bustard, which however she saw reason to believe was not materially injured. She remarked to me that it was cruel to keep her any longer blinded and her legs tied together on the sledge. To please her, I took off the covering and loosened the string on the legs, but still left it so as to be a guard against its running away or inflicting blows on those who might approach. I contented myself with tying her by a long string to the trunk of a tree, that she might relieve herself by walking about. She had by no means the savageness of manners I should have expected, excepting when the dogs went near her. She did not appear to have any dread of man; which confirmed my previous belief, that the island in which we existed, had absolutely no human inhabitants but ourselves.

The boys now amused themselves with making a large fire, which they joyously surrounded. I took the liberty to laugh at them, and asked if they had become salamanders, or inhabitants of the planet Mercury, who, it is said, make fires to refresh themselves from the burning heat of the sun; the heat of our island could scarcely be less ardent, and this irony was therefore fair and admissible.

The fire, father, is to enable us to cook the magician.—Ah, hah, that is quite another thing, replied I. It was then for the same purpose, I suppose, that I saw you picking up some large shells: you mean no doubt to use them in the cooking, instead of the rind of the gourds which would not bear sufficient heat.

They all agreed to my conclusion. Begin then, continued I, by making the dish you will want for dressing your crab, before you make a large fire and get roasted yourself by its side.

I require also, said my wife, that some vessels to contain milk, and a large flat spoon to cut out my butter by pieces, and next some pretty plates for serving it at table, should be completed, gentlemen, among you all.

*Father.*—You are perfectly reasonable in your demand, dear wife, said I; and for me there must be manufactured some nests for the pigeons, some baskets for eggs, and some hives for bees.

*All.*—Oh yes, these things must all be made, we will set earnestly to work.

*Jack.*—But first, father, let me make a dish for my crab; the excessive heat would certainly make him unfit to be eaten by the evening, and I should be sorry to be obliged to throw away what it cost me so much trouble to obtain: I should soon have finished, if you will tell me how to divide one of the rinds with a string.

*Father.*—Well, well, it is but fair to allow you to enjoy the fruit of your victory. As to the cutting with a string, it was good for something when we had no saw. I will however show you, for fear of the worst, how to do it, though I took care to bring here

Johann David Wyss

the different instruments I thought we might want. Gather then a sufficient quantity of the gourds, of different sizes, and you shall see how soon we will cut them.

They all began to gather or collect, and we were soon in possession of a sufficient number or this valuable commodity. We found a certain quantity already dry upon the tree, and these we considered fit for immediate use: many also were so bruised or broken in falling, and others so immature, that we threw them aside as useless. We now began our work: some had to cut; others to saw, scoop out, and model into agreeable forms. It was a real pleasure to witness the activity exhibited in this manufacture of porcelain: each tried what specimens of imagination he could present for the applause of his companions. For my own part, I made a pretty basket, large enough to carry eggs, with one of the gourds, leaving an arch at the top to serve as a cover. I likewise accomplished a certain number of vessels, also with covers, fit to hold our milk, and then some spoons to skim the cream. My next attempt was to execute some bottles large enough to contain a supply of fresh water, and these occasioned me more trouble than all the rest. It was necessary to empty the gourd through the small opening of the size of one's finger which I had cut in it; I was obliged after loosening the contents by means of a stick, to get them out by the friction of shot and water well shaken on the inside. Lastly, to please my wife I undertook the labour of a set of plates for her use. Fritz and Jack engaged to make the hives for the bees, and nests for the pigeons and hens. For this last object, they took the largest gourds, and cut a hole in front proportioned to the size of the animal for whose use it was intended: they had when finished so very pretty an appearance, that little Francis was ready to cry that he was not quite small enough to get into and live in one of them. The pigeons' nests were intended to be tied to the branches of our tree; those for the hens, the geese, and the ducks, were to be placed between its roots or on the sea-shore, and to represent a sort of hen-coop. When the most essential of the utensils were finished, I allowed them, as they had requested, to add a dish to dress their crab in. This also was soon accomplished; but when the cooking was completed, they discovered that they had no water. We found nothing on this spot like our providential *fountain* plants, as we had named them. The boys entreated me to go about with them in different directions, and try, to find a small supply of this precious article, not daring by themselves to venture further into the wood.

I was therefore of necessity compelled to accompany them. Ernest with great eagerness proposed relieving me of this trouble, and putting himself in my place. He had found it impossible to succeed in assisting to make the utensils; he broke more than half the pieces of gourd he took in hand; and to make amends for his awkwardness, he exerted himself in every direction to discover a water-spring, or to do something else that might be useful. It was not long before we heard him calling loudly to us, and saw him returning in great alarm. Run quick, father, said he, here is an immense wild boar. Oh, how he frightened me! I heard him grunting quite close to me, and then he scampered away to the wood, and I hear him at this very moment.

Here, here! I then called out to the boys: call the dogs quickly; here is fine game for us, if we are so lucky as to catch it. Halloo, here, Turk, Ponto! The dogs arrived full gallop. Ernest was our leader, and conducted us to the place where the boar had approached him; but he was gone, and we saw nothing but a plot of potatoes which had the appearance of having been ransacked by the animal. The ardour for the chase had been somewhat checked in Jack and Ernest, when they considered for a moment that they had so formidable a creature as a boar to encounter; they stopped short, and began to dig potatoes, and left it to Fritz and me to follow the traces of the dogs. We soon heard the cry of the latter; for they had overtaken the runaway, and soon after the most hideous growling assailed our ears from the same quarter. We advanced with caution to the spot, holding our guns before us in readiness to fire together, the instant the animal should show itself within the proper distance. Presently the spectacle of the two brave creatures attacking him on the right and left presented itself; each held one of his ears between their teeth. But the beast was not a boar, as the account of Ernest had made me suppose, but a pig of the true common breed, which on our approach, appeared rather to ask for our assistance, than to have any inclination to attack us. Contrary to our expectation, Fritz and myself also suddenly lost the relish for sporting against this animal; for we immediately recognised in the supposed boar, our own sow which had run away and had so long been lost. After the first surprise we could not resist a hearty laugh; and then we hastened to disincumber our old friend of the teeth of her two adversaries. Her frightful squalling resounded through the wood and drew the attention of our companions, who now ran to the place, when a warfare of banter and accusation went round among the parties:—Fritz knew certain persons whose passion for the chase ended in digging potatoes! Jack and Ernest returned the sally by complimenting Fritz on the fine martial appearance of the wild boar they had been so fortunate as to make captive!—Why, Fritz, we knew in a moment, by the grunting, that it was only our old sow.—You however believed it to be a wild boar, Mr. Ernest, returned Fritz, and even after you had seen it. I know not what Ernest would have answered; for the attention of all was attracted to a kind of small potatoe which we observed lying thick on the grass around us, and which had fallen from some trees which appeared loaded with the same production: our sow devoured them greedily, thus consoling herself for the fright she had been put into, and the pain the dogs had occasioned her.

The fruit was of different colours, and extremely pleasing to the eye. Fritz expressed his apprehension that it was the pernicious kind of apple called the mancenilla, against which I had so strenuously cautioned them; but the sow ate them with so much eagerness, and the tree which bore them being neither so high, and having neither the form nor foliage ascribed by naturalists to the mancenilla, made me doubt of the truth of his idea. I forbore from immediately pronouncing its condemnation; but I desired my sons to put some of the fruit in their pockets, to make an experiment with them upon the monkey. I was shortly after nearly satisfied of their harmless quality, from seeing that the two dogs also fell upon them with eagerness; but I persisted in forbidding the boys to taste them till I had further examined into their nature and properties; and they all of course obeyed me. We now again, from extreme thirst, began to recollect our want of water, and determined to seek for some in every direction. Jack sprang off and sought among the rocks, hoping, and with reason, that he should discover some little stream: but scarcely had he left the wood, than he bawled to us that he had found a crocodile. . . .

A crocodile! cried I with a hearty laugh, you have a fine imagination, my boy! who ever saw a crocodile on such scorching rocks as these, and with not a drop of water near? Now, Jack, you are surely dreaming. . . .

Not so much of a dream as you may think, father, answered Jack, trying to speak in a low voice;—fortunately he is asleep;—he lies here on a stone at his full length;—he is exactly like our mother.

*Father.*—This is excellent, upon my word! So then your mother is like a crocodile?—This is really an indiscreet sort of a joke.

*Jack.*—I meant, father, that the crocodile is about as long as the height of our mother; I had not, I assure you, the least idea of a joke; for it is certainly a crocodile, though perhaps only a young one. . . . Do, father, step here and look at it, it does not stir in the least.

I knew not what to think: we stole softly to the place where the animal lay; but instead of a crocodile I saw before me an individual of a large sort of lizard, named by naturalists *Leguana* or *Yguana*, and the flesh of which is considered in the West Indies as the greatest delicacy. I explained this to my sons, and tranquillised them as to the danger of approaching this animal, formed by nature of a mild character, and excellent as food. All were then immediately seized with the hope of seizing the lizard and presenting so rare a prize to their mother. Fritz in a moment had his gun ready, and was taking his aim, but that I was in time to lay hold of his arm and prevent him: You are always too quick, said I, in your determinations; your piece might have missed, or you might have wounded him only slightly; for this sort of animal is protected by a coat of scales as you see, and it is extremely difficult to destroy him. I think too that he is known to be extremely dangerous if approached when he is angry. Let us try another sort of experiment; as he is asleep, we need not be in a hurry: only a little contrivance is necessary to have him safe in our power alive, and the process will afford us all an amusing spectacle.

I cut a stout stick from a bush, to the extremity of which I tied a string with a running knot. I guarded my other hand simply with a little switch, and thus with cautious steps approached the sleeping animal. When I was very near to him, I began to whistle a lively air, taking care to make the sounds low at first, and to increase in loudness till the lizard was awaked. The creature appeared entranced with pleasure as the sounds fell upon his ear; he raised his head to receive them still more distinctly, and looked round on all sides to discover from whence they came, I now advanced by a step at a time, without a moment's interval in the music, which fixed him like a statue to the place. At length I was near enough to reach him with my switch, with which I tickled him gently, still continuing to whistle, one after the other, the different airs I could recollect.

The lizard was bewildered by the charms of the music; the attitudes he threw himself into were expressive of a delirious voluptuousness; he stretched himself at full length, made undulating motions with his long tail, threw his head about, raised it up, and by this sort of action, disclosed the formidable range of his sharp-pointed teeth, which were capable of tearing us to pieces if we had excited his hostility. I dexterously seized the moment of his raising his head, to throw my noose over him. When this was accomplished, the boys drew near also, and wanted instantly to draw it tight and strangle him at once; but this I positively forbad, being unwilling to cause the poor animal so unmerited a suffering.

PLATE 9
"At length I was near enough to reach him
with my switch."

I had used the noose only to make sure of him in case it should happen that a milder mode of killing him, which I intended to try, failed of success, in which case I should have looked to the noose for protection; but this was rendered unnecessary. Continuing to whistle my most affecting melodies, I seized a favourable moment to plunge my switch into one of his nostrils; the blood flowed in abundance, and soon deprived him of life, without his exhibiting the least appearance of being in pain; on the contrary, to the last moment he seemed to be still listening to the music.

As soon as he was dead I allowed the boys to come quite near and to tighten the noose, which we now found useful to draw him to the ground from the large stone on which he lay. My sons were delighted with the means I had used for killing him without pain.—But little praise is due to me, I replied; for I have often in books of travels, read the description of the manner of deluding and destroying this animal, so well known in the West Indies. But now let us consider of the best way for transporting to Falcon's Stream so large and valuable a booty. After a moment of reflection, I perceived that I had better come at once to the determination of carrying him across my shoulders: and the figure I made with so singular an animal on my back, with his tail dragging on the ground, was not the least amusing circumstance of the adventure. Fritz and Jack presented themselves as pages, contending which should support my train, as they called the tail, which, independently of the good-humour inspired amongst us, considerably eased me of the weight, and gave me the air of an old Chinese emperor habited in a superb royal mantle of many colours, for those of the lizard shone like precious stones in the eyes of the sun.

We were already far advanced in our return, when we distinguished the voice of my wife calling upon my name in a tone which indicated great uneasiness; and in addition, we heard loud sobs from little Francis. Our long absence had excited painful apprehensions concerning us: we had forgot on this occasion to give them notice of our approach, by firing our gun, and they had imagined some terrible disaster must have befallen us. No sooner, however, did our cheerful notes in speaking reach their ear, than their fears and lamentations were changed to joy, and we soon found ourselves assembled together, the happiest of beings, under a large gourd-tree, where we related to our dear companions every particular of the excursion we had made; not forgetting Jack's singular fancy of finding a resemblance between his mother and the lizard, who now lay extended at her feet. We had so many things to inform her of, that we lost sight of the principal object which caused our separation; and till she reminded us with some regret at our ill success, we forgot to mention that we had failed of procuring any water. My sons had taken out some of the unknown apples from their pockets, and they lay on the ground by our side. Knips soon scented them, and according to custom he came slily up and stole several, and fell to chewing them with great eagerness. I myself threw one or two to the bustard, who also ate them without hesitation. Being now convinced that the apples were not of a poisonous nature, I announced to the boys, who had looked on with envy all the time, that they also might now begin to eat them, and I myself set the example. We found them excellent in quality, and I began to suspect that they might be the sort of fruit called *guava*, which is much esteemed in such countries. The tree which bears them is sometimes twenty feet in height; no doubt therefore, those from which we procured the fruit, were too young to have attained their full stature. The tree itself is of so fertile a nature, that in inhabited countries they are constantly obliged to be thinned and cut down, on account of the quantity of land they would occupy.

This regale of the apples had in some measure relieved our thirst; but on the other hand, they had increased our hunger; and as we had not time for preparing a portion of the lizard, we were obliged to content ourselves with the cold provisions we had brought with us. But we contrived to have an excellent dessert of potatoes, which the boys had had the foresight to lay under the cinders of the fire they had made to cook their crab.

We had scarcely finished taking this refreshment, before my wife earnestly entreated that we might immediately begin our journey home, to be sure of arriving before dark. In fact, it appeared to me, as the evening was so far advanced, that it would be prudent to return this once without the sledge, which was heavy laden, and the ass would have drawn it but slowly: I was besides, inclined to take a shorter road by a narrow path that divided a plantation of thick bushes, which would have been too difficult a passage for the ass burthened with the sledge. I therefore determined to leave it on the spot till the following day, when I could return and fetch it, contenting myself with loading the ass for the present, with the bags which contained our new sets of porcelain; with the lizard, which I feared might not keep fresh so long; and our little Francis, who began to complain of being tired. I took these arrangements upon myself, and left to my wife and Fritz, the care of confining the bustard in such a manner that she could walk before us without danger of escaping.

When these preparations were complete, our little caravan was put in motion, taking the direction of a straight line to Falcon's Stream. On leaving the wood of gourds, we arrived at a spot where we found more of the guava trees, and could not resist the temptation to stay a few moments and secure a new supply. The course of our route lay next along a majestic wood of oaks, agreeably interspersed with fig-trees of luxuriant growth, and of the same species as those at Falcon's Stream. The ground in this place was absolutely covered with acorns. My young travellers, ever on the watch for something new and gratifying to the palate, could not refrain from tasting them: in form they exactly resembled the same fruit in Europe, though from the difference of climate, they would probably not be the same in regard to quality and flavour. One of the boys bit an acorn in two; and finding it both sweet and mild to the taste, he told his brothers, who soon fell eagerly to filling their own pockets with them, as well as mine and those of their mother. I always hailed with satisfaction every occasion that presented, of increasing the number of our resources for support: in the one that now presented itself, I perceived the hope that we might not only be ourselves nourished but our poultry also: I more than ever admired the magnificence of the trees which at this moment covered us with their shade, and made us a present of so inestimable a value: on considering, I recognised that they were a kind of oak which remains always green, and are a common production of the woods in Florida, and that the Indians of North America extract from its fruit an excellent kind of sweet oil, which they use in cooking their rice. Numerous kinds of birds subsist upon these acorns. This we were led to remark, by the wild and discordant cries of several sorts of jays and parrots, which were skipping merrily among the foliage and the branches. The boys would instantly have fired their guns; and I could only prevail upon them to desist, by observing how late it was, and promising that we would return another time, and thus procure them an opportunity for their favourite amusement.

We arrived shortly, and sooner than we expected, at Falcon's Stream; the path we had taken had so considerably lessened the distance, that we were in time to employ ourselves in some trifling arrangements, before it was completely dark. My wife had great pleasure in taking out her service of porcelain and using some of the articles that very evening; particularly the handsome egg-basket and the vessels for the milk. Fritz was instructed to dig a place in the ground to serve for a kind of cooler, the better to preserve the milk; and we covered it with boards and put heavy stones to keep them down. Jack took the pigeons' nests, and scampered up the tree, where he nailed them to the branches; he next laid some dry moss within, and placed one of the female pigeons we had contrived to tame, and which at the time was brooding, upon it; he put the eggs carefully under the mother, who seemed to accept his services, and to coo in return, with gratitude.

Ernest was occupied in distributing and fixing those intended for the fowls among the roots of the trees: when he had finished, it was of importance to observe how well they would accustom themselves to this their new abode; they were already on their perches, with their head under their wing and half asleep, and took very much amiss the being thus disturbed; while Ernest, for his part, was enraged at the little inclination they discovered to inhabit their new abode.

JOHANN DAVID WYSS

My own employment was to clean the inside of the lizard and prepare a piece of it for our supper, my wife having expressed an extreme repugnance to both the lizard and the crab; we therefore added some potatoes and some acorns, and dressed them together, and thus suited every palate. Francis had the care of turning the spit, and liked his office all the better, for its allowing of his being constantly near his mother. We all drew near a clear brisk fire while the supper was in hand: a sea breeze had refreshed the air, and after great fatigue, a good fire seldom fails to occasion agreeable sensations. This well-spent and useful day was concluded by a refreshing repast, at which all but my wife bestowed encomiums on the palatable properties of the yguana. My wife could not prevail upon herself even to taste it; she therefore supped on the potatoes. The crab we found to have but little flavour, and was put aside as useless. We concluded the exertions of the day, by contriving a comfortable bed for the bustard by the side of the flamingo, and then hastened to stretch our weary limbs upon the homely couch, but rendered by fatigue luxurious, that waited for us in the giant tree.

# XXIII

# EXCURSION INTO UNKNOWN COUNTRIES

I T IS SCARCELY NECESSARY TO RELATE, THAT MY FIRST THOUGHT the next morning, was to fetch the sledge from the wood. I had a double motive for leaving it there, which I had refrained from explaining to my wife, to avoid giving her uneasiness. I had formed a wish to penetrate a little further into the soil, and ascertain whether any thing useful would present itself beyond the wall of rocks. I was, besides, desirous to be better acquainted with the extent, the form, and general productions of our island: I wished Fritz only, who was stronger and more courageous than his brothers, to accompany me; and accordingly left the three others, and Ponto, to protect my wife. We allowed Turk to be our travelling companion, who did not fail to testify his joy by jumping about, and barking loud. We set out very early in the morning, and drove the ass before us for the purpose of drawing home the sledge.

On reaching the wood of ever-green oaks, we found the sow feeding voluptuously upon the acorns under the trees. We wished her a good appetite, and begged her to admit us to the honour of partaking her breakfast; and accordingly Fritz filled the pockets of his waistcoat with some of them. We perceived with pleasure that the lecture of the preceding day had rendered the animal more tractable: she did not now seek to avoid us; and we might even have induced her to return home, if we had had time to take the pains. As we were quietly picking up some of the acorns, we observed some birds, which occupied the wood in every direction, advancing towards us. Some of them were clothed with a plumage of exquisite beauty; and for this once, I could not refuse Fritz the pleasure of firing upon them, that we might in consequence obtain a nearer view, and inform ourselves respecting their species. He brought down three. I recognised one to be the great blue Virginia jay, and the other two were parrots. One of the two was a superb red parrot; the other was green and yellow.

While Fritz was reloading his gun, we heard a singular sort of noise which came from a distance: at one moment it resembled a muffled drum, at another, the noise made in sharpening a saw. My first idea was of music played by savages, and we retreated quickly to hide ourselves among the bushes to listen. By degrees we advanced towards the place from whence the sound appeared to come; but perceiving nothing to alarm us, we separated some of the branches with our hands, and then discovered a handsome bird about the size of the English cock; and, like it too, adorned with elegantly-formed smooth feathers round the neck, and a comb upon his head. The animal stood erect on a decayed trunk of a tree, which was lying on the ground, and at this moment exhibited some singular gestures. His tail was spread in the form of a fan, similar to that of the turkey-cock, but shorter; the feathers round his neck and head were erect and bristling. He sometimes agitated them with so quick a motion, as to make them appear like a vapour which suddenly inclosed him; sometimes he whirled himself round and round on the trunk of the tree; at others he moved his head and eyes in such a manner as to express a state of distraction, making at the same time, the singular kind of noise with his voice, which had alarmed us, and which was preceded and followed by a sort of explosion. This last was caused by a motion of his wing striking in a quick measure on the trunk, which was hollow and dry, and made the noise resemble a muffled drum. All around him, there was assembled a great number of birds of the same species, but much smaller, and of a less beautiful form. One and all fixed their eyes upon him, and seemed delighted with the pantomime. I contemplated this extraordinary spectacle, of which I had formerly read an account, with astonishment. The number of the spectators of the feathered actor, increased every moment; and the performance increased in spirit also, in proportion, presenting the idea of a perfect intoxication or delirium of the creature. At this moment, Fritz, who stood a little behind me, put an end to the scene by firing his gun. The actor fell from the stage, and stretching himself on the sand, breathed his last, and the spectators betook themselves suddenly to flight. I must confess, the interest I took in the scene was of so lively a nature, that I could not refrain from reproaching Fritz in an angry tone. Why, said I, must we be always applying the means of death and annihilation to the creatures that fall in our way? Is not nature a thousand time more exhilarating in her animated movements, which express life and enjoyment, than in the selfish scheme of destruction you seem so fond of? Some allowance should no doubt be made for the curiosity of youth, for necessities caused by our situation, and even for the taste you have acquired for sporting; I therefore, as you well know, do not object to your killing now and then a little game, or some singular or dangerous kind of animal; but moderation is on all occasions useful, and the spectacle of this bird, employed in such earnest endeavours to draw his females around him, was at least as amusing, as to see him stretched there at length, and lifeless, who but two minutes ago exhibited such rapid and lively motions! His pretty hens too all dispersed in terror, and deprived of the possibility of ever more admiring him or being his companions.

Fritz looked down, ashamed and sorry. I observed to him that the thing being done, there was now no remedy; that the fetras or heath-cock was much esteemed as game; and that as the mischief had occurred, he had better take it from the ground and carry it to his mother.

He did as I desired; and in spite of my lecture I saw that he was rejoiced to have acquired such a prize. Is it not a beautiful creature, father? said he: but I am most curious to be informed what all his action was intended to represent.

*Father.*—I imagine his gestures and his cries were intended to assemble his females, of which he has a large number, similar to the common cock of Europe. I cannot help thinking, Fritz, how cruel it was thus to interrupt the poor creature's innocent amusements.

*Fritz.*—I am now extremely sorry for it, father; particularly when I recollect that we might have caught him alive, and that it is so desirable to have possessed this kind of fowl at Falcon's Stream.

*Father.*—This is precisely what I was going to observe; I am not sure that it is now too late to effect such a plan;—when we see either of the hens disposed to brood, we will bring the monkey here to search about for the eggs of these animals; if we should be so lucky as to find a nest, which I think probable, we will take away the eggs, and put them under the brooding hen; by these means we shall procure some of this handsome race of fowls.

We now laid the dead cock upon the ass's back, and proceeded on our journey. We soon arrived at the guava trees, and a little after at the spot where we had left the sledge in the wood of gourds, when we found our treasures in the best possible condition: but as the morning was not far advanced, we entered upon our intended project of penetrating beyond the wall of rocks.

We pursued our way in a straight line at the foot of these massy and solid productions of nature, every moment expecting to reach their extremity, or to find some turn, or breach, or passage through them, that should conduct us into the interior of the island, if, as I presumed, it was not terminated by these rocks. We walked on, continually looking about, that nothing might escape us worthy of notice, or to be enabled to anticipate and avoid such dangers as should threaten. Turk with his usual bravery took the lead, the ass followed with lazy steps shaking his long ears, and Fritz and I brought up the rear. We met from time to time with some small streams which afforded a most agreeable refreshment; we passed a wood of guava trees and fields of potatoes and manioc, the stalks of which perplexed our way; but we were recompensed for this inconvenience by the fine views which every where presented themselves, and which the low stature of the plants enabled us to see in perfection. To the right, on the high grounds, we saw hares and agoutis in considerable numbers, amusing themselves on the grass in the morning sun. Fritz mistook them for marmots, but not one of them made the whistling kind of sound which is customary with these animals when they see a strange object. The idea of my son seemed therefore to be unfounded: again he wished to be convinced by firing his gun; but fortunately, the rock on which they were stationed, was at too great a distance for it to take effect.

We next entered a pretty little grove, the trees of which were unknown to us; their branches were loaded with large quantities of berries of an extraordinary quality, being entirely covered with a wax which stuck to our fingers as we attempted to gather them. I knew of a sort of bush producing wax that grows in America, and named by botanists *Myrica cerifera*; I had no doubt that this was the plant, and the discovery gave me great pleasure. Let us stop here, said I to Fritz, for we cannot do better than collect a great quantity of these berries as a useful present to your mother.

A short time after, another kind of object presented itself with equal claims to our attention; it was the singular modes of behaviour of a kind of bird scarcely larger than a chaffinch, and clothed in feathers of a common brown colour. These birds appeared to exist as a republic, there being among them one common nest, inhabited at pleasure by all their tribes. We saw one of these nests in a tree in a somewhat retired situation; it was formed with considerable skill of platted straws and bulrushes intermixed; it appeared to us to inclose great numbers of inhabitants, and was constructed in an irregular sort of form round the trunk of the tree where the branches sprout: it appeared to us to have a kind of roof formed of roots and bulrushes, but more carefully knit together than the rest of the structure. In the sides, which were unequally formed, we observed a quantity of small apertures seemingly intended as doors and windows to each particular cell of this general receptacle; from a few of these apertures, issued some small branches, which served the birds as points of rest for entering and returning: the external appearance of the whole, excited the image of an immensely large, open spunge. The birds which inhabited it were very numerous; they passed in and out continually, and I estimated that it might contain at least a million. The males were somewhat larger than the females, and there was a trifling difference in their plumage: the number of the males was very small in proportion to the females; I do not know whether this had been the cause of their thus assembling together.

While we were attentively examining this interesting little colony, we perceived a very small kind of parrot, not much larger than the birds themselves, hovering about the nest. Their gilded green wings and the variety of their colours produced a beautiful effect; they seemed to be perpetually disputing with the colonists, and not unfrequently endeavoured to prevent their entrance into the building; they attacked them fiercely, and even endeavoured to peck at us if we but advanced our hand to the structure. Fritz, who was well trained in the art of climbing trees, was earnestly desirous to take a nearer view of such extraordinary beings, and to secure, if possible, a few individuals. He threw his whole equipage to the ground, and climbed till he reached the nest; he then tried to introduce his hand into one of the apertures, and to seize whatever living creature it should touch, in that particular cell; what he most desired, was to find a female brooding, and to carry both her and the eggs away. Several of the cells were empty, but by perseverance he found one in the situation he wished. But he did not pursue his plan without meeting with the full punishment of his curiosity and ungenerous behaviour. He received so violent a stroke from the beak of an invisible bird, that his only care was now to withdraw his hand, which he shook in the air to ease the pain, uttering all the time the most dismal lamentations. But though punished, he was not cured of his fault: no sooner had the pain subsided, than he ventured a second time to pass his hand into the nest, and succeeded in seizing his prey, which he laid hold of by the middle of the body; and in spite of the bird's resistance, its cries and wailings, he drew it through the aperture and squeezed it into the pocket of his waistcoat; and buttoning it securely, he slided down the tree and reached the ground in safety. The signals of distress sent forth by the prisoner collected a multitude of birds from their cells, who all surrounded him, uttering the most hideous cries, and flying at him with their beaks, till he had made good his retreat. The birds pursued him till he was quite close to my side, when by making a loud noise and waving my pocket-handkerchief, I succeeded in driving them away. He now released the prisoner, and we discovered him to be a beautiful little green parrot, which Fritz entreated he might be allowed to preserve, and make a present of to his brothers, who would make a cage to keep him in, and would then tame him and teach him to speak. I did not oppose his request; but thinking we had spent too much time upon this singular phenomenon of the bird colony, I bade him prepare quickly for returning home. The birds were naturally the subject of our conversation on the road. It was the first time I had ever witnessed such a spectacle as a swarm of birds living together in a state of society in one nest; and I was surprised at it. From the circumstance of so young a bird being nestled within the structure, it appeared probable that the true right of property was in this species, and that the brown-coloured birds we at first observed, were intruders, endeavouring to deprive them of it. Thus we find, said I to Fritz, the existence of social dispositions in almost every class of the animal kingdom, which leads to the combining together for a common cause or benefit. I have not hitherto observed these dispositions among amphibious animals, but it is not unlikely that instances will at some time or other present themselves. A multitude of causes may induce animals to form a body or society, instead of living singly; among them may be supposed the deficiency of females or of males; the charge of the young; providing them with food; or as a means for their safety and protection. Who shall dare to fix limits to the instinct, or to the faculties of the animal creation?

*Fritz.*—I do not, however, recollect any kind of animals who live thus together in society, except the bees.

*Father.*—What say you then, my boy, to wasps, drones, and different kinds of ants?

*Fritz.*—I did not indeed recollect the ants, though I have so often amused myself with looking at them: nothing can be more interesting than the ingenious little houses they construct; observing them attentively, we perceive their industry, their economy, their care of their young;—in a word, all their undertakings, conducted on a plan of society and numbers.

*Father.*—Have you also observed with what a provident kind of instinct they bring out their eggs to be warmed by the sun, and for this end remove them from place to place till the time of their maturity?

*Fritz.*—Is it not probable, father, that what we take for eggs, are chrysales of ants, which, like many other insects, are thus shut up while the process of their taking wings is in the operation?

*Father.*—You may be right. Writers on natural history have considered the industry and frugality of these insects, as a subject not unworthy of their close consideration; but if the common ant of our own country excited so much of your admiration, in what words will you express your astonishment at the almost incredible labours which are performed by the ants of foreign countries! Of these there is a kind which build nests of four, six, and eight feet in height, and large in proportion: the external walls of these structures are formed so thick and solid, that neither sun nor rain can penetrate them. These houses contain within, little streets, arched roofs, piazzas, colonnades, and particular apartments for the offices of housewifery: and the whole of this complicated mass is put together with so much solidity of workmanship, that if emptied and cleaned, it might serve for an oven. The ant is for the most part an animal of pilfering propensities, on the profits of which it principally lives; it is also remarkable for constancy in its designs, and remaining ever in one place: a species of them exists, however, in America, which is known by the name of the *cephalate* or visiting ant; they make their appearance in numerous troops every two or three years, and disperse themselves abundantly in every house: as soon as this visitation is observed, it is customary to open all the apartments, and every receptacle for stores; they enter every where, and in a short time it is found that they have exterminated as effectually the rats, mice, bugs, kakerles (a sort of insect that gives great annoyance in hot countries);—in a word, all the different animals offensive or injurious to man, as if sent on a special mission to remedy the evils these occasion. They do no injury to man, unless they find in him an enemy, who pursues and disturbs their quiet; in which case they attack his shoes so violently, that they are destroyed with incredible rapidity. On the other hand, they cause terrible devastations in plantations of trees, of which they will entirely strip the leaves in a single night: some of the ants crawl up and separate them from the tree, and then throw them down to their fellow-labourers, who are in waiting to receive and carry the leaves to the ant-house. This curious species does not build its house above ground, but they dig holes, sometimes not less than eight feet in depth, and plaster the walls according to the rules of the art of masonry. Some travellers assert that one of the islands of the South Sea is infested by them to such a degree, that human beings cannot venture to disembark in it. The place is therefore, as it were, yielded to them, and is known to mariners by the name of Ant-island.

*Fritz.*—And has no means been found to stop the progress of their devastations?

*Father.*—As to what in this respect relates to the Ant-island, I am not able to answer your question. In Europe, fortunately for the inhabitants, they are not so formidable: they however occasion sufficient inconvenience to make us study by what means we can best destroy them; and the surest methods are found to be fire and boiling-water. They have, besides, numerous enemies among insects and birds: the most terrible of all is the *myrmecophage*, or great ant-eater. Nature, who no doubt intended in this animal to produce a counterpoise against the abundant increase of ants, furnished it with a long gluey tongue, which it drops into the holes of the ant-house: the ants crawl upon it, and remain fixed. When the tongue is sufficiently covered with them, the ant-eater draws it back, swallows its mouthful greedily, and drops it again with the same success. It is pretended, that two ant-eaters hostilely engaged against an ant-house, will destroy every inhabitant in a short time. They raise small channels of light sand in the ants' road, which the creatures in passing, fall entirely through, and are received by the enemy, who swallows them in an instant. Different savage nations, the Hottentots in particular, also devour ants by handfuls.

*Fritz.*—What a frightful idea! I can scarcely believe the account, father: but this is enough on the chapter of ants. You mentioned just now, that in each class of the animal creation there were some individuals to be found which formed themselves into societies; pray tell me which they are.

*Father.*—I know of no instance among birds, but that we have just been witnessing; but among quadrupeds there is at least one striking example of the social principle:—try to recollect it yourself.

*Fritz.*—It is perhaps the elephant or the sea-otter?

*Father.*—You have not guessed the one I thought of: in reality, however, the animals you have named discover also a strong disposition to live in society with their species, but they build nothing like a common house of reception:—try again; when you mentioned the sea-otter, you were not far from the right creature.

*Fritz.*—Ah, now I have found it: Is it not the beaver, father? These animals are said to possess so much intelligence, that they are able to contrive and place dams to such streams or rivers as obstruct their design of building entire villages: by this operation they are furnished with a sort of ditch, which they use for their purpose.

*Father.*—This is well observed; and, strictly speaking, the marmoset also may be included in the number of sociable quad-rupeds: but these latter cannot be said to build, in the literal sense of the word; they dig themselves a common place of abode, a sort of cavern, in the mountains, and in these whole families of them pass the winter comfortably, in a continual sleep. It would have been more blameable in us to have forgotten them, as they are natives of our country; for it is principally in the highest Alps of Switzerland that the animal is found.

We had proceeded a considerable way in this kind of conversation, and had reached a wood, the trees of which were unknown to us: they in a small degree resembled the wild fig-tree; at least the fruit they bore, like the fig, was round in form, and contained a soft juicy substance full of small grains: there was, however, a sharpness and sourness in the taste. We took a nearer view of these trees, so remarkable for their height, which was from forty to sixty feet; the bark of the trunk was prickly or scaly, like the pine-apple, and wholly bare of branches, except at the very top, where they are loaded with them; some growing straight, and others bent in different directions. The leaves of these trees, at the extremity of the branches, are very thick; in substance, tough, like leather; and their upper and under surfaces presented different tints. But what surprised us the most, was a kind of gum, or bituminous matter, which appeared by some accidental means to issue in a liquid state from the trunk of the tree, and to become immediately hardened by the air. This discovery awakened Fritz's whole attention: in Europe he had often made use of the gum produced by cherry-trees, either as a cement or varnish in the process of some of his youthful occupations; and the thought struck him, that he could do the same with what he now saw. He accordingly collected with his knife a certain quantity.

As we continued walking, he looked frequently at his gum, which he tried to soften with his breath, or with the heat of his hand, as he had been accustomed to do with that from the cherry-trees; but he found he could not succeed. On the other hand, his endeavours revealed a still more singular property in the substance, that of stretching considerably on being pulled by the two hands at its extremities; and, on letting go, of reducing itself instantly, by the power of an elastic principle. He was struck with surprise at this phenomenon, and sprang towards me, repeating the experiment before my eyes, and exclaiming, Look, father! if this is not the very kind of Indian rubber we formerly used, to rub out the bad strokes in our drawings: see! I can stretch it, and it instantly shrinks back when I let go.

Ah! what do you tell me? cried I with joy: such a discovery would be an invaluable benefit. The best thanks of all will be due to you, if you have discovered the true *caoutchouc* tree which yields the Indian rubber. Quick, hand it here, that I may examine it.

*Fritz.*—Look, father, how it will stretch! But I do not however understand how it can be so immensely valuable to us: can it be made to serve any other purpose than rubbing out a pencil mark? Nor am I quite sure that it is the very same ingredient. Why is it not black, like that we used in Europe?

*Father.*—How many questions you ask at once! But give me time to breathe, and I will answer them. Caoutchouc is a kind of milky sap, which runs from certain trees, and no doubt from these before us, in consequence of incisions made in the bark. This liquor is received in vessels placed expressly for the purpose: it is afterwards made to take the form of dark-coloured bottles of different sizes, such as we have seen them, in the following manner. Before the liquor which runs out has time to coagulate, some small earthen bottles are dipped into it a sufficient number of times to form the thickness required. These vessels are then hung over smoke, which completely dries them, and gives the dark colour you allude to. Before they are entirely dry, a knife is drawn across them, which produces the lines or figures with which you have seen them marked. The concluding part of the operation is to break the bottle, which has served for a mould, and to get out the pieces by the passage of the neck, when the ingredient remains in the complete form of a bottle; soft to the touch, firm in substance, yet flexible and convenient to carry about, from being not subject to break; and may be even used as a vessel to contain liquor if necessary. In later times it has been discovered that this remarkable substance would extract the mark of black lead from paper; and it is common for artists to cut them into pieces, and to be generally provided with one of them.

*Fritz.*—The fabrication of this article seems simple enough; therefore let us try to make some bottles of it, father, which will be convenient for carrying something for us to drink, when we go a long way in pursuit of game. But still I do not perceive how the discovery is, as you say, of so much value to us?

*Father.*—Not by this use of it alone, certainly; but its quality is admirable for being made into shoes and boots without seams, if we can add the assistance of earthen moulds of the size of the leg or foot to be fitted. Now then I suppose you can understand my reason for the joy I expressed at the sight of so unexpected a benefit. We must consider of some means of restoring masses of the caoutchouc to its liquid form, for spreading upon the moulds; and if we should not succeed, we must endeavour to draw it in sufficient quantities, when wanted for use and in its liquid state, from the trees themselves. There is besides another use for which this substance is both fit and excellent;—that of rendering waterproof any kind of linen or woollen production to which it may be applied.

Well satisfied with the discovery we had made, and our fancy already heated by the image of our fine India rubber boots and shoes, we continued our way, endeavouring still further to explore the wood, which stretched before us to a considerable distance. After passing through it, we reached another called Cœos, with a small part of the skirts of which we were already acquainted, it being the same which stretches from the sea-shore to the top of the rocks. There we rested ourselves with great pleasure for a few minutes, and were regaled with two cocoa-nuts, which Turk had forced from two little monkeys which were playing on the ground like children. Upon the loss of their food they left him and scampered to the top of the trees, while we on our parts devoured the booty. After this refreshment, we once more resumed our route; we were determined to reach the furthest outlet of this great wood of cocoa-trees, to examine the dimensions and limits of our empire: in a short time we had taken some observations that enabled us to ascertain this point; and looking attentively, we recognised the great bay on the right, and on the left Cape Disappointment, which latter had been the furthest point of our earliest excursion.

In this spot alone, and mixed with a quantity of cocoa-trees, I discovered a sort of tree of smaller growth which I presumed must be the sago palm: one of these had been thrown down by the wind, so that I was able to examine it thoroughly. I perceived that the trunk of it contained a considerable quantity of a mealy substance; I therefore, with my hatchet laid it open long-ways, and cleared it of the whole contents; and on tasting the ingredient,

I found it was exactly like the sago I had often eaten in Europe. The operation of cutting the trunk had disclosed also a new treasure, and one which confirmed my belief of having found the real sago palm-tree; it was the perceiving in the powder, the particular kind of larva which lives entirely on sago, and is considered the greatest delicacy of the West Indies for the palate. The interest I felt on the subject, made me eager for an experiment which would immediately determine my conclusion. I directed Fritz to get some dry branches and make a fire; I ran a sharp stick through half a dozen of the larvæ, and toasted them on the flame; the agreeable odour which exhaled from them, and is peculiar to the species, made me certain I was not mistaken: I soon ate one or two of them with a potatoe, which served for bread, and I may venture to assure the epicures of Europe, that if they desire to obtain a delicious morsel, this alone is worth the pains of a sea-voyage for the purpose. Fritz, who from the first had taken the liberty to smile at my fancy, and to assure me that nothing in the world should induce him to partake of my dish, attracted by the delicious smell and good appearance of the food, had no longer the power to desist: he asked me to give him a small share, and joined me in a chorus of the highest praise. It was now his turn to search for more, and to use the same ceremony in dressing them.

After our repast, we got up and began to consider how much further we would go: the thick bushes of bamboo, through which it was impossible to pass, seemed to furnish a natural conclusion to our journey. We were therefore unable to ascertain whether we should or should not have found a passage beyond the wall of rocks: we perceived then no better resource than to turn to the left towards Cape Disappointment, where the luxurious plantations of sugar-canes we had discovered on our first visit, now again drew our attention. That we might not return empty-handed to Falcon's Stream, and might deserve forgiveness for so long an absence, we each took the pains to cut a large bundle of the canes, which we threw across the ass's back, not forgetting the ceremony of reserving one apiece to refresh ourselves with along the road. We soon arrived on the well-known shore of the sea, which at length afforded us an open and shorter path; we next, and not long after, reached the wood of gourds, where we found our sledge loaded as we had left it the night before: we took the sugar-canes from the ass, and fastened them to the sledge, and then we harnessed the ass, and the patient animal began to draw towards home.

We arrived at Falcon's Stream without any further adventure, and rather early in the evening. We received at first some kind reproofs; we were next questioned, and lastly thanked, as we displayed our various treasures, but particularly the sugar-canes: each of the boys seized one and began to suck it, as did their mother also. Nothing could be more amusing than to hear Fritz relate, with unaffected interest, the recent discoveries we had made, and imitate the gestures of the heath-cock as he held it up for them to examine:—the whole company continued to shout with laughter for many minutes. Then came the history of the colony of birds and their singular habitation, and of the green parrot, all of which was listened to with the delight excited by a fairy tale. Fritz showed them the handsome red parrot dead, also the great blue jay, both of which they did not cease to admire; but when Fritz took out of his waistcoat pocket the little parrot all alive, there was no bounds to their ecstasy: they jumped about like mad things, and I was obliged to interpose my authority to prevent their tearing him to pieces, in the struggle who should have him first. Francis asked his eldest brother if he had not already taught him some words in their way home? I intended the office of preceptor for you, said Fritz, who are such a little prate-apace that the parrot would not be long in learning. Francis nearly devoured the little animal with kisses, repeating a thousand times *pretty little parrot*! At length the bird was fastened by the leg to one of the roots of the trees, till a cage could be made for him; and was fed with acorns, which he appeared exceedingly to relish. We next gave an account of the excellent dinner we had made on the larvæ found in the sago-meal, which excited the envy of all but my wife, who was never partial to new kinds of food. I therefore promised her for her share of so many dainties, some real mushrooms which grew spontaneously from the powder of the sago. She was delighted with the prospect of the candles I assured her I was now able to furnish, and also of the boots and shoes. Fritz took a bit of the rubber from his pocket and drew it to its full length, and then let it suddenly go, to the great amusement of little Francis.

Soon after night fall, being much fatigued, and after partaking of a hearty supper, we all mounted the ladder; and having carefully drawn it up, we fell exhausted, into sound and peaceful slumbers.

# XXIV

# USEFUL OCCUPATIONS AND LABOURS— EMBELLISHMENTS; A PAINFUL BUT NATURAL SENTIMENT

O N THE FOLLOWING DAY, NEITHER MY WIFE NOR THE BOYS LEFT me a moment's tranquillity till I had put my manufactory of candles in some forwardness: I therefore set myself to recollect all I had read on the subject. I soon perceived that I should be at a loss for a little suet or mutton fat to mix with the wax I had procured from the berries, for making the light burn clearer; but as I had neither of these articles, I was compelled to proceed without them. I put as many berries into a vessel as it would contain, and set it on a moderate fire; my wife in the mean time employed herself in making some wicks with the threads of sail-cloth. When we saw an oily matter of a pleasing smell and light green colour, rise to the top of the liquid the berries had yielded, we carefully skimmed it off and put it into a separate vessel, taking care to keep it warm. We continued this process till the berries were exhausted and had produced a considerable quantity of wax; we next dipped the wicks one by one into it, while it remained liquid, and then hung them on the bushes to harden: in a short time, we dipped them again, and continued repeating the operation, till the candles were increased to the proper size, and they were then put in a place and kept, till sufficiently hardened for use. We, however, were all eager to judge of our success that very evening, by burning one of the candles, with which we were all well satisfied. In consequence of this new treasure, we should now be able to sit up later, and consequently spend less of our time in sleep; but independently of this advantage, the mere sight of a candle, which for so long a time we had been deprived of, caused ecstasies of joy to all.

Our success in this last enterprise, encouraged us to think of another, the idea of which had long been cherished by our kind steward of provisions: it was to make fresh butter of the cream we every day skimmed from the milk, and which was frequently, to her great vexation, spoiled, and given to the animals for want of such a process. The utensil we stood in need of, was a churn, to turn the cream in. Having earnestly applied my thoughts, as to the most effectual manner of conquering the difficulty, I suddenly recollected what I had read in a book of travels, of the method used by the Hottentots for making butter; but in adopting it, I determined to introduce one feature of proceeding, for which, apparently, they have not a partiality; and this was, the utmost attention to cleanliness. Instead of a sheep-skin sewed together at its extremities, I emptied a large gourd of its natural contents, and filled it again with cream, and stopped it quite close with the piece I had cut from the top. I placed my vase of cream on a piece of coarse linen cloth with four corners, which last I tied to four stakes; I placed one boy midway between each stake, and directed them to shake the linen briskly, but with a steady measure, for a certain time. This exercise, which seemed like children's play, pleased them mightily, and they called it rocking the cradle. They performed their office singing and laughing all the time, and in an hour, on taking off the cover, we had the satisfaction of seeing some excellent butter. We heartily congratulated each other, and praised the workmen, who by their constancy of labour, had thus produced one of the first conveniences in the list of articles for food.

The employments we had thus been engaged in, were little different from play; but now a question occurred of one that would require our most serious attention:—it was the constructing a cart, in all its forms, for the better conveyance of our effects from place to place, instead of the sledge which caused us so much fatigue to load and draw. Many reasons induced me to confine my attempt in the first instance to a two-wheel cart, and to observe the result before I ventured on one with four wheels.

I will not fatigue the reader with the detail of my undertaking: I tried earnestly and long to accomplish my machine; but it did not entirely succeed to my wishes, and I wasted in the attempt both time and timber. I however produced what from courtesy we called a cart; but I would not advise my readers to take it for a model, though, to say the truth, to us it answered the purpose for which it was designed.

While I was thus laboriously engaged, the boys and their mother were no less busy in matters of use or convenience; and I now and then left my cart to assist them with my advice, though, to do them justice, I must say, they seldom stood in need of it. They undertook to transplant the greatest part of the European fruit-trees, to place them where they would be in a better situation for growth, according to the properties of each. They planted vine shoots round the roots of the magnificent tree we inhabited, and round the trunks of some other kinds of trees which grew near; and we watched them in the fond anticipation that they would in time ascend to a height capable of being formed into a sort of trellis, and help to cool us by their shade. In the climate we inhabited, the vine requires the protection of the larger trees against the scorching rays of the sun. Lastly, we planted two parallel lines of saplings, consisting of chesnut, cherry, and the common nut-trees, to form an avenue from Family Bridge to Falcon's Stream, which would hereafter afford us a cool shade in our walks to Tent-House. This last undertaking was not to be effected without a degree of labour and fatigue the most discouraging:—the ground was to be cleared of every thing it had produced, and a certain breadth covered with sand, left higher in the middle than on the sides, for the sake of being always dry. The boys fetched the sand from the sea-side in their wheel-barrows, and I also nailed together a few pieces of wood, in the form of a tub, which could be harnessed to the ass to ease in some measure their fatigue.

Our next concern was to introduce, if possible, some shade and other improvements on the barren site of Tent-House, and to render our occasional abode or visits there more secure. We began by planting in a quincunx all those sorts of trees that thrive best in the sun, such as lemon, pistachio, almond, mulberry, and lime-trees; lastly, some of a kind of orange-tree which attains to a prodigious size, and bears a fruit as large as the head of a child, and weighs not less than twelve or fourteen pounds. The commoner sorts of nut-trees we placed along the shore in the most favourable situations. The better to conceal and fortify our tent, which inclosed all our stores, we formed on the accessible side, a hedge of wild orange and lemon-trees, which produce an abundant prickly foliage; and to add to the agreeableness of their appearance, we introduced here and there the pomegranate; nor did I omit to make a little arbour of the guava shrub, which is easily raised from slips, and bears a small fruit rather pleasant to the taste. We also took care to introduce at proper places a certain number of the largest sorts of trees, which in time would serve the double purpose of shading annual plants, and, with benches placed under them, of a kind of private cabinet. Should any accident or alarm compel us to retire to the fortress of Tent-House, a thing of the first importance would be to find there sufficient food for our cattle. For the greater security, I formed a plantation of the thorny fig-tree, of sufficient breadth to occupy the space between our fortress and the river, thus rendering it difficult for an enemy to approach.

The curving form of the river having left some partial elevations of the soil within the inclosure, I found means to work them into slopes and angles so as to serve as bastions to our two cannon from the pinnace and our other fire-arms, should we ever be attacked by savages. When this was all complete, we perceived that one thing more was wanting, which was to make such alterations in Family Bridge as would enable us to use it as a drawbridge or to take it away entirely, this being the only point at which the passage of the river could be easily effected. But as we could not do all at once, we contented ourselves, for present safety, with taking away the first planks of the bridge at each end every time we passed it. My concluding labour was to plant some cedars along the usual landing-places, to which we might fasten our vessels.

We employed six whole weeks in effecting what for the present it was possible to effect, of these laborious arrangements; but the continual exercise of mind and body they imposed, visibly contributed to the physical and moral health of the boys, and to the support of cheerfulness and serenity in ourselves. The more we embellished our abode by the work of our own hands, the more it became dear to our hearts. The constant and strict observance of the sabbath-day afforded such an interval of rest, as could not fail to restore our strength and inspire us with the desire of new exertions. The sentiment of gratitude which filled our minds towards the Supreme Being, who had saved us from destruction and supplied us with all things needful, demanded utterance, and on Sundays we might allow ourselves the indulgence of pouring out our hearts in thankfulness. Thus our religious exercises, succeeded by gymnastic recreations, and these again by pleasing rambles near Falcon's Stream, during which I did not fail to inculcate some moral truth, served to increase at once, our usefulness and our happiness. It was deserving of remark, that though the boys had been employed in severe labour through the week, yet they were ever ready to encounter the climbing of trees, running races, swimming, shooting with the bow and arrow, when Sunday came; a proof that it is not so much inaction which renews the strength, as a change of occupations.

But the repetition of these exercises wore out our clothes so fast, that another trip to the vessel was absolutely necessary. We had nearly exhausted the stock we had already brought away; we were now absolutely in rags, and we feared we saw the time when we should be compelled to renounce the European modes of dress. I had also another reason; the cart I had just completed, and with which at first I was quite enchanted on further acquaintance disclosed a defect which it was scarcely possible to endure; it was a violent creaking of the wheels at every turn, and in addition the wheels moved so imperfectly round the axle-tree, that the united strength of the ass and the cow could scarcely drag the machine along. It was in vain that, in spite of my wife's reproofs, I applied a little butter now and then; in an hour or two the butter was dried, and the wheels remained the same.

These two circumstances compelled us then once more to have recourse to the vessel, which heaven and the waves had still preserved. We knew there remained on board five or six chests containing apparel, and we suspected there were also some tubs of pitch and grease for wheels in her hold, which we should thus obtain. To these motives were added, that of an earnest desire to take another look at her, and, if practicable, to bring away a few pieces of cannon which might be fixed on the new bastions at Tent-House, and thus we should be prepared for the worst.

The first fine day I assembled my three eldest sons, and put my design into execution. We reached the wreck without any striking adventure, and found her still fixed between the rocks, but somewhat more shattered than when we had last seen her. We did not lose a moment in searching for the tubs of pitch, which, with the help of the pulley, we soon conveyed into the pinnace; we next secured the chests of clothes, and whatever remained of ammunition stores; powder, shot, and even such pieces of cannon as we could remove, while those that were too heavy, we stripped of their wheels, which might be extremely useful.

But to effect our purpose, it was necessary to spend several days in visits to the vessel, returning constantly in the evening, enriched with every thing of a portable nature which the wreck contained; doors, windows, locks, bolts, nothing escaped our grasp: so that the ship was now entirely emptied, with the exception of the heavy cannon and three or four immense copper caldrons, which were too heavy to be got into the boat. We by degrees contrived to tie these heavy articles to two or three empty casks well pitched, which would effectually sustain themselves and the cannon above water. When these measures were taken, I came to the resolution of blowing up the wreck by a process similar to that with which I had so well succeeded with the pinnace. I directed my views to that part of the vessel which had been entirely stripped of everything; I supposed that the wind and tide would convey the beams and timbers ashore, and thus with little pains we should be possessed of a sufficient quantity of materials for erecting a building at some future time.

We accordingly prepared a cask of gunpowder, which we left on board for the purpose: we rolled it to the place most favourable for our views: we made a small opening in its side, and at the moment of quitting the vessel, we inserted a piece of match-wood which we lighted at the last moment, as before. We then sailed with all possible expedition for Safety Bay, where we arrived in a short time. We could not, however, withdraw our thoughts from the wreck and from the expected explosion for a single moment. I had cut the match a sufficient length for us to hope that she would not go to pieces before dark. I proposed to my wife to have our supper carried to a little point of land from whence we had a view of her, and here we waited for the moment of her destruction with lively impatience.

About the time of night-fall, a majestic rolling sound like thunder, accompanied by a column of fire and smoke, announced that the ship, so awfully concerned with our peculiar destiny, which had brought us to our present abode in a desert, and furnished us there with such vast supplies for general comfort, was that instant annihilated, and withdrawn for ever from the face of man!—At this moment, love for the country that gave us birth, that most powerful sentiment of the human heart, sunk with a new force into ours. The ship had disappeared for ever! Could we then form a hope ever to behold that country more! We had made a sort of jubilee of witnessing the spectacle; the boys had clapped their hands and skipped about in joyful expectation; but the noise was heard;—the smoke and sparks were seen;—while the sudden change which took place in our minds could be compared only to the rapidity of these effects of our concerted scheme against the vessel. We all observed a mournful silence, and all rose, as it were, by an impulse of mutual condemnation, and with our heads sinking on our bosoms, and our eyes cast upon the ground, we took the road to Tent-House.

My wife was the only person who was sensible of motives for consolation in the distressing scene which had been passing; she was now relieved from all the cruel fears for our safety in our visits to a shattered wreck, that was liable to fall to pieces during the time we were on board. From this moment she conceived a stronger partiality for our island, and the modes of life we had adopted. A night's repose had in some measure relieved the melancholy of the preceding evening, and I went rather early in the morning with the boys, to make further observations as to the effects of this remarkable event. We perceived in the water, and along the shore, abundant vestiges of the departed wreck, and among the rest, at a certain distance, the empty casks, caldrons, and cannon,

PLATE 10

"I went rather early in the morning with the boys, to make further observations as to the effects of this remarkable event."

all tied together, and floating in a large mass upon the water. We jumped instantly into the pinnace, with the tub-boat fastened to it, and made a way towards them through the numberless pieces of timber, etc., that intervened, and in a little time reached the object of our search, which from its great weight moved slowly upon the waves. Fritz with his accustomed readiness flung some rope round two four pounders, and contrived to fasten them to our barge, after which he secured also an enormous quantity of poles, laths, and other useful articles. With this rich booty we returned to land.

We performed three more trips for the purpose of bringing away more cannon, caldrons, fragments of masts, etc., all of which we deposited for present convenience in Safety Bay: and now began our most fatiguing operations, the removing such numerous and heavy stores from the boats to Tent-House. We separated the cannon and the caldrons from the tub-raft, and from each other, and left them in a place which was accessible for the sledge and the beasts of burden. With the help of the crow we succeeded in getting the caldrons upon the sledge, and in replacing the four wheels we had before taken from the cannon; and now found it easy to make the cow and the ass draw them. We in the same manner conveyed away all the pieces of wood we wished to preserve dry, and what stores remained, we tied with cords to stakes along the shore, to protect them from the tide.

The largest of the boilers or copper caldrons, which had been intended as principal utensils for a proposed manufactory of sugar, we now found of the most essential use. We brought out all our barrels of gunpowder, and placed them on their ends in three separate groups, at a short distance from our tent; we dug a little ditch round the whole, to draw off the moisture from the ground, and then put one of the caldrons turned upside down upon each, which completely answered the purpose of an out-house. The cannon were covered with sail-cloth, and upon this we laid heavy branches of trees; the larger casks of gunpowder we prudently removed under a projecting piece of rock, where, should they even blow up, no mischief could arise to the inhabitants of Tent-House: these we covered with planks, till we should have leisure for executing the plan of an ammunition storehouse, about which we had all become extremely earnest.

My wife, in taking a survey of these our labours, made the agreeable discovery that two of our ducks and one of the geese had been brooding under a large bush, and at the time were conducting their little families to the water. The news produced general rejoicings; Fritz and Ernest looked forward to some luxurious Sunday-dinners, and Jack and Francis wondered what the young birds could think, when they first saw any human creatures! We in a short time found means to tame them, by throwing them occasionally some crumbs of manioc. This last employment, together with the gambols of the little creatures, so forcibly carried our thoughts to Falcon's Stream, that we all conceived the ardent desire of returning to the society of the numerous old friends we had left there. One sighed for his monkey, another for his flamingo; Francis for his parrot, and his mother for her poultry-yard, her various housewifery accommodations, and her comfortable bed. We therefore fixed the next day for our departure, and set about the necessary preparations.

# XXV

# A NEW EXCURSION—PALM-TREE WINE

ON ENTERING OUR NEW PLANTATION OF FRUIT-TREES FORMING the avenue to Falcon's Stream, we observed that they had not a vigorous appearance, and that they inclined to curve a little in the stalk: we therefore immediately resolved to support them with sticks, and I proposed a walk to the vicinity of Cape Disappointment, for the purpose of cutting some bamboos. I had no sooner pronounced the words, than the three eldest boys and their mother exclaimed at once that they would accompany me. Their curiosity had been excited by the accounts Fritz and I had given of the variety of amusing objects we had met with in our visit to the spot: each found a sound and special reason why he must not fail to be of the party:—one of the hens was observed to be brooding, and some of the eggs of the heath-fowl were to be fetched and laid under her;—our provision of candles was nearly exhausted, and a new stock of berries must therefore be procured, for my wife now repaired our clothes by candle-light, while I employed myself in composing a journal of the events of every day:—Then, the sow had again deserted us, and nothing could be so probable as that we should find her in the acorn wood:—Jack would fain gather some guavas for himself, and Francis must needs see the sugar-canes he sucked with so keen a relish. In short, all would visit this land of Canaan.

We accordingly fixed the following morning, and set out in full procession. For myself, I had a great desire to explore with more attention this part of our island, and to reap some more substantial advantages from its produce. I therefore made some preparations for sleeping, should we find the day too short for all we might have to accomplish: I took the cart instead of the sledge, having fixed some planks across it for Francis and his mother to sit upon when they should be tired; I was careful to be provided with the different implements we might want, some rope machinery I had contrived for rendering the climbing of trees more easy, since we could not always expect to meet with a crab who should obligingly give us his assistance; and lastly, some provisions, consisting of a piece of the salted tortoise, some water in a gourd-flask, and one bottle of wine from the captain's store. When all was placed in the cart, I for this time harnessed to it both the ass and the cow, as I expected the load would be increased on our return; and we set out, taking the road of the potatoe and manioc plantations. Our first halt was at the tree of the colony of birds; close upon the same spot were also the trees whose berries produced the wax for candles, and intermixed with these some of the guava kind. On this second occasion of seeing the birds, I recollected to what species they belonged, which by naturalists is named *Loxia gregaria* (Sociable Grossbeak).

It was not without much difficulty that we conducted the cart through the thick entangled bushes, the most intricate of which

I every where cut down, and we helped to push it along with all our strength. We succeeded tolerably well at last; and that the poor animals might have time to rest, we determined to pass several hours in this place which furnished such a variety of agreeable and useful objects. We began by gathering a bag full of the guavas; and after regaling ourselves plentifully upon them, we put the remainder into the cart. We next examined anew, and with close attention, the interesting structure of the nest inhabited by the colony of birds, and concluded, contrary to the opinion I had formerly entertained, that the little green parrot was an invader who had seized upon an empty place, and fixed himself in it; for numerous flocks of the brown-coloured birds now passed in and out, rested upon the bushes which produced the wax, and devoured large quantities of the berries, which explained the reason of their building their singularly-contrived abode in this particular spot. We claimed the same privilege as the birds, and had soon filled another bag with the berries we found means to beat down from the bushes. Seeing them so greedily consumed by those little animals, the boys desired to follow their example, and accordingly tasted them, but found them too insipid for their palate.

We had brought the monkey with us to search out the nests of the heath-fowl, that we might seize upon the eggs; but we postponed the setting him on this employment till we should again reach the place on our way back, for fear of breaking the eggs in carrying. We continued our way, and soon arrived at the caoutchouc, or gum-elastic trees: I thought we could not do better than to make a halt here, and endeavour to collect a sufficient quantity of the sap, to make the different kinds of utensils, and the impenetrable boots and shoes, as I had before proposed. It was with this design that I had taken care to bring with me several of the most capacious of the gourd rinds. I made deep incisions in the trunks, and fixed some large leaves of trees partly doubled together lengthways, to the place, to serve as a sort of channel to conduct the sap to the vessels I had kept in readiness to receive it. We had not long begun this process before we perceived the sap begin to run out as white as milk, and in large drops, so that we were not without hopes by the time of our return to find the vessels full, and thus to have obtained a sufficient quantity of the ingredient for a first experiment.

We left the sap running, and pursued our way, which led us to the wood of cocoa-trees; from thence we passed to the left, and stopped half way between the bamboos and the sugar canes, intending to furnish ourselves with a provision of each. We aimed our course so judiciously, that on clearing the skirts of the wood we found ourselves in an open plain, with the sugar-cane plantations on our left, and on our right those of bamboo interspersed with various kinds of palm-trees, and in front the magnificent bay formed by Cape Disappointment, which stretched far out into the sea.

The prospect that now presented itself to our view was of such exquisite beauty, that we determined to choose it for our resting place, and to make it the central point of every excursion we should in future make: we were even more than half disposed to desert our pretty Falcon's Stream, and transport our possessions hither: a moment's reflection, however, betrayed the folly of quitting the thousand comforts we had there with almost incredible industry assembled: and we dismissed the thought with promising ourselves to include this ravishing spot ever more in our projects for excursions. We disengaged the animals, that they might graze and refresh themselves under the shade of the palm-trees, and sat down to enjoy our own repast, and to converse on the beauty of the scene.

Our next proceeding was to divide amongst us the different occupations which were the objects of our walk. Some scampered away to the right to cut bamboos; others to the left, to secure the sugar-canes, of both which a large bundle was collected, tied together, and put into the cart. The bodily exertions made by the boys again excited their desire to eat; they sucked some of the canes, but their hunger was not appeased. Their mother, however, refused to let them have the remainder of the provisions, and they therefore cast a longing eye to the tops of the trees, where they saw a great number of cocoa-nuts suspended. After a short deliberation, it was determined that two of them should venture on climbing to the top, a height of from sixty to eighty feet, and with the hatchet which would be fastened to his waist, should beat them down. Fritz and Jack had no hesitation; they selected the trees which had most fruit for their attempt, and with my assistance they proceeded a considerable way; but when left to themselves, their legs and arms were too short to embrace the trunk of the tree, and having no place of rest for either, they scampered down again much quicker than they had ascended, chagrined and out of countenance. It was now my part to interfere: I wished, said I, to let you try for yourselves first; but though it may be well to be possessed of personal courage, yet at your age, my boys, it is advisable to distrust your own suggestions and to ask advice from persons of experience: had you applied for mine, I should have told you how impossible it would be for you to mount such a tree as this without assistance. It is true, very young sailor-boys mount to the heads of masts, which are nearly as high; but then the mast is of small circumference, and the boys have, besides, the aid of ropes. I have something here which may answer the same purpose;—here are some pieces of prepared shagreen, which must be tied round your legs; then with this cord I shall fasten you by the body to the trunk of the tree, but so loosely that it will move up and down when you do; by sitting occasionally on this cord, you will be enabled to rest when necessary, and so push on by little and little. This manner of climbing trees is practised by savages and by negro slaves with success. At first you will make but slow progress, but after two or three experiments you will find no further difficulty.

The boys had listened with entire attention: excited by the description I had made, they eagerly demanded to be equipped for the experiment, and their success exceeded our expectation; they with tolerable ease reached the top of the tree, where the thick tufted foliage furnished a commodious seat, and from whence they sent forth exulting salutations. They now took their hatchets and set to work, when presently a shower of cocoa-nuts descended, from which the persons below had barely time to escape by running to a distance. The monkey having observed what was going on, took the fancy of imitating his young masters, and springing from the ground into one of the trees, he with his teeth and his paws sent down as many nuts as the hatchet: he then came down with equal swiftness, and seating himself on the ground began to crack one of the nuts, making all the time such strange grimaces as to occasion us all much merriment. The two boys had descended with more caution than the monkey, and with perfect safety: they received our compliments on the skill and address they had evinced in so promptly making themselves masters of so valuable an art.

Ernest was the only person who took no part in this animated scene: his brothers began to banter him a little on the old subject of his indolence; they approached him gravely, and offered him some cocoa-nut, *to refresh him after so much fatigue*; he made no reply, and pushed the offering aside. He then rose from his seat, and began to examine the trees one by one with deep attention; he requested me to saw off the top of a cocoa-nut for him, which he emptied, and fastened round it cross-ways a string with a loop to hang it to the button of his waistcoat. Not one of us could imagine what he was going to do; he placed a small hatchet in his girdle, and then advancing a few paces out of the group we formed, he in a graceful manner pronounced the following little address:

"I am sensible, my dear parents, that in our republic, or rather in our kingdom (for our father is to us as a beloved sovereign, and our mother as a much cherished queen,) I am I say sensible, that here, as in Europe, he who has sufficient talent to raise himself above the rest, is held in high consideration and esteem. For my own part, I must confess I had more pleasure in remaining in tranquillity without endeavours to obtain distinction. I have but little ambition, and am fond of quiet, and therefore the greater will be my desert, if I, like the rest, resolve to contribute to the general good of this our country, by executing, as the other subjects have done, the task of climbing trees; well satisfied if, like them, I should obtain the applauses of my king and of my fellow-citizens!—To the tree then, since climbing is the question," said he, saluting us with his hand as he sprang away to a high palm-tree of the cabbage species.

I looked with extreme curiosity; but when I saw him courageously grasp the trunk with his legs and arms, and proceed to climb without assistance, I approached the tree and offered him the shagreen and the cord; he accepted the first, but refused the cord. I am naturally somewhat awkward, observed he, and to have to draw a cord after me would only add to my difficulty; besides, I think I have no occasion for it. In fact, he employed so much earnest desire in the undertaking, and exerted his limbs with so much spirit, that I was astonished at the rapidity of his ascent, and conceived at every remove the most terrible alarm, since the further from the ground, the more danger would attend him, should any slip or other accident occasion him to fall. I kept my station near the foot of the tree, continually encouraging him by calling out: Bravo, bravo, boy Ernest, though last in attempt, yet it is you who have shown the greatest courage, for you have not, like your brothers, had assistance from the cord. Fritz and Jack, who were spectators also, now, instead of seeming humbled by my repeated commendation of Ernest, to my great surprise, were observed whispering each other with an air of self-satisfaction; I could not for my own part conceive what could be the subject of their seeming exultation, but I soon learnt the truth. When Ernest now showed himself at the very top of the tree, Fritz and Jack burst into an immoderate fit of laughter:—Pains enough for nothing, master Ernest, bawled they as loud as they could: in your sublime wisdom, master Ernest, you have chosen a tree which has no fruit upon it. Not a single cocoa-nut will you bring down; your most devoted fellow-subjects can truly assure you!

Not a cocoa-nut, certainly, replied Ernest in his loudest voice; but, brothers, you shall receive a crown instead, and at the same instant he with his hatchet cut off the tufted summit of the palm-tree, and a large mass of tender leaves fell at our feet.

Mischievous boy! cried his mother: disappointed of his cocoa-nuts, see if he has not cut off the head of this magnificent palm-tree, and it will perish in consequence! Ah! Ernest, what do you not deserve for thus giving way to anger!

I am happy, mother, to be able to correct your mistake, cried Ernest from his stately column, where he stood erect, and looked exactly like a statue. What I have done was not from anger, but from a desire to procure you one of the finest kinds of food this country affords; the tree is the cabbage palm-tree, and believe me you will find it a more valuable acquisition than even our highly prized cocoa-nuts!—A cabbage! exclaimed Fritz: Ah, ah! Master Ernest, so you would make us believe that cabbages grow on palm-trees, and that we are in a land of wonders!

In a land of wonders, my son, we can never fail to be, in whatever place we may abide, for the whole scheme of nature is a perpetual tissue of wonders proceeding from the hand of a beneficent Creator; and those we now behold appear to us extraordinary, only because we view them for the first time. Examine this production, to which the name of palm-cabbage has been given by naturalists; it has not the shape of our European cabbage; but, as Ernest tells you, it is a most delicious and refreshing food: he has also had the merit of distinguishing this tree from others: and let me seize the present occasion, young ones, to reprove you for the taunting spirit in which you viewed your brother's proceedings, who, though less enterprising and less alert than you, so far surpasses any one of you in observation and reflection. To him we are indebted for the most useful of the discoveries which have been made—the potatoes and the manioc: if, instead of envying each other, you were to unite your various endowments, what happiness and what success might be the result! Ernest would think for you, you would execute for him; thus, all would share in the advantages which would result from this spirit of concord, so necessary among mankind, but particularly among brothers. Let me also recommend to you to accustom yourselves to suspend your judgement on the actions of another, till those actions are complete and you are quite sure both of their object and effect. Even you, well-beloved of my heart, were not on this occasion free from blame towards your boy! Try then to make him such reparation as your kind maternal heart shall dictate!

Most willingly, cried she, her eyes filling with tears of tenderness; and she looked up to invite him to come down: mine and the boys followed in the same direction; when we beheld Ernest in a fixed erect position in the very centre of the palm-tree, which he had stripped of its crown, as motionless as if he had become a cabbage. The whole effect of this spectacle was irresistibly ludicrous; and accordingly the boys, in spite of the lecture I had that moment concluded, burst into an immoderate fit of laughter.

I now called out to Ernest: Do you mean, said I, to stay all night in your tree, or are you afraid to trust yourself with coming down?

Far from it, father, answered he; but I am engaged in preparing you here some good sauce for the cabbage, and the operation takes a longer time than I imagined: but have a little patience, and I will bring down something for you to drink to my health.

What can he mean? asked little Francis; I dare say he has found a fountain in the tree; do you know, papa, I have been thinking that this must be an enchanted forest, like those I have read about in my little books; perhaps some of those trees are all the time princes and princesses:—do you not think it very likely, brother Fritz? said the young innocent with so real and fearful a persuasion, that we all laughed heartily as we answered his question. His mother took him on her knee and explained to him the nature of a fairy-tale, while the scene for my own part strengthened me in the opinion that children should be told nothing but the truth.

By this time Ernest had finished his work, and was descending cautiously from the tree. When he reached the ground, he released the cocoa-shell from his button, held it delicately in one hand, while with the other he drew from his pocket a small bottle, and pulling out the cork he emptied the contents into the shell, and presented it to me, saying: Most gracious sovereign, permit your devoted cup-bearer to present you with a specimen of a new and choice beverage he has been so fortunate as to procure for you: may it be pleasing to your royal taste: it is called palmist wine, and your faithful slave waits but your commands to obtain a larger supply! . . .

My wife and the other boys looked on in astonishment. I was myself less surprised, having read accounts of this production in different books. I was, however, much gratified to owe the acquisition to the study and reflection of my young philosopher, as I now called Ernest. It is excellent, my boy, said I, and we shall unite in drinking it to your health, with sensations of gratitude and affection. This was accordingly done.

I then made some inquiries of Ernest, as to his previous knowledge of the tree and its properties; and he answered, that if he had been quite sure of these being the kind producing cabbage, he should sooner have ascended. I knew, continued he, that there was a sort of palm which bore a cabbage at the top; and while my brothers were getting up for the cocoa-nuts, I was looking about in hopes to find it, and presently I thought that the tree which had no cocoa-nuts was most likely to be the sort; and you see I was lucky in my guess. He then related his expectation of finding some of our famous palm-wine also. When I had cut off the cabbage, said he, a quantity of juice issued from the place, which I tasted and found delicious: you know the rest, father, added he; and I have only to regret that I had not a larger bottle to receive it; but now that we know the means, we can obtain the liquor when we please.

A small quantity at a time, observed I, will always be best; for the juice, though so like to champain in flavour, and which would perhaps affect our heads as soon if we were to use it freely, would by to-morrow, like the cocoa-milk, be quite sour: as there are abundance of the trees, we can, as you say, procure the liquor at pleasure, only taking care to be moderate; for it is affirmed by writers on natural history, that if the cabbage at the top is cut off, the tree dies, and we should therefore in time destroy the species. There are other sorts of palm-trees besides those we have noticed; one in particular, which yields a kind of oil which burns whatever it is applied to; we shall perhaps meet with it. In the mean time, let us render thanks to Providence for the benefits he has bestowed.

It was now past noon; and as we had determined to pass the night in this enchanting spot, we began to think of forming some large branches of trees into a sort of hut, as is practised by the hunters in America, to shelter us from the dew and the coolness of the air, for we had dismissed our fears of the approach of wild-beasts, not having in so long a time been visited by any. I accordingly set to work; I had brought a piece of sail-cloth with me from Falcon's Stream, and I drove some stakes into the ground, and covered them with it, filling the opening in the front with some branches I had cut for the purpose. While we were engaged in our work, which was nearly completed, we were suddenly roused by the loud braying of the ass, which we had left to graze at a distance but a short time before. As we approached nearer to the place, we saw him throwing his head in the air, and kicking and prancing about in a most extraordinary manner; and while we were thinking what could be the matter, he set off on a full gallop, leaving us in a state of astonishment at all we saw. Unfortunately, Turk and Ponto, whom we sent after him, took the fancy of entering the plantation of the sugar-canes, while the ass had preferred the direction of the bamboos on the right. We began to fear the approach of some wild beast might have frightened the creature, and to think of assembling our fire-arms. In a little time the dogs returned, and showed no signs, by scenting the ground or otherwise, of any pursuit. I made a turn round the hut to see that all was well, and then sallied forth with Fritz and the two dogs in the direction the ass had taken, hoping the latter might be enabled to trace him by the scent; but the familiar creatures could not be made to understand our meaning; they lived habitually with the ass, and had no notion of the new reason for following him; so that they did no more than run from place to place for their amusement; and as night was coming on, I prudently gave up the pursuit and returned to my companions.

Fatigued, and vexed with the loss of the ass, which was so eminently useful to us, I entered the hut, which I found complete and provided with the necessary branches strewed on the ground for sleeping, and with some reeds for making a fire, which the freshness of the evening air rendered agreeable to all: it served us also for cooking our supper; and after it had been partaken by us all, we were glad to lie down upon the branches and enjoy the blessing of sleep. When all was safe, I watched and replenished the fire till midnight, rather from habit than the fear of wild beasts, and then took possession of the little corner assigned me near my slumbering companions.

# XXVI

# A NEW COUNTRY DISCOVERED—
# THE TROOP OF BUFFALOS;
# A PRECIOUS ACQUISITION

T HE FOLLOWING MORNING FOUND US ALL IN GOOD HEALTH, and thankful for the Divine protection we had enjoyed. We breakfasted on some milk from the cow, some boiled potatoes, and a small portion of Dutch cheese, and formed during our meal the plan of the business for the day: we had in vain hoped that night and our bright fire would bring back the fugitive; we had therefore no resource but to depend upon our own exertions for recovering him. It was accordingly decided that one of the boys and myself, attended by the two dogs, should seek him in every direction through the bamboo plantation; and if we should not succeed in finding him, I was to return to the hut, where I knew my wife and the other boys would have been employed in cutting sugar-canes and collecting a provision of the different articles we had met with, preparatory to our return the following day to Falcon's Stream. As I was to take both the dogs, it seemed but reasonable that I should leave the two eldest boys to protect little Francis and his mother, and to take for my own escort the agile Jack, who was almost beside himself with joy at this determination.

We took then our hatchets, our fire-arms, a little saw for the cocoa-nuts we might happen to find, and began our course with the first dawn of the morning. We soon reached the bamboo plantation, which we entered, preceded by the dogs, and found means, though not without difficulty, to force ourselves along its intricate entanglements. After the most exhausting fatigue, and when we were on the point of relinquishing all further hope, we discovered the print of the ass's hoofs on the soil, which inspired us with new ardour in the pursuit. After spending a whole hour in further endeavours, we at length, on reaching the skirts of the plantation, perceived the sea in the distance, and soon after found ourselves in an open space which bounded the great bay. A considerable river flowed into the bay at this place, and we perceived that the ridge of rocks which we had invariably observed to the right, extended to the shore, terminating in a perpendicular precipice, leaving only a narrow passage between the rocks and the river, which during every flux of the tide must necessarily be under water, but which at that moment was dry and passable. The probability that the ass would prefer passing by this narrow way, to the hazard of the water, determined us to follow in the same path: we had also some curiosity to ascertain what might be found on the other side of the rocks, for as yet we were ignorant whether they formed a boundary to our island, or divided it into two portions; whether we should see there, land, or water. We continued to advance, and at length reached a stream which issued foaming from a large mass of rock and fell in a cascade into the river; the bed of this stream was so deep, and its course so rapid, that we were a long time finding a part where it might be most practicable for us to cross. When we had got to the other side, we found the soil again sandy and mixed with a fertile kind of earth: in this place we no longer saw naked rock; and here we again discovered the print of the ass's hoofs.

By observing with attention, we beheld with astonishment that there were the prints of the feet of other animals also, that they were somewhat different from those of the ass, and much larger. Our curiosity was so strongly excited by this appearance, that we resolved to follow the traces; and they conducted us to a plain at a great distance, which presented to our wondering eyes the exhilarating image of a terrestrial paradise. We ascended a hill which partly concealed from our view this delicious scene, and then with the assistance of the glass we looked down upon a range of country exhibiting every rural beauty that the mind could conceive, and where a profound tranquillity had seemed to take up its abode. To our right appeared the majestic wall of rocks which divided the island, some of which appeared to touch the heavens, others seemed to imprint the clouds with wild fantastic forms, while mists broken into pieces partially concealed their tops. To the left, a chain of gently rising hills, the long green verdure of which was tinged with blue, stretched as far as the eye could discern, and were interspersed at agreeable distances with little woods of palm-trees of every kind. The river we had crossed flowed in a serpentine course through this exquisite valley, presenting the idea of a broad floating silver ribbon, while its banks were adorned with reeds and various aquatic plants. I could with difficulty take my eyes from this enchanting spectacle, and I seated myself on the ground to contemplate and enjoy it at my leisure. Neither on the plain nor on the hills was there the smallest trace of the abode of man, or of any kind of cultivation; it was every where a virgin soil in all its original purity; nothing endowed with life appeared to view, excepting a few birds which flew fearlessly around us, and a quantity of brilliantly coloured butterflies, which the eye frequently confounded with the different sorts of unknown flowers, which here and there diversified the surface of the soil.

By straining our eyes, however, as far as we could see, we thought we perceived at a great distance some specks upon the land, that seemed to be in motion. We hastened towards the spot; and as we drew nearer, to our inexpressible surprise discovered a group of animals, which in the assemblage presented something like the outline of a troop of horses or of cows; I observed them sometimes run up to each other, and then suddenly stoop to graze. Though we had not lately met with further traces of the ass, I was not entirely without hope of finding him among this group of animals. We accordingly drew near by a path we found in a plantation of reeds, that we might not give notice of our approach, being ignorant of the kind of animal we were about to meet. We had not gone far when the soil became so marshy, and the reeds entangled to such a degree, that we were obliged to get out of the plantation and wind along on the outside. We were soon near the animals, which we perceived consisted of rather a numerous troop of wild buffalos. This animal is formed at first sight to inspire the beholder with terror; it is endowed with an extraordinary degree of strength, and two or three of them were capable of destroying us in a moment, should they feel the desire of attacking us. My alarm was so great, that I remained for a few moments fixed to the spot like a statue. By good luck the dogs were far behind us, and the buffalos having never beheld the face of man, gave no sign of fear or of displeasure at our approach; they stood perfectly still, with their large round eyes fixed upon us in astonishment; those which were lying down got up slowly, but not one among them seemed to have any hostile disposition towards us. The circumstance of the dogs' absence was most likely, on this occasion, the means of our safety, for on the least demonstration from these, no doubt the fierce animals would instantly have fallen upon us. As it was, we had time to draw back quietly and prepare our fire-arms. It was not, however, my intention to make use of them in any way but for defence, being sensible that we were not strong enough for the encounter, and recollecting also to have read that the sound of a gun drives the buffalo to a state of desperation. I therefore thought only of retreating; and with my poor Jack, for whom I was more alarmed than for myself, was proceeding in this way, when unfortunately Turk and Ponto ran up to us, and we could see were noticed by the buffalos. The animals instantly, and altogether, set up such a roar, as to make our nerves tremble with the shock of so terrible a noise; they struck their horns and their hoofs upon the ground, which they tore up by pieces and scattered in the air. I with horror foresaw the moment when confounding us with the dogs, which no doubt they mistook for jackalls, they would seize upon and tear us to pieces. Our brave Turk and Ponto, fearless of danger, ran among the troop in spite of all our efforts to detain them, and according to their manner of attacking, laid hold of the ears of a young buffalo which happened to be standing a few paces nearer to us than the rest; and though the creature began a tremendous roar and motion with his hoofs, they held him fast, and were dragging him towards us. Thus hostilities had commenced; and unless we could resolve to abandon the cause of our valiant defenders, we were now forced upon the measure of open war, which, considering the strength and number of the enemy, wore a face of the most pressing and inevitable danger. Our every hope seemed now to be in the chance of the terror the buffalos would feel at the noise of our musketry, which for the first time would assail their organs, and perhaps excite them to flight. With, I must confess, a palpitating heart and trembling hands, we fired both at the same moment: the buffalos, terrified by the sound and by the smoke, remained for an instant motionless, as if struck by a thunderbolt, and then one and all betook themselves to flight with such incredible rapidity that they were soon beyond the reach of our sight. We heard their loud roaring from a considerable distance, which by degrees subsided into silence, and we were left with only one of their terrific species near us; this one, a female, was no doubt the mother of the young buffalo which the dogs had seized and still kept a prisoner; she had drawn near on hearing its cries, and had been wounded by our guns, but not killed; the creature was in a furious state: after a moment's pause, she took aim at the dogs, and with her head on the ground, as if to guide her by the scent, was advancing in her rage, and would have torn them to pieces, if I had not prevented her by firing upon her with my double-barrelled gun, and thus putting an end to her existence.

It was only now that we began to breathe. A few moments before, death, in the most horrible and inevitable form, seemed to stare us in the face! But now we might hope that every danger was over! I was enchanted with the behaviour of my boy, who, instead of giving way to fears and lamentations, as other lads of his age would probably have done, had stood all the time in a firm posture by my side, and had fired with a steady aim in silence. I bestowed freely on him the commendation he had so well deserved, and made him sensible how necessary it is in times of danger to preserve a presence of mind, which in many cases is of itself sufficient to effect the sought for deliverance. But I had not time for a long discourse. The young buffalo still remained a prisoner with his ears in the mouths of the dogs, and the pain occasioned him to be so furious that I was fearful he might do them some injury. I therefore determined to advance and give them what assistance I might find practicable. To say the truth, I scarcely knew in what way to effect this. The buffalo, though young, was strong enough to revenge himself, if I were to give the dogs a sign to let go his ears. I had the power of killing him with a pistol at a stroke; but I had a great desire to preserve him alive, and to tame him, that he might be a substitute for the ass, which we now had no hope of recovering. I found myself altogether in a perplexing state of indecision, when Jack suddenly and unexpectedly interposed a most effective means for accomplishing my wishes. He had his string with balls in his pocket; he drew it out hastily, and making a few steps backward, he threw it so skilfully as to entangle the buffalo completely, and throw him down. As I could then approach him safely, I tied his legs by two and two together with a very strong cord; the dogs released his ears, and from this moment we considered the buffalo as our own. Jack was almost mad with joy. What a magnificent creature! How much better than the ass he will look, harnessed to the cart! How my mother and the boys will be surprised and stare at him as we draw near! repeated he many and many times.

*Father*.—Ah hah! What, you already fancy him exactly to your wishes, Jack; already you have harnessed him to the loaded cart, while for my part I have not yet been able to conceive a means for even removing him from this place! Will you carry him upon your back?

*Jack*.—If I were Sampson or Hercules I would most willingly; but, father, he will be able to walk if we untie his legs.

*Father*.—And if we bid him do so, you think he will implicitly obey us?

*Jack*.—The dogs would make him get on.

*Father*.—And the buffalo might kill the dogs, Jack, and then turn back at a full gallop:—on reflection, the best way I think will be to tie his two fore-legs together, so tight that he cannot run, and loose enough for him to walk, as they do to mischievous horses: I will assist the scheme by trying a method which is practised in Italy for subduing the buffalo; you will think it somewhat cruel, but the success will be certain; it shall afterwards be our study to make him amends by the kindest care and treatment. Hold you the cord which confines his legs with all your strength, that he may not be able to move:—I then called Turk and Ponto, and made each again take hold of the ears of the animal, who was now keeping his head quite still; I took from my pocket a sharp and pointed knife, and held a piece of string in my hand in readiness; I placed myself before the buffalo, and taking hold of his snout, I made a hole in his nostril, into which I quickly inserted the string, which I immediately tied so closely to a tree, that the animal was prevented from the least motion of the head which might have inflamed the wound and increased his pain. I drew off the dogs the moment the operation was performed. The creature, thus rendered furious, would have run away, but the stricture of the legs and the pain in the nostril prevented it. The first attempt I made to pull the cord, found him docile and ready to accommodate his motions to our designs, and I perceived that we might now begin our march. I left him for a short time to make some other preparations.

I was unwilling to leave so fine a prey as the dead buffalo behind us: I therefore, after considering what was to be done, began by cutting out the tongue, which I sprinkled with some of the salt we had in our provision-bag: I next took off the skin from the four feet, taking care not to tear it in the operation. I remembered that the Americans use these skins, which are of a soft and flexible quality, as boots and shoes, and I considered them as precious articles. I lastly cut some of the flesh of the animal with the skin on, and salted it, and abandoned the rest to the dogs, as a recompense for the valour of their behaviour, and I then repaired to the river to wash myself after the performance of these butcher-like employments.

We now seated ourselves under the shade of a large tree; and as we ate the remaining portion of our provisions, amused ourselves with an animated review of the scene which had been passing. Our dogs were no less busily employed in greedily devouring the flesh of the buffalo.

As we were not disposed to leave the spot in a hurry, I desired Jack to take the saw and cut down a small quantity of the reeds, which from their enormous size might hereafter be of use to us. We set to work, but I observed that he took pains to choose the smallest.—What shall we do, said I, with these small-sized reeds? You are thinking, I presume, of nothing better than providing a bag-pipe to announce a triumphal arrival to our companions! You are mistaken, father, answered Jack; I am thinking rather of some candlesticks to present to my mother, who will set so high a value on them!

This is a good thought, my boy, said I, tapping him on the shoulder, I am well pleased both with the kindness and the readiness of your invention, and I will give you my assistance in trying to empty the reeds without breaking them; if we should not succeed, at least we know where to provide ourselves with more. I now helped him to choose some reeds, and soon after we set out on our return home.

We had so many and such heavy articles to remove, that I did not hesitate to dismiss, for that day, all thoughts of looking further for the ass, that we might return the sooner to our companions to relieve any uneasiness they might have felt at our long stay, and also to be myself satisfied respecting their safety during our absence. I began now to think of untying the young buffalo; and on approaching him, perceived with pleasure that he was asleep, which afforded me a proof that his wound was not extremely painful. When I awaked him he gave a start as I began to pull him gently with the string; but he afterwards seemed to forget his pain, and followed me without resistance. I fastened another string to his horns, and led him on by drawing both together; and he performed the journey with little inconvenience, and with so unexpected a docility, that to case ourselves of a part of the heavy burdens we had to carry, we even ventured on the measure of fastening the bundles of reeds upon his back, and upon these we laid the salted pieces of the buffalo. The creature did not seem aware that he was carrying a load; he followed in our path as before, and thus on the first day of our acquaintance he rendered us an essential service.

In a short time we found ourselves once more at the narrow passage between the torrent and the precipice of the rocks, which I have already mentioned. Near this spot, we met with a large jack-all, who on perceiving us, slunk away, but was stoutly pursued by our brave dogs, who overtook him at the entrance of a cavern, and forced him to give them battle. The fight, however, was unequal; the dogs were two to one, besides being protected by their pointed collars, which enabled them to resist the most skilful attacks of the enemy. When we got up to them, the jackall was already killed. On examining our prey, we found it was a female, which from appearances had lately brought forth young, and we therefore concluded that she was going to suckle them in the cavern, where no doubt they lay concealed. Jack would instantly have entered to search for them; but I prevented him, from the apprehension that the male might also be there for the purpose of guarding them. I accordingly used the precaution of shooting off my piece into the dark profundity which presented itself, when finding all quiet, I gave him leave to enter, being myself both proud and gratified by every proof he gave of personal courage.

For some moments after entering the cavern, the complete darkness which prevailed prevented him from seeing any thing around him; but when his eyes had become accustomed to it, he discerned in a corner a litter of young jackalls: the dogs who accompanied had before discovered them by the smell; they flew upon the creatures without mercy, and with the exception of one, which Jack found means to preserve, put an end to their existence. He came out of the cavern with the young jackall in his arms, asking if he might have leave to rear it as Fritz had done his monkey; and to this I made no objection, being unwilling to refuse to one of my children what I had granted to another; besides that it appeared to me that nothing could be so cruel as to kill the innocent little being in cold blood, or to leave it there to perish. I also felt the inclination to make an experiment on the effects and power of education, and to observe if it should be possible to succeed in taming him in such a degree as to obtain in consequence a race of good running dogs; at all events it seemed worth while to convince ourselves by the experiment. Jack therefore obtained leave to keep him, and could scarcely express the joy he felt: he pressed the animal to his bosom and devoured it with kisses, and promised to bestow upon him so faultless an education, that he should become the gentlest and most engaging little creature in the world.

We now left the cavern. I had fastened the young buffalo to a tree near the cascade without remarking of what species it might be; when I went to release him, I saw that it was a kind of small palm-tree, and on looking about me I observed also some other kinds of the palm which I had not before met with. One of the kinds I now remarked was from ten to twelve feet in height; its leaves were armed with thorns, and it bore a fruit resembling a small cucumber in form, but which at this time was immature, so that we could not taste it. The second, which was smaller, was also thorny; it was now in blossom, and had no fruit, I suspected that the first of these was the *little royal palm*, sometimes called *awiva*, or *Adam's needle*; and the other, the dwarf palm. I resolved to avail myself of both for further fortifying my enclosure at Tent-House, and also to protect the outer side of the narrow pass immediately over the torrent of the cascade, I determined to return and plant a line of them there, as close to each other as the consideration of their growth would allow; for my intention, of course, was to effect this by means of the young shoots which presented themselves in great abundance; we also hoped by that time to find their fruit ripe, and to ascertain their kind.

We repassed the river in safety, and accompanied by the agreeable noise of its foaming cascades, we regained the hazardous and narrow pass at the turn of the rocks. We however proceeded with caution, and finding ourselves safe on the other side, we thought of quickening our pace to arrive the sooner at the hut: we accordingly had the happiness to rejoin our friends before the close of the evening; and though we were somewhat fatigued, yet in other respects we were well and satisfied with the success of our various undertakings. We were received with the liveliest demonstrations of joy, and, as usual, a thousand questions asked at once. Where, how and where did we procure such interesting creatures as the buffalo and the golden fox? Shall we see the precipice and the cascade at the end of the wall of rocks?—Questions were so rapidly proposed to us, that we were obliged to demand on our parts the necessary time for answering them. This being granted, the story of our different adventures served for the amusement of the evening: conversing happily together concerning them, we enjoyed the sober meal which had been prepared for us; and having warmed ourselves by the fire, we retired in thankfulness to rest.

# XXVII

# THE MALABAR EAGLE, AND
# SAGO MANUFACTORY

M Y WIFE THE NEXT MORNING BEGAN THE CONVERSATION. SHE told me the children had been good and diligent, that all of them had ascended Cape Disappointment together, that they had gathered wood and made some torches for the night; and, what I could scarcely think possible, they had ventured to fell an immense palm-tree, to the top of which Ernest had again climbed for amusement; and afterwards they undertook the laborious and perilous work of bringing it down, which they also happily executed. This monarch of the forests lay prostrate on the ground, and covered a space of at least seventy feet in length. To effect their purpose, Ernest had got up the tree a second time, with a long rope which he fastened tight to the top of it. As soon as he had come down again, he and Fritz worked with the axe and saw, to cut it through. When it was nearly divided, they cautiously managed its fall with the rope, and in this manner they succeeded. But during their excursion and labours, a somewhat unfortunate visit took place. A numerous group of monkeys had found their way to the hut: every drop of the palm-wine we had preserved in our gourd-shells, these intrusive gentry contrived to swallow; they had upset and thrown about all the potatoes, stolen the cocoa-nuts, and disturbed, nay even almost wholly demolished, the order of the branches and other contrivances we had recourse to for our hut; so that my children on their return were employed a full hour in repairing the damage effected by those mischievous creatures. Fritz was in high spirits with the luck he had met with and secured; he brought me on his wrist a young bird of prey, of the most beauteous plumage; he had taken it from a nest in one of the rocks near the hill at Cape Disappointment. Very young as the bird was, it had already all its feathers, though they had not yet received their full colouring; but it was evidently not an European eagle, and I supposed it to be the beautiful eagle of Malabar. I viewed it with the admiration it was entitled to:—meeting with one of these birds is thought a lucky omen; and as this species of eagle is neither large nor expensive in its food, I was desirous to train it like a falcon to pursue smaller birds. Fritz had already covered its eyes and fastened the foot with packthread; I advised him to hold it often, and for a length of time, on his hand, and to tame it with hunger as falconers do.

When we had all finished our narratives, my wife began her usual lamentations upon the subject of so many living and devouring animals being brought to her, and which she said must in no long time, from the food they required, become burthensome to us. I consoled her with some difficulty, by observing that the buffalo would be a good substitute for the ass; and I established as an invariable law, that he who wished to have a useful animal in his service, should also have the care of keeping it. It is a cruelty, said I, to deprive a feeling creature of its liberty, for a transient pleasure or amusement to ourselves, and to make it suffer; we ought, on the contrary, to recompense it for the privation it would have to endure, by kind treatment and feeding it well. I declare then, that he who neglects the animals committed to his charge shall no longer be thought worthy of having so important a care intrusted to him. This warning intimidated my hearers; for man is a creature so formed for society, and so dependent upon it for his comforts and content, that, when by accidents deprived of intercourse with his own species, he attaches himself to the brute creation with even warm affection. This satisfied the kind temper of my wife; and as she was herself very partial to animals, she promised her sons to take the charge of one and all of the animals upon herself whenever their absence from home should render this necessary. We communicated to each other our hopes that such attentions would form them to more active, regular, and constant habits of affection and mildness towards us. I have said, I frequently noticed that treating animals with kindness tends to produce the benign effects I have been speaking of.

I next ordered a fire to be lighted and a quantity of green wood to be put on it, for the purpose of raising a thick smoke, over which I meant to hang the buffalo meat I had salted, to dry and preserve it for our future use; and this was done accordingly. We fixed pieces of it on long forked poles. I cut away what appeared not quite fresh, and saw our little eagle feast upon it voraciously. The young buffalo was beginning to browse, but the cow's milk was still given it; and Jack succeeded in making his little jackall drink some occasionally, likewise. We added to the buffalo's meal, whose appetite we found to be enormous, a heap of sliced potatoes, the whole of which he greedily devoured, and this led us to conclude that the pain from the wound in his nose was subsided, and that he would soon become tame.

Supper-time was now arrived, and we did not fail to acquit ourselves at it, as well, to say the least, as our cattle, seasoning our repast with lively anecdotes and affectionate conversation. The combat with the buffalos excited much raillery; but we saw that it was no less intended for compliment also, nor was our design to make boots and shoes of their hoofs passed over in silence; the candle-moulds too came in for a share in these their playful attacks upon what they called the wonderful feats we had per-formed. Jack persisted in defending himself, and this he did so cleverly as to point the laughter at the adversary. The arrange-ments for this night were much the same as for the preceding. We left our meat suspended over the smoke of our fires during our sleep; we tied the young buffalo by the side of the cow, and were pleased to see them agree and bid fair to live in peace together. The dogs were set upon the watch, Fritz resolved to go to bed with his eaglet fastened on his wrist, and its eyes still bound: it remained in this state throughout the night without disturbing its master. The time of repose elapsed so calmly that none of us awoke to keep in the torch lights, which now for the first time the industry of the boys had supplied us with, and we did not get up till after sun-rise. Directly after a moderate breakfast I chaunted the accustomed summons for our setting out; but my young ones had some proj-ects in their heads, and neither they nor their mother were just then in the humour to obey me.

Let us reflect a little first, said my wife: as we had so much difficulty in felling the palm-tree, would it not be a pity to lose our labour by leaving it in this place? It is the one from which Ernest cut out the famous cabbage: as it was thus deprived of future growth and bearing fruit, we wished to reap benefit from it in another way; Ernest assures me it is a sago-tree; if so, the pith would be an excellent ingredient for our soups. I request you will examine it, and let us see if in any way we can turn it to account.

I found she was in the right: but in that case it was necessary to employ a day in the business, since to open from one end to the other the trunk of a tree sixty feet long was not a trivial task. I assented however with some readiness, as, independent of the use of the farinaceous pith, I could, by emptying it, obtain two handsome and large troughs for the conveyance of water from Jackall's River to my wife's kitchen garden at Tent-House, and thence to my new plantations of trees.

*Fritz.*—One of the halves, father, will answer that purpose, and the other will serve as a conduit for our little stream from Falcon's Nest into my pretty bason lined with tortoise-shell; we then shall be constantly regaled with the agreeable view of a fountain close to our dwelling:—I fancy it now before my eyes and that I see its course. And I, for my part, said Ernest, long for a sight of the sago formed into small grains as I have seen it in Europe. Can you, father, make it up into that sort of composition?

With your help I think I could. Come, let us set up a famous manufactory of vermicelli and macaroni! and what other delicacy shall I say?

*Francis.*—Oh! yes, papa, I intreat you, macaroni! it is so nice, I will assist in making that.

Little glutton! answered I, you would, I imagine, rather assist in eating up all we can make. I do not however promise that our manufactory will produce such good and well made articles as those of Genoa and Naples; but let us first make the sago-paste, and afterwards work it up for such purposes of magnificence as in our profound wisdom we may afterwards be led to desire. Have we not one of our manioc graters here at hand?

Yes certainly, replied Ernest. We were even thinking of making some of them here for our amusement, but we found we were not likely to want employment: and he accordingly scampered away to fetch it me, while the rest crowded round me. Patience, children, patience, exclaimed I; we are not yet in readiness to use it, many other matters are previously requisite: in the first place you must assist me to raise this palm-tree from the ground, and it must be done by filing at each end two small cross-pieces or props to support it; to split it open as it lies, would be a work of too much labour: this done, I shall want several wooden wedges to keep the cleft open while I am sawing it, and afterwards a sufficient quantity of water. There is the difficulty, said my wife; our Falcon's Stream is too far off, and we have not yet discovered any spring in the neighbourhood of this place.

*Ernest.*—That is of no consequence, mother; I have seen hereabouts so great an abundance of the plants which contain water, that we need not be at a loss; for they will fully supply us, if I could only contrive to get vessels enough to hold it.

We now produced the enormous reeds we had brought home, which being hollow would answer the purpose of vessels: and as some time was required to draw off the water from such small tubes, he and Francis at once set to work; they cut a number of the plants, which they placed slantingly over the brim of a vessel, and whilst that was filling they were preparing another. The rest of us got round the tree, and with our united strength we soon succeeded in raising the heavy trunk, and the top of it was then sawed off. We next began to split it through the whole length, and this the softness of the wood enabled us to effect with little trouble. We soon reached the pith or marrow that fills up the middle of the trunk the whole of its length. When divided, we laid one half on the ground, and we pressed the pith together with our hands so as to make temporary room for the pith of the other half of the trunk, which rested still on the props. We wished to empty it entirely, that we might employ it as a kneading-trough, leaving merely enough of the pith at both ends to prevent a running out, and then we proceeded to form our paste. We had fastened the grater at one end, for the purpose of squeezing the paste through the small holes as soon as it was made.

My young manufacturers with stripped arms joyfully fell to work, and really surpassed my expectation; they brought water in succession and poured it gradually into the trough, whilst we mixed it with the flour. In a short time the paste appeared sufficiently fermented; I then made an aperture at the bottom of the grater on its outside, and pressed the paste strongly with my hand; the farinaceous parts passed with ease through the small holes of the grater, and the ligneous parts, blended with particles of wood, which did not pass, were thrown aside in a heap in the hope that mushrooms, etc. might spring from them. My boys were in readiness to receive in the reed vessels, what fell from the grater, and conveyed it directly to their mother, whose business was to spread out the small grains in the sun upon sail-cloth for the purpose of drying them. The subsequent process was the making of vermicelli, by working up the paste into a thicker consistence and pressing it more forcibly against the perforations of the grater; they passed through in slender rolls of different lengths, which were quickly dried by means of a gentle fire. To remunerate our toil my wife promised to dress us an excellent dish of this new manufacture, with some Dutch cheese, similar to Italian macaroni. Thus we procured a good supply of a wholesome and pleasant food; and should have had a larger stock of it, had we not been restricted as to time; but the privilege of renewing the process at pleasure, by felling a sago-tree, added to some impatience to take home our two pretty conduits and employ them as proposed, prompted us to expedite the business. The paste which remained was thrown upon the mushroom-bed, and watered well to promote a fermentation.

We employed ourselves the remainder of the evening in loading the cart with our tools and the two halves of the tree. Night coming on, we retired to our hut, where we enjoyed our usual repose, and early next morning were ready to return to Falcon's Stream. Our buffalo now commenced his service, yoked with the cow; he supplied the want of the ass, and was very tractable: it is true I led him by the cord which passed through his nose, and thus I restrained him within the bounds of his duty whenever he was disposed to deviate.

We returned the same way as we came, in order to load the cart with a provision of berries, wax, and elastic gum. I gave up looking for eggs this day, as I was very desirous to get back as soon as possible to Falcoln's Stream, to look after the beasts we had left there. I sent forward Fritz and Jack as a van-guard, with one of the dogs; they were to cut a commodious and secure road through the bushes for our cart. The two water conductors, which were very long, produced numerous difficulties and somewhat impeded our progress. My sons well performed their task, and we reached with tolerable speed and without any accident the wax and gum trees, where we halted to place our sacks filled with berries in the cart. The elastic gum had not yielded as much as I expected, from the too rapid thickening caused by an ardent sun, and an incrustation formed over the incision; we obtained however about a quart, which sufficed for the experiment of the impenetrable boots I had so long desired.

We set out again, still preceded by our pioneers, who cleared the way for us through the little wood of guavas. Suddenly we heard a dreadful noise which came from our van-guard, and beheld Fritz and Jack hastening towards us. I began now to fear a tiger or panther was near at hand, or had perhaps attacked them. Turk began to bark so frightfully, and Ponto running up to him joined in so hideous a yell, that I prepared myself, not without terror, for a bloody conflict. I advanced at the head of my troop, who expressed their determination to follow me to the assistance of those I thought in danger, and my high-mettled dogs ran furiously up to a thicket, where they stopped, and with their noses to the ground and almost breathless strove to enter it: I had no doubt some terrible animal was lurking there; and Fritz, who had seen it through the leaves, confirmed my suspicion; he said it was about the size of the young buffalo, and that its hair was black and shaggy. I was going to fire at it promiscuously in the thicket, when Jack, who had thrown himself on his face on the ground to have a better view of the animal, got up in a fit of laughter—It is only, exclaimed he, dame pig, that has played us another trick—our old sow, who is never tired of playing off her tricks upon us. He had hardly spoken, when the grunting of the concealed monster justified the assertion made by Jack. Half vexed, half laughing, we broke into the midst of the thicket, where in reality we found our sow stretched supinely on the earth, but by no means in a state of dreary solitude; the good matron had round her seven little creatures, which had been littered a few days, and were sprawling about contending with each other for the best place near their mother for a hearty meal. This discovery gave us considerable satisfaction, and we all greeted the corpulent creature, who seemed to recollect and welcome us with a sociable kind of grunting, while she licked her young without any ceremony or show of fear. We rewarded her docility with potatoes, sweet acorns, and manioc bread; for the boys one and all readily consented to go without themselves for her accommodation: they felt obliged to her for the new family she had given them, and anticipated ideally the pleasure of beholding a nice crisp suckling pig before the fire. But their mother censured their greedy impatience and cruelty, in already thinking about roasting the poor animals on their very entrance into life. A general consultation took place—should this swinish family be left where we found it, or conveyed to Falcon's Stream? Fritz voted for their being all left, to run at large like the wild boars in Europe, that he might have the sport of hunting them. My wife, like a good housewife, proposed that two of them at least should be domesticated for breeding; and as to the old sow, as she was always running away, it would be better to kill her when done suckling, and she would afford a large provision of salt meat;—and her opinion was adopted. For the moment they were suffered to keep quiet possession of their retreat; we resolved to rear three of them, and allow the other four to take to the woods, where they might be hunted if they injured our plantations.

We then, so many adventures ended, pursued our road to Falcon's Stream, and arrived there in safety and content;—so true it is, that home is always dear and sacred to the heart, and anticipated with delight. All was in due order, and our domestic animals welcomed our return in their own jargon and manner, but which did not fail to be expressive of their satisfaction in seeing us again. We threw them some of the food we knew them to be the most partial to, which they greedily accepted, and then voluntarily went back to their usual stand. It was necessary to practise a measure dictated by prudence, which was to tie up again the buffalo and jackall, to inure them by degrees to confinement; and the handsome Malabar eagle shared the same fate: Fritz deemed himself remarkably clever in placing it near the parrot on the root of a tree; he fastened it with a piece of packthread of sufficient length to allow it free motion, and uncovered its eyes: till then the bird had been tolerably quiet; but the instant it was restored to light, it fell into a species of rage that surprised us; it proudly raised its head; its feathers became ruffled, and its eye-balls seemed to whirl in their orbits and dart out vivid lightnings. All the poultry was terrified and fled; but the poor luckless parrot was too near the sanguinary creature to escape. Before we were aware of the danger, it was seized and mangled by the formidable hooked beak of the eagle in an almost inconceivably short space of time. Fritz vented his anger in loud, severe, and passionate reproaches: he would have killed the murderer on the spot, had not Ernest run up and entreated him to spare its life: Parrots, said he, we shall find in plenty, but never

JOHANN DAVID WYSS

perhaps so beauteous, so magnificent a bird as this eagle, which, as father observes, we may train for hawking. You may too blame only yourself, continued Ernest, for the parrot's death;—why did you uncover the eagle's eyes? If you had consulted me, I could have told you that falconers keep them covered six weeks, till they are completely tamed. But now, brother, let me for a certain time have the care of him, let me manage the unruly fellow; he shall soon, in consequence of the methods I shall use, be as tractable and submissive as a new-born puppy; say then that you consent, I will pledge myself you shall not be disappointed.

Yes, forsooth, said Fritz, but I shall not give you my eagle neither; it is mine, and I will not part with it to anyone; I can bring it up myself, only tell me how; it will be very unkind not to teach me the way—Father, is not Ernest very ungenerous to keep his management of eagles a secret, and wanting to bring it up himself?—Ernest, by the by, had signified his refusal by a shake of the head.

Gently, gently, children, said I: Fritz, listen to a little moral fable. "A dog placed himself on a truss of straw, which he considered as his property. An ass and an ox extremely hungry entreated permission to eat some of it, as it could not serve him for food; but the surly selfish cur would not even suffer them to approach it. Envious animal, said the ox, *eat thy straw, or permit it to be eaten by another*; but the dog was deaf to their entreaties, and dismissed them with snarling selfishness." Now tell me, boy, is not your conduct on this occasion similar to the selfish dog's? You know not how to tame your eagle, you a few minutes ago would even have inflicted death upon it, and now you refuse to give it to Ernest, who promises to bring it up, because you are envious of his knowing more than you do: as he has reflected more than you on what he has read, it is but just he should wish to derive some advantage from his reading and knowledge; you cannot do less than make him a civil offer of something for his secret, if you persist in not resigning your eagle. Should Ernest after this, have the generosity to impart it without the reward, the greater will be his merit, and I shall be pleased with you both.

Right, father, replied Fritz briskly; well, I will give him my monkey if he chooses to have it.—An eagle is a more noble and heroical animal; as I found it, I mean to keep it; but you will teach me to tame it? What say you, Ernest? Do you accept my offer?

*Ernest.*—With all my heart; but I value the heroism you talk of, very little: I, for my part prefer being learned; you shall be knight of the eagle if you think proper, and I your historiographer and poet. I will write a grand epic poem to record the splendid deeds of the knight and his eagle.

*Fritz.*—Poor jeering this, master Ernest! but, no matter; take the monkey, and teach me to tame my eagle: How shall I render it more docile and quiet?

*Ernest.*—I have read somewhere that the Caribs puff tobacco-smoke into the nostrils of the birds of prey and of the parrots they catch, until they are giddy and almost senseless;—this stupefaction over, they are no longer wild and untractable.

*Fritz.*—And this is the great witchcraft! Tobacco-smoke! it was worth puffing off to be sure! Your secret is not equivalent to the property of my monkey, is it, father?

Why not? If the bargain is fair, as I think it is, it should by all means hold good; if not, Ernest will not require any thing for useless counsel; but I have reason to think well of the method, and therefore approve of it. Bees may be stupefied in the same manner, so as to take them without resistance, or how could the honey-comb be obtained? The notion I assure you, boys, is far from bad.

*Francis.*—Oh! then there is a way to hinder the naughty bees from stinging poor little boys who want just to taste their honey? Good papa, pray go and smoke awhile opposite that hole in the tree, and make these stinging gentry sleep long enough for us to take away at least half of their honey without being devoured by them.

Fritz having consented to the experiment, took some tobacco and a pipe, of which we had found plenty in the sailors' chests, and began to smoke, at the same time gradually approaching the unruly bird. As soon as it was somewhat composed, he replaced the fillet over the eyes, and smoked close to its beak and nostrils so effectually, that it became motionless on the spot, and had the exact air of a stuffed bird. Fritz thought it dead, and was inclined to be angry with his brother; but I told him it would not hold on the perch if it were lifeless, and that its head alone was affected,— and so it proved. The favourite came to itself by degrees, and made no noise when its eyes were unbound; it looked at us with an air of surprise, but void of fury, and grew tamer and calmer every day. The monkey was adjudged unanimously to Ernest, who took possession of it the same evening, and made it lie down near him. We all passed an excellent night in our green castle, and in our good beds, which we returned to with abundant satisfaction.

# XXVIII

# ORIGIN OF SOME EUROPEAN
# FRUIT-TREES—BEES

W E COMMENCED EARLY THE NEXT DAY A BUSINESS WHICH WE had long determined to engage in: it was to plant bamboos close to all the young trees, to support them effectually in their growth. We quitted our tree with great alertness, having our cart loaded with canes and a large pointed iron to dig holes in the ground. We left my wife this time with only her dear little Francis, requesting them to prepare us a plentiful dinner, and to include the palm-tree cabbage and the sago-macaroni mixed with some Dutch cheese; in addition to these performances, they volunteered the melting some of the wax berries for our store of candles.

We did not take the buffalo with us, as I wished to give it a day's rest for its nose to heal up; the cow was sufficient for drawing the load of light bamboo canes. Before setting out, we gave the buffalo a few handfuls of salt, to ingratiate ourselves with our horned companion; and this treat pleased him so highly, that he showed by many signs his inclination of accompanying us;

and to prevent this, we were compelled to fasten him securely till we were out of sight.

We began our work at the entrance of the avenue which we had formed, and nearest to Falcon's Stream. The walnut, chestnut, and cherry-trees we had planted in a regular line and at equal distances, we found disposed to bend considerably to one side, seemingly as they had been directed by the wind. Being the strongest, I took the task of making holes with the implement, upon myself, which, as the soil was light, I easily performed, taking care to go deep enough to fix the stake firmly. In the mean time the boys selected the bamboos, cut them of equal lengths, and pointed the ends to go into the ground. When they were well fixed, we threw up the earth compactly about them, and fastened the saplings by the branches to them with some long, straight tendrils of a plant which we found near the spot. In the midst of our exertions we entered with much detail into a conversation respecting the culture of trees. Till then my boys had only thought of eating fruits, without giving themselves much trouble about theft production; but now their curiosity was excited, and they questioned me so closely on the subject, that I was somewhat at a loss in answering them. I communicated however, with pleasure, all within my knowledge: I perceived that the occasion was particularly favourable for rendering my lessons instructive and truly profitable, as the occupation we were engaged in gave me an opportunity to illustrate the lesson by means of the objects before our eyes. I shall briefly relate the summary of our discourse, which may be of use to young persons designed for an agricultural life.

*Fritz.*—Are the young trees that we have recently planted, and just propped up, wild or cultivated?

*Jack.*—A pretty question indeed! Do you imagine that trees are tamed like buffalos and eagles? You would perhaps teach them to stoop politely when we come to gather their fruit, to avoid giving us the trouble of reaching to their branches.

*Fritz.*—You suppose, friend Jack, that your speech is very witty, while in reality it is only nonsense. Do you think then that all created beings are brought up alike? If so, papa should punish the first occurrence of ill behaviour in you, by passing a cord through your nose, like the buffalo, to render you more considerate and compliant.

*Ernest.*—We should soon, if this plan were adopted, see brother Jack with a bridle round his neck.

*Father.*—All of you, children, would be exposed to such discipline as this, if there were no other means: but the observation of Fritz is perfectly just; men are not brought up like brutes, nor are brutes trained like plants, though the education of all ever tends to the same end—that of subjecting the will to the yoke of necessity and duty, and to make them walk upright: for did not these trees bend to every wind till we raised and supported them. Every creature is capable of improvement, if not susceptible of perfection, that is to say, with care and cultivation, every being may become better, and acquire virtues and qualities which, left to himself and nature, he would be destitute of; thus I render our buffalo, and you your jackall, tame and manageable, by making them feel the power of man over brutes; thus I strive, my dear children, to lead you on towards perfection, by cultivating your understanding, giving you, as far as I am able, good lessons and good examples; so these trees, which at first were mere wild stocks, produced from kernels or seeds, and bearing only small imperfect fruits, have been made to produce those of an excellent quality by grafting on them a superior species. Come here, examine this branch; it is easy to see it has been inserted into this other branch; all the rest were lopped away, and this alone preserved; the whole of the sap or nutritious juice flowed then to this point, and thence diffused itself; and thus the wild sapling is become a fine fruitful tree, producing as good fruit as that from which the graft was taken.—Such is the process of ingrafting.

*Fritz.*—There are many things in it I do not yet understand; I have often heard of the inoculation of trees—is that the same as ingrafting them?

*Father.*—Nearly so; to *inoculate* is, I believe, the appropriate term for the operation, and *graft* that for the branch, or part inserted. According to the different species of trees, different methods and seasons are chosen; different terms are also adopted; and when the first insertion fails, a second, and even a third attempt is made.

*Jack.*—Can good fruits be grafted on every kind of tree, such as firs, or oaks?

*Father.*—No, my son; trees of an homogeneous kind must be selected.

*Jack.*—Ah! now that's a fruit I am a stranger to; *homogeneous*—is it very good? are they to be found here? I long to taste them.

*Father.*—It is not a fruit, my dear child: it is, I confess, rather too learned a word which I was wrong to use without explanation. It is derived or comes from the Greek, and signifies *of the same nature, or bearing great similitude*; thus an apple, a pear, a quince-tree, may be ingrafted on each other, because their wood and their seeds are homogeneous or resemble each other. It is the same with a variety of fruits having stones and kernels; the cherry, plum, peach, and almond-tree: to attempt to graft any of these on a pine or oak, would be useless; so with the best education every man is not constituted to be learned, to form an artist or a general.

*Fritz.*—You said, father, that the wild stocks or trees, produced only from seed, bear but indifferent fruits; how is it, then, with all those in our island—our good cocoas and guavas were not grafted, as no gardeners or other persons were here to perform the operation?

*Father.*—Your remark is just; but I spoke only of our fruit-trees in Europe, where, almost without exception, the fruits require to be meliorated by a better soil, ingrafting, and culture. No doubt kind Providence has meant to indemnify these burning climes for many inconveniences, in bestowing on them palm-trees and other agreeable fruits that grow spontaneously and without trouble or labour on the soil.

*Ernest.*—I comprehend all this: yet one thing puzzles me; how were the scions and grafts of the best kinds first procured in Europe?

*Jack.*—What a question! From those who had them, certainly.

*Ernest.*—And what a reply! I answer. And where did those from whom they were obtained get them? I wish to know where the first branches of the best species were had, before any persons had undertaken the husbandry of trees, or thought of ingrafting them. All trees, I presume, were wild originally. . . .

*Jack.*—Indeed! What think you then of the terrestrial paradise? Do you not believe that excellent fruits of all kinds were there? And might not the scions and grafts you are so puzzled about, have been taken there to any number?

*Father.*—My dear young pupil, if you had read the Bible with attention, you would have seen that our father Adam was driven out of the terrestrial paradise for having eaten of one of those goodly fruits, contrary to the positive prohibition of God; and as he and his wife Eve were then alone on the earth, none could go and take grafts in that beautiful garden, which moreover was not in Europe; therefore the inquiry of Ernest is just and sensible. Good fruit-trees are doubtless natives of some part of the earth, where they bear spontaneously, in their natural climate, as good fruits as those we raise in ours with care and art. Such trees were torn from their native soil when young, and transplanted into Europe, where, by the assiduous attentions of the gardener, they prospered, and furnished grafts for their multiplication; for the European climate is so little fitted to the natural production of good fruits, that the best tree, propagated from their seed, soon resumes the wild state, and requires to be grafted. Gardeners usually collect a number of tender shoots or saplings in an inclosure, which they first raise by seed and afterwards ingraft; these inclosures are called nurseries, where such plants are purchased, and where all these shipped for our use were procured.

*Fritz.*—Do you know, father, the native country of all these trees?

*Father.*—Of most of them, I think. The vine I have ventured to plant near our tree at Falcon's Stream, grows only in the temperate zone; it neither thrives in very cold countries nor under the torrid zone, though it generally prefers the south to the north. The vine is of ancient date, for we find in the Bible that Noah was acquainted with the use of it. It seems then that the vine is a native of Asia Minor and Armenia; and it appears to have been brought at a very remote period into Egypt, Greece, and most parts of Europe. The fabulous accounts in mythology of Bacchus, relate, no doubt, to the propagation of the vine. Italy probably received it from the emigrant Greeks and from the Romans, who became masters of the known world; thence it was carried into Gaul, Spain, Germany, and those parts of Switzerland in which it promised to thrive: perhaps the Phoenicians too had previously transported it to some of the above-mentioned countries.

*The boys speaking together.*—And the apple, pear, chestnut, walnut, almond, peach, and mulberry-trees?

*Father.*—Patience, patience, prattlers! Can I tell you every thing in a breath? And pray speak one after the other, gentlemen.— Fruits with shells or pods, such as the nut, almond, and chestnut, generally called *glands* or *kernels* by the Romans, come from the East; but that is too general a term—for the East being the quarter in which the sun rises, includes too many regions. Chestnuts were called by the ancients *glandes Sardes*, from Syria, a province of Asia Minor, and they received their present name from a Grecian town, near which they were cultivated in abundance. As to walnuts, they were formerly named *glandes Jovis*, (*Jupiter's acorns* or *kernels*) by the Romans; they are originally from Persia, and were spread through Europe by the Roman conquests. The great filberd-tree, bearing the Portugal nut or filberd, is originally from Pontus, a country of Asia Minor, and has been transplanted in the same way as the preceding. The origin of the almond-tree is uncertain; it is found wild in Asia and Africa: its fruit bore the name of *thalos* in Greece, because it had been first transplanted from an island of that name in the Archipelago.

*Jack.*—And cherries, papa,—cherries I like so much? Such quantities of them are in Switzerland, on the high roads and every where, that I think them natives of my country.

*Father.*—Not so, my friend; but of all exotic fruits it is certainly the one that thrives the most with us. They derived their name from *Cerasus*, another town of the Pontus already mentioned to you, and if I recollect right, the place is called *Chirisarda*. The celebrated Roman general Lucullus, after his victory over Mithridates king of Pontus, was the first who transported them into Europe, seventy years before the birth of Christ.

*Ernest.*—I have not read any thing about cherries in Eutropius, where I should have been glad to find some account of them.

*Father.*—I am of your opinion, Ernest, that historians would have done as well to give the names of those who procured an agreeable fruit, as in recording the destroyers of mankind.

In this kind of instructive conversation we had got to the end of our alley of trees, which looked all the better for the uprightness we had restored them to. This accomplished, we crossed Family Bridge on our way to the southern plantation of trees, in order to raise and prop them also. We were delighted with the view of beautiful orange, citron, and pomegranate trees, that had all taken root and were thriving to our satisfaction, as well as the pistachio and mulberry trees. Some of these were in blossom, and inspired us with the most pleasing hope. We quickly set to work, and my sons with increased curiosity renewed their inquiries concerning the origin of these delicious fruits.

Ah! how charming the country must be where such fruits as these grow spontaneously! exclaimed Fritz.

Considered as confined to this question only, said I, this country, no doubt, may be termed propitious; but in some other respects it has likewise its unfavourable side. All the fruits abounding with acid and refreshing juices, are natives of the torrid or burning zone, or of parts of the temperate zone most adjacent to it; they seem to have been designed to cool the mass of blood, and keep off the inflammatory diseases so frequent in these climates. Orange and lemon trees are certainly, as I think, from Medea and Assyria; the Romans called them *mala Medica*, or Medean apples; they were brought by the Persians to Albina, and thence into Sicily and the island of Malta, where the best species of orange trees is still found; they were afterwards transplanted to Italy, and in succession to many other parts of Europe. Pomegranates were named mala *Puniçea* (*Punic apples*,) and doubtless were brought by the Phoenicians and Carthaginians into the southern provinces of Europe. I have no positive knowledge of the original growth of pistachios. You are now, children, tolerably well informed on the subject of fruit trees.

*All.*—No no, dear father, since you have gone so far, and are so kind as not to be tired of instructing us, pray tell us the primitive country of all the trees we have to straighten and prop; the description amuses us exceedingly.

I am glad of it, and all I know is entirely at your service; but hearing in this sudden and rapid succession, the species, qualities, and countries of such variety of fruits, you will, I fear, overload your memory and forget the whole.

*Fritz.*—Pardon me, father, every one will recollect perfectly what relates to his favourite fruit, and we shall often talk on the subject in our walks under the shade of the very trees so principally concerned.

*Father.*—Well, be it so! Thus it is in fact with all the sciences; we do not easily forget what we wish to know, what is connected with our desires and hopes;—propose your questions then, and I will answer you as fully as I am able.

*Fritz.*—Well then, father, from what part do olives come originally?

*Father.*—From Armenia and Palestine. Authors of antiquity say that Hercules brought the first into Europe, and planted them on Mount Olympus; they were gradually cultivated throughout Greece, and especially in the territory of Athens, whence they came into Italy, and from thence were spread over the south of France, and in Spain, where they are cultivated with the greatest care, on account of the excellent oil which is extracted from them. Figs belong to the same native soil; they were brought from Lydia and the isle of Chios into the Archipelago, in the time of Cato the Elder: they were transplanted into Gaul a long while after by the emperor Julian, who was previously prefect or governor of that Roman province. Peaches are from Persia, and were first named *mala Persica* (*Persian apples*). In Pliny's time, who lived under the emperor Vespasian, they were still a novelty in Italy: the family of apricots from Armenia came amongst the Romans about the same time.

But now let us go on to plums, your favourite fruit:—Whence do they originate? Some of the inferior kinds are probably European; but those of the finest qualities are from other parts: they have reached us from Damascus, a town of Syria, from which their name is borrowed. In course of time the crusaders brought several species of them into Europe, and prunes most likely were among them.

Your favourite apples and pears now claim, I think, a few observations. We find them first noticed in Greek authors, under the denomination of *Peloponnesian fruits*; they were obtained from that country by the Romans; they found also several kinds of them in Syria and Alexandria. These two fruits, of all others offer the greatest varieties, and no doubt several of them are the result of culture, or of the influence of soil and climate. It is in general a law of nature, that care and attentive management produce in the same species a more considerable number of shades and varieties, than is met with in the wild uncultivated state, in which much sameness prevails throughout. Man in the rude state of nature is nearly alike every where, and is destitute of those diversities of character that naturally unfold themselves in his civilized condition. Every class of animals and plants, which man renders subservient to his use by cultivation and due care, exhibits beyond comparison greater differences in the same species, more varieties, more families, than those which remain in their native state, remote from and unaided by his fostering care:—it would appear as if Providence had thus meant to encourage and reward activity and labour.

*Jack*.—But, father, you left off with the apples too soon; do pray resume their history: I wish you may tell us they are of Swiss or German origin; they are so useful as a fruit, keep so well through the winter, and may be eaten raw as well as dressed.

*Father*.—This refreshing fruit, my apple-eating boy, is not a native of Switzerland or Germany, as you desire it should be, but comes to us from more favoured climates; at least this is the case with the best sorts of them. We have a number of wild pear and apple trees, the fruit of which is crabbed, harsh, and scarcely eatable; whether they were so originally, or have degenerated, remains to be determined. As I have said, none of these valuable fruits are indigenous or native in the colder parts of Europe: yet this ungrateful and rough climate it is that operates on the European so as to distinguish him from the inhabitants of the other parts of the world, by his intelligence, his fitness for toil, and his skill in agriculture. There exist abundant means and facilities for rendering man effeminate and indolent, but necessity and want stimulate him to industry and useful inventions; and by these blessings the inconveniences of climate are amply compensated.

*Jack.*—I dare say you are quite right, father;—but tell me where then do apples come from?

*Father.*—From the eastern countries, my son; and it is to the victories of the Romans we are indebted for some of the best kinds, which have been diversified by experiments, ingrafting, or in other words the influence of soil and labour and intelligence.

*Fritz.*—Quince and mulberry-trees are the last we have to inquire about; and then, father, we will cease our importunities for the present.

*Father.*—It is almost time, I must confess. Mulberry-trees are in general from Asia; they have, I presume, been cultivated more for the sake of their leaves, on which silkworms feed, than for their fruit: however, it cannot be denied that the juicy berry of the dark-coloured mulberry-tree merits to be held in some estimation, and the white-coloured, whose fruit is small and indifferent, contributes to the production of the finest silk. The quince-tribe must have taken its name from the town of Cydonia in the isle of Crete; the Romans called them *pyrus Cydoniæ*. On the quince-tree may be most successfully grafted pear-trees designed to be afterwards planted as espaliers.

*Fritz.*—But why is it thought right to stunt the growth of a fine tree, and force it to remain diminutive?

*Father*.—This, in several respects, is useful; wall-trees, being sheltered on one side, bear earlier and more choice fruits; it is easier to defend them from insects; their fruits are more conveniently gathered. The tree, giving less shade, is not so injurious to the culinary plants that are near it.—Are not these substantial reasons?

*Jack*.—Then I must ask, why are not all trees set in this way?

That would not be a judicious plan by any means; an espalier takes up too much ground; besides, trees with high stems produce more fruit, they form orchards; a crop of hay too may be raised under them, whereas espaliers serve in general as fences or boundaries in gardens.

This is a compendium of our morning's conversation, in the course of which we finished our work in the completest manner. Towards noon, a keen appetite hastened our return to Falcon's Stream, where we found an excellent and plentiful dinner prepared by our good and patient steward, of which the palm-tree cabbage was the chief dish. We all agreed that to eat of a better or more delicate food was impossible; and Ernest, who had procured it, received the thanks of all the board.

When the sharpness of hunger was appeased, a new subject was introduced which I and my wife had been seriously revolving for some time; she found it difficult and even dangerous to ascend and descend our tree with a rope ladder: we never went there but on going to-bed, and each time felt an apprehension that one of the children, who scrambled up like cats, might make a false step and perhaps be lamed for ever. Bad weather might come on and compel us for a long time together to seek an asylum in our aerial apartment, and consequently to ascend and descend oftener.

My wife addressed me constantly on the subject, incessantly asking whether my inventive genius could not suggest some easier and less perilous mode of getting to our dwelling. I smiled at her implicit confidence that I could accomplish wonders: I assured her that if I were an enchanter or magician no desire of hers should remain ungratified, and that with a single touch of my wand I would instantly produce for her a commodious firm stair-case of perfect workmanship; but that not being the case, I acknowledged myself at a loss for the means to effect such an accommodation for her: still her reiterated appeals and my own anxiety had often made me reflect if the thing were really possible? A stair-case on the outside was not to be thought of, the considerable height of the tree rendered that impracticable, as I had nothing to rest it on, and should be at a loss to find beams to sustain it; but I had for some time formed the idea of constructing winding stairs within the immense trunk of the tree, if it should happen to be hollow, or I could contrive to make it so: Francis had excited this idea in speaking of the bees.

Did you not tell me, dear wife, said I, that there is a hole in the trunk of this enormous tree of ours, in which a swarm of bees is lodged?

Without doubt, answered she; it was there little Francis was so severely stung in attempting to thrust in a stick; look at it yourself, you will see the bees go in and come out in throngs.

Then, replied I, we have only to examine how far this excavation goes, whether it extends to the roots, and what the circumference of it is; this done, we shall have gained the first difficult step in favour of our stair-case.

All my children seized the idea with ardour; they sprang up, and prepared themselves to climb the tops of the roots like squirrels, to

PLATE 11
"Jack, whose temper was on all occasions rash, had
struck fiercely upon the bees' nest."

succeed in striking at the trunk with axes, and to judge from the sound how far it was hollow; but they soon paid dearly for their attempt: the whole swarm of bees, alarmed at the noise made against their dwelling, issued forth, buzzing with fury, attacked the little disturbers, began to sting them, stuck to their hair and clothes, and soon put them to flight, bearing along with them their enemies, and uttering lamentable cries. My wife and I had some trouble to stop the course of this uproar, and cover their little wounds with fresh earth to allay the smart. Jack, whose temper was on all occasions rash, had struck exactly upon the bees' nest, and was more severely attacked by them than the rest; it was necessary, so serious was the injury, to cover the whole of his face with linen.

The less active Ernest got up the last, and was the first to run off when he saw the consequences, and thus avoided any further injury than a sting or two; but some hours elapsed before the other boys could open their eyes or be in the least relieved from the acute pain that had been inflicted. When they grew a little better, the desire of being avenged of the insects that had so roughly used them had the ascendant in their minds: they teased me to hasten the measures for getting every thing in readiness for obtaining possession of their honey. The bees in the mean time were still buzzing furiously round the tree. I prepared tobacco, a pipe, some clay, chisels, hammers, etc. I took the large gourd long intended for a hive, and I fitted a place for it by nailing a piece of board on a branch of the tree; I made a straw roof for the top to screen it from the sun and rain; and as all this took up more time than I was aware of, we deferred the attack of the fortress to the following day, and got ready for a sound sleep, which completed the cure of my little wounded patients.

# XXIX

# VICTORY OVER THE BEES;— WINDING STAIR-CASE; TRAINING OF VARIOUS ANIMALS; DIVERS MANUFACTURES; FOUNTAIN, ETC.

NEXT MORNING ALMOST BEFORE DAWN ALL WERE UP AND IN motion; the bees had returned to their cells, and I stopped the passages with clay, leaving only a sufficient aperture for the tube of my pipe. I then smoked as much as was requisite to stupefy without killing the little warlike creatures. Not having a cap with a mask, such as beecatchers usually wear, nor even gloves, this precaution was necessary. At first a humming was heard in the hollow of the tree, and a noise like a gathering tempest, which died away by degrees. All was become calm, and I withdrew my tube without the appearance of a single bee. Fritz had got up by me: we then began with a chisel and a small axe to cut out of the tree, under the bees' hole of entrance, a piece three feet square. Before it was entirely separated, I repeated the fumigation, lest the stupefaction produced by the first smoking should have ceased, or the noise we had been just making revived the bees. As soon as I supposed them quite lulled again, I separated from the trunk the piece I had cut out, producing as it were the aspect of a window, through which the inside of the tree was laid entirely open to view; and we were filled at once with joy and astonishment on beholding the immense and wonderful work of this colony of insects. There was such a stock of wax and honey, that we feared our vessels would be insufficient to contain it. The whole interior of the tree was lined with fine honey-combs: I cut them off with care, and put them in the gourds the boys constantly supplied me with. When I had somewhat cleared the cavity, I put the upper combs, in which the bees had assembled in clusters and swarms, into the gourd which was to serve as a hive, and placed it on the plank I had purposely raised. I came down, bringing with me the rest of the honey-combs, with which I filled a small cask, previously well washed in the stream. Some I kept out for a treat at dinner; and had the barrel carefully covered with cloths and planks, that the bees, when attracted by the smell, might be unable to get at it. We then sat round the table, and regaled ourselves plentifully with the delicious and odoriferous treat of the honey. Having finished our meal, my wife put by the remainder; and I proposed to my sons to go back to the tree, in order to prevent the bees from swarming again there on being roused from their stupor, as they would not have failed to do, but for the precaution I took of passing a board at the aperture, and burning a few handfuls of tobacco on it, the smell and smoke of which drove them back from their old abode, whenever they attempted to return to it. At length they desisted from approaching it, and became gradually reconciled to their new residence, where their queen no doubt had settled herself. I took this opportunity to relate to my children all I had read in the interesting work by Mr. Huber of Geneva of the queen-bee, this beloved and respected mother, of her subjects, who are all her children, and who take care of and guard her, work for her, nourish the rising swarms, make the cells in which they are to lodge, prepare others of a different structure, as well as nutriment for the young queens destined to lead forth the fresh colonies: and I entered into all those details which celebrated observers, and particularly the one we have just mentioned, have described so interestingly. These accounts highly entertained my youthful auditory, who almost regretted having molested by their depredation the repose of a fine peaceable kingdom that had flourished so long without interruption in the huge trunk. As to me, it so well suited my intended stair-case, that I readily adopted the prevailing moral amongst conquerors, who dispense with scruples when the seizing a country is convenient to their policy, and I resolved to take full possession next day. In the mean time I advised all to watch during the night, over the whole provision of honey obtained while the bees were torpid, who when recovered would not fail to be troublesome, and come in legions to get back to their property. That we might not be ourselves injured by so much fatigue, we went and threw ourselves on our beds, and in our clothes, to take a short doze before the hour of retreat; we were lulled to sleep with their buzzing, which had quite ceased when we awoke at the coming on of night; they had remained quiet in the gourd or suspended in clusters from some branches: without concerning ourselves about them, we went promptly to business; the cask of honey was emptied into a kettle, except a few prime combs which we kept for daily consumption; the remainder mixed with a little water was set over a gentle fire and reduced to a liquid consistence, strained and squeezed through a bag, and afterwards poured back into the cask, which was left upright and uncovered all night to cool. In the morning the wax was entirely separated, and had risen to the surface in a compact and solid cake that was easily removed; beneath was the purest, most beautiful and delicate honey that could be seen: the cask was then carefully headed again, and put into cool ground near our wine vessels; and now we promised ourselves an abundant supply of an agreeable article for desserts. This task accomplished, I mounted to revisit the hive, and found every thing in order; the bees going forth in swarms and returning loaded with wax, from which I judged they were forming fresh edifices in their new dwelling place. I was surprised to see the numbers that had occupied the trunk of the tree find room in the gourd; but on looking round me, I perceived a part of them collected in a cluster upon a branch, and I thence concluded a young queen was amongst them. On perceiving this, I procured another gourd, into which I shook them and placed it by the former: thus I had the satisfaction of obtaining at an easy rate two fine hives of bees in activity.

We soon after these operations proceeded to examine the inside of the tree. I sounded it with a pole from the opening I had made towards the top; and a stone fastened to a string served us to sound the bottom, and thus to ascertain the height and depth of the cavity. To my great surprise the pole penetrated without any resistance to the branches on which our dwelling rested, and the stone descended to the roots. The trunk, it appeared, had wholly lost its pith, and most of its wood internally; nothing therefore was more practicable than to fix winding stairs in this capacious hollow, that should reach from top to bottom. It seems that this species of tree, like the willow in our climates, receives nourishment through the bark; for it did not look decayed, and its far-extended branches were luxuriant and beautiful in the extreme. I determined to begin our construction that very day. The undertaking appeared at first beyond our powers; but intelligence, patience, time, and a firm resolution vanquished all obstacles. We were not disposed to relax in any of these requisites; and I was pleased to find opportunities to keep my sons in continual action, and their minds and bodies were all the better for exertion. They grew tall, strong, and were too much engaged to regret, in ignoble leisure, any of their past enjoyments in Europe.

We began to cut into the side of the tree, towards the sea, a door-way equal in dimensions to the door of the captain's cabin, which we had removed with all its framework and windows; by means of which we should at once be guarded against every attack on that side. We next cleared away from the cavity all the rotten wood, and rendered the interior even and smooth, leaving sufficient thickness for cutting out resting places for the winding stairs, without injuring the bark. I then fixed in the centre, the trunk of a tree ten or twelve feet high and a foot thick, completely stripped of its branches, in order to carry my winding stair-case round it: on the outside of this trunk, I and the inside of the cavity of our own tree, we formed grooves, so calculated as to correspond with the distances at which the boards were to be placed to form the stairs. These were continued till I had got to the height of the trunk round which they turned. The window I had opened at the top to take out the honey gave light enough. I made a second aperture below, and a third above it, and thus completely lighted the whole ascent. I also effected an opening near our room, that I might more conveniently finish the upper part of the stair-case. A second trunk was fixed upon the first, and firmly sustained with screws and transverse beams. It was surrounded like the other with stairs cut slopingly; and thus we happily effected the stupendous undertaking of conducting it to the level of our bed-chamber. Here I made another door directly into it; and I then found I could add nothing further to my design. If my stair-case was not in strict conformity to the rules of architecture, it at least answered the purpose it was built for, that of conducting us with safety and shelter to our nocturnal residence. To render it more solid and agreeable, I closed the spaces between the stairs with plank. I then fastened two strong ropes, the one descending the length of the little tree, the other along the side of the large one, to assist in case of slipping. I fixed the sash-windows taken from the captain's cabin in the apertures we had made to give light to the stairs; and when the whole was complete, it was so pretty, solid, and convenient, that we were never tired of going up and coming down it; and I fear I must add, for the sake of truth, with no small admiration of our united talents. I must, however, candidly own, that we succeeded in this arduous attempt by mere dint of efforts, patience, industry, and time; for it occupied us for several weeks together with no intermission. It more than once reminded me of the wise system of education of the philosopher of Geneva, J.J. Rousseau; and particularly where he recommends that boys of all classes in society should learn a trade, and especially that of a carpenter. How happy should I have been in our circumstances to have known this trade myself, and to have taught it to my eldest son! I cannot too earnestly exhort all fathers to put their sons in early possession of a resource which, though it may not become of the first necessity, has, at all events, the advantage of making a young man stronger, and more dexterous; of filling up many of the dangerous idle hours of ardent youth; and of being able, in maturer age, if it be unnecessary to work ourselves, at least to overlook the workmen we employ. I am not an enthusiast for the system of Rousseau, though I admire his style and genius; yet if humanity were indebted to him for no more than this sagacious counsel, and the felicity conferred by his maxims on early childhood, it would still suffice to make us love and consider him as a benefactor.

But our new acquisition of a handsome stair-case did not exclusively occupy the whole of our time; as in our solitude we had nothing to consider but our own pleasure or convenience, and our daily wants were not subject to the occurrence of other social duties, we saw no occasion for tormenting ourselves with a greater degree of labour in every day than was wholesome for our bodily health. We had no harsh surveyor, no inquisitive examiners; no troublesome neighbours nor counselors. If we occasionally regretted not being members of a large society under just laws and agreements established between societies of men, we more frequently complimented ourselves on not being subjected to this restraint and the inconveniences that arise from it. If we happened now and then to feel the want of some of the high-wrought pleasures of social existence, we were speedily solaced by reflecting that we did not stand in need of money; that we had no uneasy care about the acquisition of it; that we excited neither envy, pity, nor censure; while the imperfection of our achievements, and the trouble they cost us, were richly compensated by the freedom and cheerfulness with which they were executed, ever without altercation, and with united hearts and souls.

I will briefly narrate the few remarkable occurrences that took place during the construction of our stair-case.

A few days after the commencement of our stair-case, the two she-goats gave us two kids, and our ewes five lambs; so that we now saw ourselves in possession of a pretty flock: but lest the domestic animals should follow the example of the ass, and run away from us, I tied a bell to the neck of each. We had found a sufficient number of bells in the vessel, which had been shipped for trading with the savages; it being one of the articles they most value. We could now immediately trace a deserter by the sound, and bring it back to the fold.

Next to the winding stairs, my chief occupation was the management of the young buffalo, whose wound in the nose was quite healed, so that I could lead it at will with a cord or stick passed through the orifice, as the Caffrarians do, I preferred the latter, which answered the purpose of a bit; and I resolved to break-in this spirited beast for riding as well as drawing. It was already used to the shafts, and very tractable in them; but I had more trouble in inuring him to the rider, and to wear a girth, having made one out of the old buffalo's hide. I formed a sort of saddle with sail-cloth, and tacked it to the girth. Upon this I fixed a burthen, which I increased progressively. I was indefatigable in the training of the animal, and soon brought it to carry, without fear or repugnance, large bags full of potatoes, salt, and other articles, such as the ass had patiently borne to be loaded with. The monkey was his first rider, who stuck so close to the saddle, that in spite of the plunging and kicking of the buffalo, it was not thrown. Francis was then tried, as the lightest of the family; but throughout his excursion I led the beast with a halter, that it might not throw the child off. Jack now showed some impatience to mount the animal in his turn. Some restraint was requisite:—

I passed the appropriate piece of wood through the buffalo's nose, and tied strong packthread at each end of the stick, bringing them together over the neck of the animal; and I then put this new-fashioned bridle into the hands of the young rider, directing him how to use it. For a time the lad kept his saddle, notwithstanding the repeated jumps of the horned steed; at length a side jolt threw him on the sand, without his receiving much injury, Ernest, Fritz, and lastly myself, got on successively, with more or less effect. His trotting shook us to the very centre, the rapidity of his gallop turned us giddy, and our lessons in horsemanship were reiterated many days before the animal was tamed, and could be rode with either safety or pleasure. At last, however, we succeeded without any serious accident; and the strength and swiftness of our saddled buffalo were prodigious. It seemed to sport with the heaviest loads. My three eldest boys mounted it together now and then, and it ran with them with the swiftness of lightning. By continued attentions it at length became extremely docile: it was not in the least apt to start; and I really felt satisfaction in being thus enabled to make my sons expert riders, so that if they should even have horses, they might get on the most restive and fiery without any fear:—none could be compared to our young buffalo; and the ass which I had intended to employ in the same way was far surpassed by this new member of our family. Fritz and Jack, with my instructions, amused themselves in training the animal as horses are exercised in a riding-house; and by means of the little stick through the nose, they were able to do what they pleased with him.

In the midst of all this Fritz did not neglect his eagle; he daily shot some small birds which he gave it to eat, placing them sometimes betwixt the buffalo's horns, sometimes on the back of one of the hens, or of a flamingo, or on a shelf, or at the end of a stick, in order to teach it to pounce like a falcon upon other birds. He taught it to perch on his wrist whenever he called or whistled to it; but some time elapsed before he could trust it to soar without securing its return by a long string, apprehending its bold and wild nature would prompt it to take a distant and farewell flight from us.

Our whole company, including even the inert Ernest, was infected with the passion of becoming instructors. Ernest tried his talents in this way with his monkey; who, it must be confessed, seldom failed to furnish him with work. It was no poor specimen of the ludicrous to see the lad; he whose movements were habitually slow and studied, now constrained to skip, and jump, and play a thousand antics with his pupil during training hours, and all the time deeply interested in carrying forward the lesson the grotesque mimic was condemned to learn, of carrying small loads, climbing the cocoa-trees, and to fetch and bring the nuts. He and Jack made a little hamper of rushes, very light: they put three straps to it, two of which passed under the fore, and one between the hind legs of the animal, and were then fastened to a belt in front, to keep the hamper steady on the back of the mischievous urchin. This apparatus was at first intolerable to poor Knips: he gnashed his teeth, rolled on the ground, jumping like a mad creature, and did every thing to get rid of it; but all in vain, for education was the standing order, and he soon found he must submit. The hamper was left on day and night; its sole food was what was thrown into it; and in a short time pug was so much accustomed to the burden, that he began to spit and growl whenever we attempted to take it off, and every thing given to the creature to hold was instantly thrown into it. Knips became at length a useful member of our society; but he would only obey Ernest, whom he at once loved and feared, thus affording a proof of at least one of the great ends of all instruction. Jack was less successful with his little jackall, which he had named *Hunter,* hoping that its qualities would justify the name. He made continual attempts to induce the animal to go after game; but for the first six months he advanced no further in the lesson than teaching him to bring what was thrown to it: and when it was dead game, Hunter was sure to devour it on the way, and to bring home the skin alone: but it was nevertheless so pretty and tractable a creature, that I intreated the boy not to relinquish a task that would prove so beneficial to us; and he persevered with considerable zeal.

These different occupations filled up several hours of the day; when, after working at our stairs, we assembled in the evening round our never-failing constant friend, the good mother, to rest ourselves: and forming a little circle, every individual of which was affectionate and cheerful, it was her turn to give us some agreeable and less fatiguing occupation in the domestic concerns of Falcon Stream: such, for example, as endeavouring to improve our candle-manufactory, by blending the berry and the bees-wax, and employing the reed-moulds invented by Jack: but having found some difficulty in taking out the candles when cold, I adopted the plan of dividing the moulds, cleaning the inside, and rubbing it over with a little butter, to prevent the wax from adhering to it; then to rejoin both halves with a band that could be loosened at pleasure, to facilitate the extraction of the tapers. The wicks gave us most trouble, as we had no cotton.

We tried with moderate success the fibrous threads of the karatta, and those of the algava or flame-wood; but each had the inconvenience of becoming a sort of coal or cinder. The production which gave us the most satisfaction was the pith of a species of elder; but it did not, however, lessen our desire to discover the only appropriate ingredient, the cotton-tree. I likewise contrived a method of rendering our candles even and shining, by rolling them between two boards: they now were only distinguishable from those of Europe by a greenish hue. On my observing to my sons that wax was bleached like linen, by spreading it on cloths, and exposing it to the dew and sun, they wished to try the process; but as our green tapers burned remarkably well, bleaching the wax would have been a useless luxury and loss of time, which I could turn to more account in manufacturing our impenetrable boots without seams, of the caoutchouc or elastic gum. I began with a pair for myself; and I encouraged my children to afford a specimen of their industry, by trying to form some flasks and cups that could not break. They commenced by making some clay moulds, which they covered with layers of gum, agreeably to the instructions I had given them.

In the meanwhile I compactly filled a pair of stockings with sand, and covered them with a layer of clay, which I first dried in the shade, and afterwards in the sun. I then took a sole of buffalo-leather, well beaten, and studded round with tacks, which served me to fix it under the foot of the stocking; and after this I poured the liquid gum into all the interstices, which on drying produced a close adhesion between the leather and stocking sole. I next proceeded to smear the whole with a coat of resin of a tolerable thickness; and as soon as this layer was dried on, I put on another, and so on till I had spread on a sufficiency with my brush. After which I emptied the sand, drew out the stocking, removed the hardened clay, shook off the dust, and thus obtained a pair of seamless boots, as finished as if made by the best English workman; being pliant, warm, soft, smooth, and completely water-proof. I hung them up directly, that they might dry without shrinking. They fitted uncommonly well, and my four lads were so highly pleased with their appearance, that they skipped about with joy in requesting me to make each of them a pair. I refrained from any promise, because I wished to ascertain their strength previously, and to compare them with boots made out of mere buffalo-leather. Of these I at once began a pair for Fritz, with a piece of the slaughtered buffalo's skin. They gave far more trouble than those manufactured with the caoutchouc, which I used to cover the seams and render them less pervious to water. The work turned out very imperfect, and so inferior to my incomparable boots, that Fritz wore them reluctantly; and the more so, as his brothers shouted with laughter at the difficulty he had to run in them. My boys had succeeded tolerably well with their new ware, though still imperfect; but as a first essay performed by tyro-artists, I was satisfied with their productions.

We had also been engaged in the construction of our fountain, which afforded a perpetual source of pleasure to my wife, and indeed to all of us. In the upper part of the stream we built with stakes and stones a kind of dam, that raised the water sufficiently to convey it into the palm-tree troughs; and afterwards, by means of a gentle slope, to glide on contiguous to our habitation, where it fell into the tortoise-shell bason, which we had elevated on stones to a certain height for our convenience; and it was so contrived that the redundant water passed off through a cane pipe fitted to it. I placed two sticks athwart each other for the gourds, that served as pails, to rest on; and we thus produced, close to our abode, an agreeable fountain, delighting with its rill, and supplying us with a pure crystal fluid, and such as we frequently could not get when we drew our water from the bed of the river, which was often blended with the leaves and earth fallen into it, or rendered turbid by our water-fowls. The only inconvenience was, that the water flowing in this open state through narrow channels in a slender stream, was heated, and not refreshing when it reached us. I resolved to obviate this inconvenience at my future leisure, by employing, instead of the uncovered conduits, large bamboo-canes, fixed deep enough in the ground to keep the water cool. In waiting the execution of this design, we felt pleasure in the new acquisition; and Fritz, who had suggested the notion, received his tribute of praise from all.

# XXX

# THE WILD ASS;—DIFFICULTY IN BREAKING IT;—THE HEATH-FOWL'S NEST

W E WERE SCARCELY UP ONE MORNING, AND HAD GOT TO WORK in putting the last hand to our winding stair-case, when we heard at a distance two strange peculiar kind of voices, that resembled the howlings of wild beasts, mixed with hissings and sounds of some creature at its last gasp, which I was at a loss to explain, and I was not without uneasiness; our dogs too pricked up their ears, and seemed to whet their teeth for a sanguinary combat with a dangerous enemy.

From their looks we judged it prudent to put ourselves in a state of defence; we loaded our guns and pistols, placed them together within our castle in the tree, and prepared to repel vigour-ously any hostile attack from that quarter. The howlings having ceased an instant, I descended from our citadel, well armed, and put on our two faithful guardians their spiked collars and side-guards: I assembled our cattle about the tree to have them in sight, and I reascended to look around for the enemy's approach. Jack wished they might be lions—I should like, said he, to have a near view of the king of beasts, and should not be in the least afraid of him, for lions are deemed generous!

I do not advise you, answered I, to trust the report, though you may not fear a lion when elevated as you are forty feet above them: but these are not lions; their roarings are more lengthened, majestic, and fill all other animals that hear them with fear and trembling; I do not observe this effect amongst ours.

*Fritz.*—I rather surmise they are a troop of jackalls, disposed to avenge the death of their comrades.

*Ernest.*—It is not the jackall's cry: I am more inclined to fear they are hyenas, whose howling must, one would think, be as frightful as their looks.

*Francis.*—Now I think they are savages come to eat their prisoners on our island; I wish we could save them, and get a good *Man Friday* as Robinson Crusoe did.

Whatever it is, children, let us not yield to fear or imagination; we are in safety here . . .

At this very instant the howlings were renewed and quite close to us. Fritz got as near the spot as he could, listened attentively and with eager looks, then threw down his gun and burst into a loud laughter, exclaiming: Father, it is our ass—the deserter comes back to us, chanting the hymn of return: listen! do you not hear his melodious brayings in all the varieties of the gamut?—We lent an ear; our doubts ceased, and we felt somewhat mortified at our premature alarms and preparations of defence against such an ignoble foe.

I, on my part, however, was soon reconciled to the offence against our pride, since it also insured our safety: and a fresh roar, in sounds unquestionable, raised loud peals of laughter among us; and then followed the usual train of jests and mutual banter at the alarm we had one and all betrayed. Shortly after, we had the satisfaction of seeing among the trees our old friend Grizzle, moving towards us leisurely, and stopping now and then to browse; but to our great joy we perceived in his train one of the same species of very superior beauty, and when it was nearer I knew it to be a fine onagra or wild ass, which I conceived a strong desire to possess, though at the same time aware of the extreme difficulty there would be in taming and rendering him subject to the use of man. Some writers who have described it under the name of the Œigitai, (or long-eared horse,) given it by the Tartars, affirm that the taming it has been ever found absolutely impracticable; but my mind furnished an idea on the subject which I was resolved to act on, if I got possession of the handsome creature. Without delay I descended the ladder with Fritz, desiring his brothers to keep still; and I consulted my privy counsellor on the means of surprising and taking the stranger captive. I got ready, as soon as possible, a long cord with a running knot, one end of which I tied fast to the root of a tree; the noose was kept open with a little stick slightly fixed in the opening so as to fall of itself on the cord being thrown round the neck of the animal, whose efforts to escape would draw the knot closer. I also prepared a piece of bamboo about two feet long, which I split at the bottom, and tied fast at top, to serve as nippers. Fritz attentively examined my contrivance, without seeing the use of it. Prompted by the impatience of youth, he took the ball-sling and proposed aiming at the wild ass with it, which he said was the shortest way of proceeding. I declined adopting this Patagonian method, fearing the attempt might fail, and the beautiful creature avail itself of its natural velocity to evade us beyond recovery: I therefore told him my project of catching it in the noose, which I gave him to manage, as being nimbler, and more expert than myself. The two asses drew nearer and nearer to us. Fritz, holding in his hand the open noose, moved softly on from behind the tree where we were concealed, and advanced as far as the length of the rope allowed him: the onagra was extremely startled on perceiving a human figure; it sprung some paces backward, then stopped as if to examine the unknown form; but as Fritz now remained quite still, the animal resumed its composure and continued to browse. Soon after he approached the old ass, hoping that the confidence that would be shown by it, would raise a similar feeling in the stranger: he held out a handful of oats mixed with salt; our ass instantly ran up to take its favourite food, and greedily devoured it; this was quickly perceived by the other. It drew near, raised its head, breathed strongly and came up so close, that Fritz, seizing the opportunity, succeeded in throwing the rope round its neck; but the motion and stroke so affrighted the beast that it instantly sprang off; it was soon checked by the cord, which in compressing the neck almost stopped its breath: it could go no further, and after many exhausting efforts, it sunk panting for breath upon the ground. I hastened to loosen the cord and prevent its being strangled. I then quickly threw our ass's halter over its head; I fixed the nose in my split cane, which I secured at the bottom with packthread. Thus I succeeded in subduing the first alarm of this wild animal, as farriers shoe a horse for the first time. I wholly removed the noose that seemed to bring the creature into a dangerous situation; I fastened the halter with two long ropes to two roots near us, on the right and left, and let the animal recover itself, noticing its actions, and devising the best way to tame it in the completest manner.

The rest of my family had by this time come down from the tree and beheld the fine creature with admiration, its graceful shape and well-turned limbs, which placed it so much above the ass, and nearly raised it to the noble structure of the horse! In a few moments the onagra got up again, struck furiously with its foot, and seemed resolved to free itself from all bonds: but the pain of its nose, which was grasped and violently squeezed in the bamboo, forced it to lie down again. My eldest son and I now gently undid the cords, and half led, half dragged it between two roots closely connected, to which we fastened it afresh so as to give the least scope for motion, and thus render its escape impracticable, whilst it enabled us to approach securely and examine the valuable capture we had made. We also guarded against master Grizzle playing truant again, and tied him fast with a new halter, confining its fore legs with a rope. I then fastened it and the wild ass side by side, and put before both plenty of good provender to solace their impatience of captivity.

We had now the additional occupation of training the onagra for our service or our pleasure as might turn out to be most practicable: my boys exulted in the idea of riding it, and we repeatedly congratulated each other on the good fortune which had thus resulted from the flight of our ass. Yet I did not conceal that we should have many difficulties to encounter in taming it, though it seemed very young and not even to have reached its full growth. But I was inclined to think proper means had not been hitherto adopted, and that the hunters, almost as savage as the animals themselves, had not employed sufficient art and patience, being probably unconscious of the advantages of either. I therefore determined to resort to all possible measures: I let the nippers remain on its nose, which appeared to distress him greatly, though we could plainly perceive their good effect in subduing the creature, for without them no one could have ventured to approach him; I took them off however at times when I gave it food, to render eating easier, and I began, as with the buffalo, by placing a bundle of sail-cloth on its back to inure it to carry. When accustomed to the load, I strove to render the beast still by degrees more docile, by hunger and thirst; and I observed with pleasure that when it had fasted a little and I supplied it with food, its look and actions were less wild. I also compelled the animal to keep erect on its four legs, by drawing the cords closer that fastened it to the roots, in order to subdue gradually by fatigue its natural ferocity. The children came in turns to play with it and scratch its ears gently, which were remarkably tender; and it was on these I resolved to make my last trial if all other endeavours failed. For a long time we despaired of success; the onagra made furious starts and leaps when any of us went near it, kicked with its hind feet, and even attempted to bite those who touched it. This obliged me to have recourse to a muzzle, which I managed with rushes, and put on when was not feeding. To avoid being struck by its hind feet, I partially confined them by fastening them to the fore feet with cords, which however I left moderately loose, that we might not encroach too much upon the motion necessary for its health. It was at length familiarized to this discipline, and was no longer in a rage when we approached, but grew less impatient daily, and bore to be handled and stroked.

At last we ventured to free it by degrees from its restraints, and to ride it as we had done with the buffalo. Still keeping the fore feet tied; but notwithstanding this precaution and every preceding means, it proved as fierce and unruly as ever for the moment. The monkey, who was first put on its back, held on pretty well by clinging to its mane, from which it was suspended as often as the onagra furiously reared and plunged; it was therefore for the present impracticable for either of my sons to get upon it. The perverse beast baffled all our efforts, and the perilous task of breaking it was still to be persevered in with terror and apprehension. In the stable it seemed tolerably quiet and gentle; but the moment it was in any degree unshackled, it became wholly ferocious and unmanageable.

I was at length reduced to my last expedient, but not without much regret, as I resolved, if it did not answer, to restore the animal to full liberty. I tried to mount the onagra, and just as in the act of rearing up violently to prevent me, I seized with my teeth one of the long ears of the enraged creature, and bit it till it bled; instantly it stood almost erect on its hind feet, motionless, and as stiff as a stake; it soon lowered itself by degrees, while I still held its ear between my teeth. Fritz seized the moment and sprung on its back; Jack, with the help of his mother, did the same, holding by his brother, who, on his part, clung to the girth. When both assured me they were firmly seated, I let go the ear: the onagra made a few springs less violent than the former, and checked by the cords on its feet, it gradually submitted, began to trot up and down more quietly, and ultimately grew so tractable that riding it became one of our chief pleasures. My lads were soon expert horsemen; and their horse, though rather long-eared, was very handsome and well broken in. Thus patience on our parts conquered a serious difficulty, and gained for us a proud advantage.

In the name of goodness, said my wife to me one evening, after one of our first essays, where did you learn this strange notion of biting the animal's ear? I learned it, replied I, from a horse-breaker whom I fell in with by chance: he had lived long in America and carried on the skin-trade with the savages, to whom he took in exchange various European goods. He employed in these journeys, half-tamed horses of the southern provinces of that country, which are caught in snares or with nooses. They are at first unruly and resist burthens, but as soon as the hunter bites one of their ears they become mild and submissive; and they become so docile, that any thing may be done with them. The journey is continued through forests and over heaths to the dwellings of the savages; skins are given in barter for the goods brought them, with which the horses are re-loaded. They set out again on their return, and are directed by the compass and stars to the European settlements, where they profitably dispose of their skins and horses.—Till now I thought this singular mode of taming a wild beast fabulous, but the young onagra convinces me of the truth of the accounts I heard. In a few weeks the onagra was so effectually tamed, that we all could mount it without fear: I still however kept his two fore legs confined together with the cord, to moderate the extreme swiftness of its running. In the room of a bit, I contrived a curb, and with this and a good bite applied, as wanted, to the ear, it went to right or left at the will of the rider. Now and then I mounted it myself, and not without an emotion of pride at my success in subduing an animal that had been considered by travellers and naturalists as absolutely beyond the power of man to tame. But how superior was my gratification in seeing Fritz spring at any time on the creature's back and do what he pleased with it, drive along our avenue like lightning, in depicting to my fond imagination that even on a desert unknown island, I could qualify my dear children to re-enter society and become in such respects its ornament! I in beholding their physical strength and native graces unfold themselves, and these keeping pace with the improvement of their intelligence and their judgement; and in anticipating that, buried as they were in a distant retreat, far from the tumult of the world, and all that excites the passions, their sentiments would be formed in exact conformity to the paternal feelings of my heart! I had not lost hope that we should one day return to Europe in some vessel chance might throw on our coast, or even with the aid of our pinnace; but I felt at the same time, and my wife still more, that we should not leave the island without a lively regret, and I determined to pursue my arrangements as if we were to close existence on a spot where all around us prospered.

During the training of our horse, which we named *Lightfoot*, a triple brood of our hens had given us a crowd of little feathered beings; forty of these, at least, were chirping and hopping about us, to the great satisfaction of my wife, whose zealous care of them sometimes made me smile. Most women's hearts are so imbued with maternal love as to excite in them a fondness for whatever bears a similitude to infancy. Thus, my admirable partner, far from complaining of the trouble such a number of young chickens gave her, took delight in it, and was constantly admiring them; yet her care and admiration did not prevent her appropriating a part of them to the table, and sending the remainder in small colonies to feed and breed in the desert, where we could find them as they were wanted for our use.

Here, she said, are animals of real utility in a family, far beyond your monkeys, jackalls, and eagles, that do nothing but eat, and are unfit to be eaten. The buffalo was not found fault with, because it brought her the provisions, nor the onagra, on which she liked to see her sons gallop. From the time we had trained it to this, the rough-paced buffalo that shook us to pieces was no longer used for riding, but kept entirely for drawing.

This increase of our poultry reminded us of the necessity of an undertaking we had long thought of, and was not in prudence to be deferred any longer; this was the building between the roots of our great tree, covered sheds for all our bipeds and quadrupeds. The rainy season, which is the winter of these countries, was drawing near, and to avoid losing most of our stock it was requisite to shelter it.

We began by forming a kind of roof above the arched roots of our tree, and employed bamboo canes for the purpose; the longest and strongest supported the roofing in the place of columns, the smaller more closely united and composed the roof itself. I filled up the interstices with moss and clay, and I spread over the whole a thick coat of tar. By these means I formed a compact and solid covering, capable of bearing pressure. I then made a railing round it, which gave the appearance of a pretty balcony, under which, between the roots, were various stalls sheltered from rain and sun, that could be easily shut and separated from each other by means of planks nailed upon the roots; part of them were calculated to serve as a stable and yard, part as an eating-room, a store-room, etc., and as a hayloft to keep our hay and provisions dry in.

This work was soon completed; but afterwards it was necessary to fill these places with stores of every kind for our supply throughout the wet season. In this task we engaged diligently, and went daily here and there with our cart to collect every thing useful, and that might give us employment whilst the weather confined us to the house.

One evening on our return from digging up potatoes, as our cart loaded with bags, drawn by the buffalo, ass and cow, was gently rolling along, seeing still a vacant place in the vehicle, I advised my wife to go home with the two youngest boys whilst I went round by the wood of oaks with Ernest and Fritz to gather as many sweet acorns as we could find room for. We had still some empty sacks. Ernest was accompanied by his monkey, who seldom left him; and Fritz, horseman like, was on his dear onagra, which he had appropriated to himself, inasmuch as he had helped to take and tame it, and indeed because he knew how to manage it better than his brothers. Ernest was too lazy, and preferred walking at ease with the monkey on his shoulder, and the more so because it spared him the trouble of gathering fruit. Jack was too giddy to be trusted alone on the horse, though he often got up behind his brother, and Francis still too little to attempt mounting it. Notwithstanding the onagra was so well broken in for riding, it continued to be very mettlesome and restive in the shafts, to which we could not inure it; but occasionally it submitted to our putting a loaded sack or two on its back; but we could seldom prevail even in this, without Fritz being seated in front; he would then take them to the house, and thus was rendered of some general use.

When we reached the oaks Lightfoot was tied to a bush, and we set actively to work to gather the acorns that had dropped from the trees. While all were busily employed, the monkey quitted its master's shoulder and skipped unperceived into an adjoining bush.

Johann David Wyss

It had been there some time when we heard on that side the loud cries of birds and flapping of wings, and this assured us a sharp conflict was going on betwixt master Knips and the inhabitants of the bushes. I dispatched Ernest to reconnoitre. He went stoutly towards the place, and in an instant we heard him exclaim, Come quickly, father! a fine heath-fowl's nest full of eggs; Mr. Knips, as usual, wished to make a meal of them; the hen and he are fighting for it: come quick, Fritz, and take her; I am holding greedy-chops as well as I can.

Fritz ran up directly, and in a few moments brought out alive the male and female heath-fowl, both very beautiful; the cock finely collar'd, similar to one he had killed on a former occasion, not without much regret on my part. I was rejoiced at this discovery, and helped my son to prevent their escape, by tying their wings and feet, and holding them while he returned to the bush for the eggs. And now Ernest came forward driving the monkey before him, and carrying his hat with the utmost care: he had stuck his girdle full of narrow sharp-pointed leaves, in shape like a knife-blade, which reminded me of the production named sword-grass; but I did not pay much attention, as I was too busily engaged in our egg-hunt, and considered his decoration as childishness. On coming up to me he uncovered his hat, and gave it me in a transport of joy, crying out. Here, dear father, here are some heath-fowl's eggs; I found them in a nest so well concealed under these long leaves that I should not have observed them had not the hen, in defending herself against the monkey, scattered them about. I am going to take them home, they will please my mother; and these leaves will so amuse Francis, they are like swords, and will be the very thing he will like for a play-thing. I applauded

Ernest's attention to both, and I encouraged him and Fritz to be thus ever considerate for the absent, so as to prove they could never be forgotten. The kindnesses conferred on those who are separated from us have in themselves more merit, and are more valued, than those which are personally received. It was now time to think of moving homeward: my two sons filled the bags with acorns and put them on Lightfoot; Fritz mounted, Ernest carried the eggs, I took charge of the hen, and we proceeded to Falcon's Stream followed by our train-waggon. Our good cattle were in such complete subjection that it was only necessary to speak to them. I remarked Ernest often applying his ear to the hat which held the eggs, as if he thought the little ones were near coming forth; I listened also, and observed some shells already broken and the young protruding; we were overjoyed at our good luck, and Fritz could not refrain from trotting on briskly to bear the tidings to his dear mother: but he went rather faster than he intended on setting out: he had taken a handful of the pointed leaves with him, which he whisked before the ears and eyes of the onagra, till the animal was frightened, lost all restraint, and darted forward with him like a shot, hurrying away bags and rider at such a rate that we soon lost sight of them. Anxious for his safety, we followed as fast as possible, though out of sight of him all the way; but on our arrival at Falcon's Stream we had the satisfaction of finding him there in perfect safety. His mother, indeed, had been some-what alarmed in seeing him dash in like a thunderbolt, but firmly seated betwixt the bags on master Lightfoot, who well deserved his name on this occasion, and who stopped short with wonder-ful precision at his stable door. Our first care was to examine the eggs: the female bird was too frightened and wild to sit upon them: fortunately we had a hen that was hatching; her eggs were immediately removed, and the new ones put in their place: the female heath-fowl was put into the parrot's cage, and hung up in the room to accustom it to our society. In less than three days all the chickens were hatched, they kept close to their foster-mother, and ate greedily a mixture of sweet acorns bruised in milk, such as we gave our tame poultry: as they grew up I plucked out the large feathers of their wings, lest they should naturally take flight; but they and their real parent gradually became so domesticated, that they daily accompanied our feathered stock in search of food, and regularly came back at night to the roost I had prepared for them, and in which this little new colony of feathered beings seemed to delight.

# XXXI

# FLAX, AND THE RAINY SEASON

F RANCIS FOR A SHORT TIME WAS HIGHLY AMUSED WITH HIS sword-leaves, and then like all children, who are soon tired of their toys, he grew weary of them, and they were thrown aside. Fritz picked up some of them that were quite soft and withered; he held up one which was pliable as a rib and in the hand: My little fellow, said he to his brother, you can make whips of your sword-grass, take up the leaves and keep them for this purpose, they will be of use in driving your goats and sheep. It had been lately decided that it should be the business of Francis to lead these to pasture.

Well then, help me to make them, said the child. They sat down together. Francis divided the leaves into long narrow slips, and Fritz ingeniously platted them into whip-cords. As they were working, I saw with pleasure the flexibility and strength of the bands; I examined them more closely, and found they were composed of long fibres or filaments; and this discovery led me to surmise that this supposed sword-grass might be a very different thing, and not improbably the flax-plant of New Zealand, called by naturalists *Chlomidia*, and by others *Phormion*. This was a valuable discovery in our situation: I knew how much my wife wished for the production, and that it was the article she felt most the want of; I therefore hastened to communicate the intelligence to her, upon hearing which she expressed the liveliest joy: This, said she, is the most useful thing you have found; I entreat you, lose not a moment in searching for more of these leaves, and bring me the most you can of them; I will make you stockings, shirts, clothes, thread, ropes. . . . In short, give me flax, looms, and frames, and I shall be at no loss in the employment of it. I could not help smiling at the scope she gave to her imagination, on the bare mention of flax, though so much was to be done between the gathering the leaves and having the cloth she was already sewing in idea. Fritz whispered a word in Jack's ear; both went to the stable, and without asking my leave, one mounted Lightfoot, the other the buffalo, and galloped off towards the wood so fast that I had no time to call them back; they were already out of sight: their eagerness to oblige their mother in this instance pleaded their forgiveness, and I suffered them to go on without following them purposing to proceed and bring them back if they did not soon return.

In waiting for them I conversed with my wife, who pointed out to me with all the animation and spirit of useful enterprise so natural to her character, the various machinery I must contrive for spinning and weaving her flax for the manufactory of cloths, with which she said she should be able to equip us from head to foot; in speaking of which, her eyes sparkled with the love of doing good, the purest kind of joy, and I promised her all she desired of me.

In a quarter of an hour our deserters came back on a full trot, and I was pleased to see them again; like true hussars, they had foraged the woods, and heavily loaded their cattle with the precious plant, which they threw at their mother's feet with joyful shouts. We could not blame their abrupt departure. Jack made us laugh in recounting with his accustomed vivacity and drollery at what a rate he had trotted his buffalo to keep up with Lightfoot, and how his great horned horse had thrown him by a side leap; yet that notwithstanding these, he and his buffalo, as in duty and allegiance bound, were, as ever, at the entire command of their acknowledged queen. Well, said I, you shall then all assist her with consummate diligence in preparations for the work she is about to engage in, and previously in steeping the flax.

*Fritz.*—How is flax prepared, father, and what is meant by steeping it?

*Father.*—Steeping flax, or hemp, is exposing it in the open air, by spreading it on the ground to receive the rain, the wind, and the dew, in order in a certain degree to liquefy the plant; by this means the ligneous or cortical parts of the flax are separated with more ease from the fibrous; a kind of vegetable glue that binds them is dissolved, and it can then be perfectly cleaned with great facility, and the parts selected which are fit for spinning.

*Fritz.*—But may not the natural texture of this part be destroyed by exposing it so long to wet?

*Father.*—That certainly may happen when the process is managed injudiciously, and the flax not duly turned; the risk, however, is not great, the fibrous part has a peculiar tenacity, which enables it to resist longer the action of humidity; flax may be even steeped altogether in water without injury. Many think this the best and quickest method, and I am of their opinion.

My wife coincided with me, especially in the sultry climate we inhabited: she therefore proposed to soak the flax in Flamingo Marsh, and to begin by making up the leaves in bundles, as they do hemp in Europe. We agreed to her proposal, and joined in this previous and necessary preparation of the flax during the rest of the day.

Next morning the ass was put to the small light car, loaded with bundles of leaves; Francis and the monkey sat on them, and the remainder of the family gaily followed with shovels and pickaxes. We stopped at the marsh, divided our large bundles into smaller, which we placed in the water, pressing them down with stones and leaving them in this state till our sovereign should direct us to remove and set them in the sun to dry, and thus render the stems soft and easy to peel. In the course of this work we noticed with admiration the instinct of the flamingoes in building their cone-shaped nests above the level of the marsh, each nest having a recess in the upper part, in which the eggs are securely deposited, while the contrivance enables the female to sit with her legs in the water: the nest is of clay closely cemented, so as to resist all danger from the element till the young can swim.

A fortnight after, my wife told us the flax was sufficiently steeped. We then took it out of the water, and spread it on the grass in the sun, where it dried so well and rapidly that we were able to load it on our cart the same evening, and carry it to Falcon's Stream, where it was put by till we had time to attend further to it, and make beetles, wheels, reels, carding-combs, etc., as required by our expert and skilful flax-manufacturer. It was thought best to reserve this task for the rainy season, and to get ready what would be then necessary during our confinement within doors. Uninformed as we were as to the duration of this season, it was highly important to lay in a competent stock of provisions for ourselves and for all the animals. Occasional slight showers, the harbingers of winter, had already come on; the temperature, which hitherto had been warm and serene, became gloomy and variable; the sky was often darkened with clouds, the stormy winds were heard, and warned us to avail ourselves of the favourable moment to collect every thing that would be wanted.

Our first care was to dig up a full supply of potatoes and yams for bread, with plenty of cocoa-nuts, and some bags of sweet acorns. It occurred to us while digging, that the ground being thus opened and manured with the leaves of plants, we might sow in it to advantage the remainder of our European corn. Notwithstanding all the delicacies this stranger land afforded us, the force of habit still caused us to long for the bread we had been fed with from childhood: we had not yet laid ourselves out for regular tillage, and I was inclined to attempt the construction of a plough of some sort as soon as we had a sufficient stock of corn for sowing. For this time, therefore, we committed it to the earth with little preparation: the season, however, was proper for sowing and planting, as the ensuing rain would moisten and swell the embryo grain, which otherwise would perish in an arid burning soil. We accordingly expedited the planting of the various palm trees we had discovered in our excursions, at Tent-House, carefully selecting the smallest and the youngest. In the environs we formed a large handsome plantation of sugar-canes, so as to have hereafter every thing useful and agreeable around us, and thus be dispensed from the usual toil and loss of time in procuring them.

These different occupations kept us several weeks in unremitted activity of mind and body; our cart was incessantly in motion, conveying home our winter stock; time was so precious that we could not even make regular meals, and limited ourselves to bread, cheese, and fruits, in order to shorten them, to return quickly to our work, and dispatch it before the bad season should set in.

Unfortunately, the weather changed sooner than we had expected, and than, with all our care, we could be prepared for: before we had completed our winter establishment, the rain fell in such heavy torrents that little Francis, trembling, asked me whether father Noah's deluge was coming on again; and I could not myself refrain from painful apprehension in surmising how we should resist such a body of water, that seemed to change the whole face of the country into a perfect lake.

The first thing to be done, and which gave us all sensations of deep concern, was to remove without delay our aerial abode, and to fix our residence at the bottom of the tree, between the roots and under the tarred roof I had erected; for it was no longer possible to remain above, on account of the furious winds that threatened to bear us away, and deluged our beds with rain through the large opening in front, our only protection here being a piece of sail-cloth, which was soon dripping wet and rent to pieces. In this condition we were forced to take down our hammocks, mattresses, and every article that could be injured by the rain; and most fortunate did we deem ourselves in having made the winding stairs, which sheltered us during the operation of the removal. The stairs served afterwards for a kind of lumber-room; we kept all in it we could dispense with, and most of our culinary vessels, which my wife fetched as she happened to want them. Our little sheds between the roots, constructed for the poultry and the cattle, could scarcely contain us all; and the first days we passed in this manner were painfully embarrassing, crowded all together, and hardly able to move in these almost dark recesses, which the foetid smell from the close-adjoining animals rendered almost insupportable: in addition, we were half stifled with smoke whenever we kindled a fire, and drenched with rain when we opened the doors. For the first time, since our disaster, we sighed for the comfortable houses of our dear country:—but what was to be done! we were not there, and losing our courage and our temper would, only increase the evil. I strove to raise the spirits of my companions, and obviate some of the inconveniences. The now doubly-precious winding stair was, as I have said, every way useful to us; the upper part of it was filled with numerous articles that gave us room below; and as it was lighted and sheltered by windows, my wife often worked there, seated on a stair, with her little Francis at her feet. We confined our live-stock to a smaller number, and gave them a freer current of air, dismissing from the stalls those animals that from their properties, and being natives of the country, would be at no loss in providing for themselves. That we might not lose them altogether, we tied bells round their necks; Fritz, and I sought and drove them in every evening that they did not spontaneously return. We generally got wet to the skin and chilled with cold, during the employment, which induced my wife to contrive for us a kind of clothing more suitable to the occasion; she took two seamen's shirts from the chest we had recovered from the wreck; and then, with some pieces of old coats, she made us a kind of cloth hoods joined together at the back, and well formed for covering the head entirely: we melted some elastic gum, which we spread over the shirts and hoods; and the articles thus prepared answered every purpose of waterproof overalls, that were of essential use and comfort to us. Our young rogues were ready with their derision the first time they saw us in them, but afterwards they would have been rejoiced to have had the same: this, however, the reduced state of our gum did not allow, and we contented ourselves with wearing them in turn, when compelled to work in the rain, from the bad effects of which they effectually preserved us.

As to the smoke, our only remedy was to open the door when we made a fire; and we did without as much as we could, living on milk and cheese, and never making a fire but to bake our cakes: we then availed ourselves of the opportunity to boil a quantity of potatoes and salt meat enough to last us a number of days. Our dry wood was also nearly expended, and we thanked Heaven the weather was not very cold; for had this been the case our other trials would have much increased. A more serious concern was our not having provided sufficient hay and leaves for our European cattle, which we necessarily kept housed to avoid losing them; the cow, the ass, the sheep, and the goats, the two last of which were increased in number, required a large quantity of provender, so that we were ere long forced to give them our potatoes and sweet acorns, which by the by they found very palatable, and we remarked that they imparted a delicate flavour to their milk;—the cow, the goats, and even the sheep, amply supplied us with that precious article: milking, cleaning the animals and preparing their food, occupied us most of the morning, after which we were usually employed in making flour of the manioc root, with which we filled the large gourds, which were previously placed in rows. The gloom of the atmosphere and our low windowless habitation sensibly abridged our daylight; fortunately, we had laid in a huge store of candles, and felt no want of that article: when darkness obliged us to light up, we got round the table, when a large taper fixed on a gourd gave us an excellent light, which enabled my wife to pursue her occupation with the needle, while I, on my part, was forming a journal and recording what the reader has perused of the narrative of our shipwreck and residence in this island, assisted from time to time by my sons and their admirable mother, who did not cease to remind me of various incidents belonging to the story. To Ernest, who wrote a fine hand, was intrusted the care of writing off my pages in a clear legible character; Fritz and Jack amused themselves by drawing from memory the plants and animals which had most struck their observation; while one and all contributed to teach little Francis to read and write: we concluded the day with a devotional reading in the Holy Bible, performed by each in turn, and we then retired to rest, happy in ourselves, and in the innocent and peaceful course of our existence. Our kind and faithful steward often surprised us agreeably on our return from looking after the cattle, by lighting up a faggot of dried bamboo, and quickly roasting by the clear and fervent heat it produced, a chicken, pigeon, duck, or penguin from our poultry-yard, or some of the thrushes we had preserved, in butter, which were excellent, and welcomed as a treat to reward extraordinary toil. Every four or five days the kind creature made us new fresh butter in the gourd-churn; and this with some deliciously fragrant honey spread on our manioc cakes, formed a collation that would have raised the envy of European epicures. These unexpected regales represented to our grateful hearts so many little festivals, the generous intention of which made us forget our bad accommodations and confinement.

The fragments of our meals belonged in right to our domestic animals, as part of the family. We had now four dogs, the young jackall, the eagle, and the monkey, to feed; they relied with just confidence on the kindness of their respective masters, who certainly would have deprived themselves to supply the wants of their helpless dependents. Francis had taken under his mighty protection the two little bull-dogs; my wife Ponto, and I the brave Turk:—thus each had his attendant, of which he took care, and no one was dispensed from the offices of tenderness and vigilance. If the buffalo, the onagra, and pig had not found sustenance abroad, they must have been killed or starved, and that would have given us much pain. In the course of these discomforts it was unanimously resolved on, that we would not pass another rainy season exposed to the same evils; even my beloved consort, who felt such a predilection for the abode at Falcon's Stream, was frequently a little ruffled and out of temper with our inconvenient situation, and insisted more than any of us on the propriety of building elsewhere a more spacious winter residence: she wished, however, to return to our castle in the tree every summer, and we all joined with her in that desire. The choice of a fresh abode now engrossed our attention, and Fritz in the midst of consultation came forward triumphantly with a book he had found in the bottom of our clothes' chest. Here, said he, is our best counsellor and model, *Robinson Crusoe*; since Heaven has destined us to a similar fate, whom better can we consult? as far as I remember, he cut himself an habitation out of the solid rock: let us see how he proceeded; we will do the same and with greater ease, for he was alone; we are six in number, and four of us able to work. Well spoken, son, said I: this activity and courage give me pleasure; let us then strive to be as ingenious as Robinson Crusoe.

And why not? observed Jack—Have we not an island, rocks, and tools from abroad as good as he had, and, as brother Fritz says, more hands to use them?

We assembled, and read the famous history with an ardent interest; it seemed though so familiar, quite new to us: we entered earnestly into every detail and derived considerable information from it; and never failed to feel lively gratitude towards God who had rescued us all together, and not permitted one only of us to be cast a solitary being on the island. The occurrence of this thought produced an overwhelming sense of affection among us, and we could not refrain from throwing ourselves into each other's arms, embracing repeatedly, and the pathetic scene ended in mutual congratulations.

Francis repeated his wish to have a Man Friday; Fritz thought it better to be without such a companion, and to have no savages to contend with. Jack was for the savages, warfare and encounters. The final result of our deliberations was to go and survey the rocks round Tent-House, and to examine whether any of them could be excavated for our purpose.

Our last job for the winter, undertaken at my wife's solicitation, was a beetle for her flax and some carding-combs. I filed large nails till they were even, round, and pointed; I fixed them at equal distances in a sheet of tin, and raised the sides of it like a box;

I then poured melted lead between the nails and the sides, to give firmness to their points, which came out four inches. I nailed this tin on a board, and the machine was fit for work. My wife was impatient to use it; and the drying, peeling, and spinning her flax, became from this time a source of inexhaustible delight.

# XXXII

# SPRING;—SPINNING;—SALT MINE

I CAN HARDLY DESCRIBE OUR JOY WHEN, AFTER MANY TEDIOUS and gloomy weeks of rain, the sky began to brighten, the sun to dart its benign rays on the humid earth, the winds to be lulled, and the state of the air became mild and serene. We issued from our dreary hovels with joyful shouts, and walked round our habitation breathing the enlivening balmy ether, while our eyes were regaled with the beauteous verdure beginning to shoot forth on every side. Reviving nature opened her arms, every creature seemed reanimated, and we felt the genial influence of that glorious luminary which had been so long concealed from our sight, now returned like a friend who has been absent, to bring us back blessings and delight. We rapidly forgot in new sensations the embarrassments and weary hours of the wet season, and with jocund, hopeful hearts, looked forward to the toils of summer as enviable amusements.

The vegetation of our plantation of trees was rapidly advancing; the seed we had thrown into the ground was sprouting in slender blades that waved luxuriantly; a pleasing tender foliage adorned the trees; the earth was enamelled with an infinite variety of flowers, whose agreeable tints diversified the verdure of the meadows. Odorous exhalations were diffused through the atmosphere; the song of birds was heard around; they were seen between the leaves joyfully fluttering from branch to branch; their various forms and brilliant plumage heightened this delightful picture of the most beautiful spring, and we were at once struck with wonder and penetrated with gratitude towards the Creator of so many beauties. Under these impressions we celebrated the ensuing Sunday in the open air, and with stronger emotions of piety than we had hitherto felt on the fertile shores upon which we had been so miraculously saved and fostered. The blessings which surrounded us were ample compensation for some uneasy moments which had occasionally intervened, and our hearts, filled with fresh zeal, were resolved to be resigned, if it should be the will of God, to pass the residue of our days in this solitude with serenity of soul and every due exertion. The force of paternal feelings, no doubt, made me sometimes form other wishes for my children; but these I buried in my own breast, for fear of disturbing their tranquillity: but if I secretly indulged a desire for some event that might prolong and even increase their happiness, I nevertheless wholly submitted all to the Divine will, the manifestation of which I awaited in becoming thankfulness and patience.

Our summer occupations commenced by arranging and thoroughly cleaning Falcon's Nest, the order and neatness of which the rain and dead leaves blown by the wind had disturbed: in other respects, however, it was not injured, and in a few days we rendered it completely fit for our reception; the stairs were cleared, the rooms between the roots re-occupied, and we were left with leisure to proceed to other employments. My wife lost not a moment in resuming the process of her flax concern. Our sons hastened to lead the cattle to the fresh pastures, already dried by the sun; whilst it was my task to carry the bundles of flax into the open air, where by heaping stones together I contrived an oven sufficiently commodious to dry it well. The same evening we all set to work to peel, and afterwards to beat it and strip off the bark, and lastly to comb it with my carding machine, which fully answered the purpose. I took this somewhat laborious task on myself, and drew out such distaffs full of long soft flax ready for spinning, that my enraptured wife ran to embrace me, to express her heartfelt acknowledgement, requesting me to make her a wheel without delay, that she might enter upon her favourite work.

At an earlier period of my life I had practised turnery for my amusement; now, however, I was unfortunately destitute of the requisite utensils; but as I had not forgotten the arrangement and component parts of a spinning-wheel and reel, I by repeated endeavours found means to accomplish those two machines to her satisfaction; and she fell so eagerly to spinning, as to allow herself no leisure even for a walk, and scarcely time to dress our dinners: nothing so much delighted her as to be left with her little boy, whom she employed to reel as fast as she could spin, and sometimes the other three were also engaged in turns at the wheel, to forward her business whilst she was occupied in culinary offices; but not one of them was found so tractable as the cool-tempered quiet Ernest, who preferred this to more laborious exertions, though such was our want of linen and clothes, that we ought all readily and even eagerly to have joined in procuring them;

but our excursions, and the necessary liberty they involved, were more agreeable to us than this female occupation. Our first visit was to Tent-House, as we were anxious to ascertain the ravages of winter there, and we found them much more considerable than at Falcon's Stream, and even dreadful: the tempest and rain had beaten down the tent, carried away a part of the sail-cloth, and made such havoc amongst our provisions, that by far the largest portion of them was spotted with mildew, and the remainder could be only saved by drying them instantly. Luckily, our handsome pinnace had been for the most part spared; it was still at anchor, ready to serve us in case of need; but our tub-boat was in too shattered a state to be of any further service.

In looking over the stores we were grieved to find the gunpowder most damaged, of which I had left three barrels in the tent instead of placing them in a more sheltered situation in the cavity of the rock. The contents of two were rendered wholly useless, I thought myself fortunate on finding the remaining one in tolerable condition, and derived from this great and irreparable loss a cogent motive to fix upon winter quarters where our stores and wealth would not be exposed to such cruel dilapidations.

Notwithstanding the gigantic plan suggested by the enterprising characters of Fritz and Jack, I had little hope of being able to effect the excavation of a dwelling in the side of the rock. Robinson Crusoe is supposed to have found a spacious cavern that merely required arrangement; no such cavity was apparent in our rock, which bore the aspect of primitive existence, and was of extreme hardness; so that with our limited powers, three or four summers would scarcely suffice to execute the design. Still, the earnest desire of a more substantial habitation to defend us from the elements, perplexed me incessantly, and I resolved to make at least the attempt of cutting out a recess that should contain the gunpowder, the most valuable of all our treasures; by which means it would be secured against injury from the vicissitudes of the weather. With this resolution I set off one day, accompanied by my two valiant workmen Fritz and Jack, leaving their mother at her spinning with her assistants Ernest and Francis. We took with us pickaxes, chisels, hammers, and iron levers, to try what impression we could make on the rock. I chose a part nearly perpendicular, and much better situated than our tent: the view from it was enchanting; for it embraced the whole range of Safety Bay, the banks of Jackall's Stream and Family Bridge, and many of the picturesque projections of the rocks. I marked out with charcoal the circumference of the opening, we wished to make, and we began the heavy toil of piercing the quarry. We made so little progress the first day, that in spite of all our courage we were tempted to relinquish the undertaking; we persevered however, and my hope was somewhat revived as I perceived the stone was of a softer texture as we penetrated deeper: we concluded from this, that the ardent rays of the sun striking upon the rock had hardened the external layer, and that the stone within would increase in softness as we advanced, and we admitted a ray of hope that the substance would prove to be a species of calcareous stone. When I had cut about a foot in depth, we could loosen it with the spade like dried mud; this determined me to proceed with double ardour, and my boys assisted me in the task with a zeal beyond their years.

After a few days of assiduous labour we measured the opening, and found we had already advanced seven feet into the rock. Fritz removed the fragments in a barrow, and discharged them in a line before the place to form a sort of terrace; I applied my own labour to the upper part to enlarge the aperture; Jack, the smallest of the three, was able to get in and cut away below. He had with him a long iron bar sharpened at the end, which he drove in with a hammer to loosen a large piece; suddenly he bawled out: It is pierced through, father! Fritz, I have pierced it through!

Hah, hah, master Jack at his jokes again!—But let us hear, what have you pierced? Is it the mountain? Not peradventure your hand or foot, Jack? cried I:

*Jack.*—No, no, it is the mountain; (the rocks resounding with his usual shout of joy) huzza, huzza, I have pierced the mountain!

Fritz now ran to him. Come, let us see then; it is no doubt the globe at least you have pierced, said he, in a bantering tone: you should have pushed on your tool boldly, till you reached Europe, which they say is under our feet; I should have been glad to peep into that hole.

*Jack.*—Well, then, peep you may, I can assure you, but I hardly know what you will see; now come and look how far the iron is gone in, and tell me if it is all my boasting;—if there were not a hollow space behind, how could it penetrate the rock so easily?

Come hither, father, said Fritz, this is really extraordinary; his iron bar seems to have got to a hollow place; see, it can be moved in every direction. I approached, thinking the incident worth attention: I took hold of the bar, which was still in the rock, and pressing it forcibly from one side to another, I made a sufficient aperture for one of my sons to pass, and I observed that in reality the rubbish fell within the cavity, the extent of which I could not ascertain, but I judged from the falling of the stones that it was not much deeper than the part we stood on. My two lads offered to go in together and examine it: this, however, I firmly opposed: I even made them remove from the opening, as I smelled the mephitic air that issued abundantly from it, and began myself to feel giddiness in consequence of having gone too near; so that I was compelled to withdraw quickly, and inhale a purer air. Beware, my dear children, said I in terror, of entering such a perilous cavern; life might be suddenly extinguished there.

*Jack.*—What, lose our lives, father! do you think then it contains lions or tigers? Only give me a gun, and let me speak a word to them.

*Fritz.*—How can you think such animals could live there? Father may indeed fear that it is inhabited by serpents or vipers.

*Jack.*—And what should hinder us, pray, from killing serpents and vipers?

I admire, said I, your courage, my brave Jack, but it shall not be tried on this occasion. Neither lions, serpents, nor men are there, yet the danger still exists: how would my young hero acquit himself, when on entering the aperture he should feel his respiration totally cease?

*Jack.*—Not be able to breathe! and why not?

*Fritz.*—Because the air is mephitic, that is, foul, and therefore unfit for breathing in, and those who are exposed to it must of course be suffocated. But in what manner, father, is this air corrupted?

*Father.*—In different ways: for example, when it is replete with noxious vapours, or when it contains too many igneous or inflammable particles, or when it is too heavy or dense, as fixed air is; but in general, when it merely loses its elasticity, it no longer passes freely into the lungs; respiration is then stopped, and suffocation speedily ensues, because air is indispensable to life and the circulation of the blood.

*Jack.*—Then all to be done is to be off quickly when one feels a stoppage of breath.

*Father.*—This is certainly the natural course when it can be taken; but the attack usually begins by a vertigo or dizziness of the head, so violent as to intercept motion, which is followed by an insurmountable oppression; efforts are made to breathe, fainting follows, and without speedy help, a sudden death takes place.

*Fritz.*—What assistance can be administered?

*Father.*—The first thing to be done is to remove the person so affected to pure fresh air, and to throw cold water over his body; he must then be well dried, and afterwards rubbed with warm cloths; vital air must be infused, or tobacco-smoke thrown up;—in short, he must be treated like a drowned person till signs of re-animation appear, which is not always the result

*Fritz.*—But why do you think, father, the air in this cavern is mephitic, as you term it, or dangerous to breathe in?

*Father.*—All air confined and wholly separated from that of the atmosphere, gradually loses its elasticity, and can no longer pass through the lungs: in this state it generates injurious qualities that interrupt the process of respiration. It is in this act that the atmospheric air diffused around us, unites intimately with the blood, to which it communicates one of its most essential parts, called vital air, for without it life cannot be supported. This air failing, respiration ceases, and death succeeds in a few minutes: the consequence is similar when this air is impregnated too abundantly with injurious parts.

*Fritz.*—And by what is good air known? How judge that one may respire freely at a few paces from this mephitic cave?

*Father.*—This becomes evident when inspiration and expiration are performed with ease; besides, there is an infallible test: fire does not burn in foul air, yet it is made the means of correcting it. We must light a fire of sufficient strength in this hole to purify the air within, and render it friendly to respiration: at first the bad air will extinguish the fire, but by degrees the fire in its turn will expel the bad air and burn freely.

*Fritz.*—Oh! if that is all, it is an easy matter. As soon as the foul air is out, we can make a huge opening, and walk about in the whole interior as if it were a level plain. The boys now hastened to gather some dry grass, which they made into bundles; they then struck a light, and set fire to them, and threw the moss blazing into the opening; but, as I had described, the fire was extinguished at the very entrance, thus proving that the air within was highly mephitic. I now saw that it was to be rarefied by another and more effectual method; I recollected opportunely, that we had brought from the vessel a chest which had belonged to the artificer, and had put it by in the tent, and that it was full of granadoes and rockets, of which and other fire-works a number had been shipped for the purpose of making signals as well as for amusement. I sought this chest hastily, and took out of it some of the most requisite materials, and an iron mortar for the purpose of throwing them into the hollow: with these I speedily returned to attack with my artillery the aerial demons: I threw the whole in, with a train that extended to where we stood, and thus ignited the space. A general explosion took place, and an awful report reverberated through the dark recess; the granadoes flew about on all sides like brilliant meteors; we hurled them back to the extremity of the cavern, they rebounded and burst with a terrific sound. We then sent in the rockets, which had also a full effect; they hissed in the cavity like flying dragons, disclosing to our astonished view its vast extent. We beheld too, as we thought, numerous dazzling bodies that sparkled suddenly, as if by magic, and disappeared with the rapidity of lightning, leaving the place wrapped in the most profound obscurity. A squib bursting in the form of a star presented a spectacle we wished to be prolonged. On its separating, a crowd of little winged genii came forth, each holding a small lighted lamp, and the whole fluttering in every direction with a thousand varied reverberations: every thing in the cavern shone brilliantly, and offered instantly a truly enchanting sight; but they dropped in succession, fell to the ground without noise, and vanished like aethereal spirits.

After having played off our fire-works, I tried lighted straw: to our great satisfaction, the bundles thrown in were entirely consumed; we could then reasonably hope nothing was to be feared from the air; but there still remained the danger of plunging into some abyss, or of meeting with a body of water: from these considerations I deemed it more prudent to defer our entrance into this unknown recess till we had lights to guide us through it. I dispatched Jack on the buffalo to Falcon's Stream, to impart our discovery to his mother and two brothers, directing him to return with them, and bring all the tapers, that were left: my intention was to fasten them together on a stick, and form therewith a large torch, and thus illuminated, proceed with our whole troop to examine the interior of this grotto. I had not sent Jack on his embassy without a meaning; the boy possessed from nature a lively and poetical imagination: I knew he would tell his mother such wonders of the enchanted grotto, of the fire-works, and all they had brought to our view, that in spite of the charms of her spinning-wheel he would induce her to accompany him without delay, and bring us lights to penetrate the obscure sanctuary.

Overjoyed at his commission, Jack sprang on the buffalo, which he had nearly appropriated to himself, gaily smacked his whip, and set off so boldly that I almost trembled for his safety. The rash intrepid boy was unincumbered by fear, and made a complete race-horse of his horned Bucephalus.

In waiting his coming back, I proposed to Fritz to widen the entrance to the subterraneous grotto, to remove the rubbish, and make a way for his mother to pass in easily. After labouring three or four hours we saw them coming up in our car of state—the one I had equipped for the potatoes—and which was now drawn by the cow and the ass, and conducted by Ernest. Francis too played his part in the cavalcade, and contended with his brother for the ropes that served as reins. Jack, mounted on his buffalo, came prancing before them, blew through his closed hand in imitation of a French horn, and now and then whipped the ass and cow to quicken their motion. When they had crossed Family Bridge, he came forward on the gallop; and when he got up to us, jumped off the beast, shook himself, took a spring or two from the ground, and thus refreshed, ran up to the car to hand his mother out like a true and gallant knight.

I immediately lighted my torches; but instead of tying them together as I had intended, I preferred each taking one in his right hand, an implement in his left in case of accident, a taper in his pocket, flint and steel; and thus we entered the rock in solemn procession, I took the lead, my sons followed me, and their beloved

PLATE 12
"Thus we entered the rock in solemn procession."

mother with the youngest brought up the rear, her interest and curiosity not unalloyed with tender apprehensions; and indeed I felt myself that sort of fear which an unknown object is apt to excite: even our dogs that accompanied us betrayed some timidity, and did not run before as usual; but we had scarcely advanced four paces within the grotto, when all was changed to more than admiration and surprise. The most beautiful and magnificent spectacle presented itself. The sides of the cavern sparkled like diamonds, the light from our six tapers was reflected from all parts, and had the effect of a grand illumination. Innumerable crystals of every length and shape hung from the top of the vault, which, uniting with those of the sides, formed pillars, altars, entablatures, and a variety of other figures, constituting the most splendid masses. We might have fancied ourselves in the palace of a fairy, or in an illumined temple. In some places all the colours of the prism were emitted from the angles of the crystals, and gave them the appearance of the finest precious stones. The waving of the lights, their bright coruscations, dark points here and there occurring, the dazzling lustre of others—the whole, in short, delighted and enchanted the sight and the fancy.

The astonishment of my family was so great as to be almost ludicrous; they were all in a kind of dumb stupor, half imagining it was a dream: I had seen stalactites and read the description of the famous grotto of Antiparos, far more considerable than this, which, however, gave an idea of it. The bottom was level, covered with a white and very fine sand, as if purposely strewed, and so dry that I could not see the least mark of humidity anywhere. All this led me to hope the spot would be healthy, convenient, and eligible for our proposed residence. I now formed a particular conjecture as to the nature of the crystallizations shooting out on all sides, and especially from the arch-roof; they could scarcely be of that species of rock crystals produced by the slow filtering of water falling in drops and coagulating in succession, and seldom found in excavations exhibiting so dry a nature, nor ever with so many of the crystals perpendicular and perfectly smooth, I was impatient to evince the truth or falsehood of my opinion by an experiment, and discovered with great joy, on breaking a portion of one of them, that I was in a grotto of sal gem, that is, fossil or rock salt, found in the earth in solid crystallized masses, generally above a bed of spar or gypsum, and surrounded by layers of fossils or rock. The discovery of this fact, which no longer admitted a doubt, pleased us all exceedingly. The shape of the crystals, their little solidity, and finally their saline taste, were decisive evidences.

How highly advantageous to us and our cattle was this super-abundance of salt, pure and ready to be shovelled out for use, and preferable in all respects to what we collected on the shore, which required to be refined!

My wife was charmed with my good fortune in having cut through the rock at this spot. I observed, that in all probability the mine extended a long way, and that I should have discovered salt had I opened at any other part, though such a wonderful grotto might not have been found every where.

Little Francis said to his brothers in a whisper, that it was certainly the palace of some good fairy, who would come with her wand and grant them every thing they wished for, if they were good. Well then, said Jack, I ask her to make you a little wiser and less credulous; don't you hear father say all these diamonds are only salt? and how often has he told you that God alone does wonders? The dear child said no more, but shook his pretty fair locks as if he gave up his enchanted palace with some reluctance; and to say the truth, his notion did not surprise me. As we advanced in the grotto, remarkable figures formed by the saline matter every where presented themselves; columns reaching from the bottom to the top of the vault appeared to sustain it, and some even had cornices and capitals: here and there undulating masses which at certain distances resembled the sea. From the variegated and whimsical forms we beheld, fancy might make a thousand creations at its pleasure; windows, large open cupboards, benches, church ornaments, grotesque figures of men and animals; some like polished crystals or diamonds, others like blocks of alabaster.

We viewed with unwearied curiosity this repository of wonders, and we had all lighted our second taper, when I observed on the ground in some places a number of crystal fragments that seemed to have fallen off from the upper part. Such a separation might recur and expose us to danger; a piece falling on any of our heads might prove instantly fatal: but on closer inspection I was convinced they had not dropped of themselves spontaneously; the whole mass was too solid for fragments of that size to have been so detached from it; and had dampness loosened them they would have dissolved gradually: I rationally concluded they were broken off by the explosion of our artillery and fire-works, that had caused a violent concussion in this subterraneous palace. However, I thought it prudent to retire, as other loosened pieces might unexpectedly fall on us. I directed my wife and three of the children to place themselves in the entrance, while Fritz and I carefully examined every part that threatened danger. We loaded our guns with ball and fired them in the centre of the cavern, to be more fully assured of what produced the separation of the former pieces; one or two more fell, the rest remained immovable, though we went round with long poles and struck all we could reach. We at length felt confident that in point of solidity there was nothing to fear, and that we might proceed to fit up our new habitation without dread of accident. Our joy on this important discovery did not fully declare itself till after these trials. Loud exclamations, mixed with numerously varied questions, projects, consultations, now succeeded to our mute astonishment! Many schemes were formed for converting this beautiful grotto into a convenient and agreeable mansion for our abode. All the force of our imagination was centred in that point: the greatest difficulty was removed; we had possession of the most eligible premises; the sole business now was to turn them to the best account, and how to effect this was our unceasing theme: some voted for our immediate establishment there, but they were opposed by more sagacious counsel, and it was resolved that Falcon's Stream should continue to be our head quarters till the end of the year.

# XXXIII

# HOUSE IN THE SALT-ROCK;— HERRING FISHERY

T HE LUCKY DISCOVERY OF A PREVIOUSLY-EXISTING CAVERN IN the rock, had, as must be supposed, considerably lessened our labour: excavation was no longer requisite: I had more room than was wanted for the construction of our dwelling; to render it habitable was the present object, and to do this did not seem a difficult task. The upper bed of the rock in front of the cavern, through which my little Jack had dug so easily, was of a soft nature, and to be worked with moderate effort. I hoped also that, being now exposed to the air and heat of the sun, it would become by degrees as hard and compact as the first layer that had given me so much trouble. From this consideration I began, while it retained its soft state, to make openings for the door and windows of the front. This I regulated by the measurement of those I had fixed in my winding stair-case, which I had removed for the purpose of placing them in our winter tenement. Intending Falcon's Nest in future as a rural retreat for the hottest days of summer, the windows of the stair-case became unnecessary; and as to the door, I preferred making one of bark similar to that of the tree itself, as it would conceal our abode the better, should we at any time experience invasion from savages or other enemies: the doors and windows were therefore taken to Tent-House, and afterwards properly fixed in the rock. I had previously marked out the openings to be cut for the frames, which were received into grooves for greater convenience and solidity. I took care not to break the stone taken from the apertures, or at least to preserve it in large pieces, and these I cut with the saw and chisel into oblongs an inch and half in thickness, to serve as tiles. I laid them in the sun, and was gratified in seeing they hardened quickly; I then removed them, and my sons placed them in order against the side of the rock till they were wanted for our internal arrangements.

When I could enter the cavern freely through a good doorway, and it was sufficiently lighted by the windows, I erected a partition for the distribution of our apartments and other conveniences. The extent of the place afforded ample room for my design, and even allowed me to leave several spaces in which salt and other articles could be stored. At the request of my children, I was cautious to injure as little as possible the natural embellishments of this new family mansion; but with all my care, I could not avoid demolishing them in the division allotted to the stables:—cattle are fond of salt, and would not have failed to eat away these ornaments, and perhaps in a prejudicial quantity: however, to gratify and reward my obedient children, I preserved the finest of the pillars and the most beautiful pieces to decorate our saloon. The large ones served us for chairs and tables, and the brilliant pilasters at once enlivened and adorned the apartment, and at night multiplied the reflection

of the lights. I laid out the interior in the following manner:—
A very considerable space was first partitioned off in two divisions; the one on the right was appropriated to our residence; that on the left was to contain the kitchen, stables, and workroom. At the end of the second division, where windows could not be placed, the cellar and store-room were to be formed; the whole separated by partition boards, with doors of communication, so as to give us a pleasant and comfortable abode. Favoured so unexpectedly by what nature had already effected of the necessary labour, we were far from repining ungratefully at what remained to be done, and entertained full hope of completing the undertaking, or at least the chief parts, before winter.

The side we designed to lodge in, was divided into three chambers; the first, next to the door, was the bed-room for my wife and me, the second a dining-parlour, and the last a bed-chamber for the boys. As we had only three windows, we put one in each sleeping-room; the third was fixed in the kitchen, where my wife would often be. A grating for the present fell to the lot of our dining-room, which, when too cold, was to be exchanged for one of the other apartments. I contrived a good fire-place in the kitchen near the window; I pierced the rock a little above, and four planks nailed together and passed through this opening answered the purpose of a chimney. We made the work-room near the kitchen, of sufficient dimensions for the performance of undertakings of some magnitude; it served also to keep our cart and sledge in: lastly, the stables, which were formed into four compartments to separate the different species of animals, occupied all the bottom of the cavern on this side; on the other were the cellar and magazine.

Johann David Wyss

It is readily imagined that a plan of this extent was not to be executed as if by enchantment, and that we satisfied ourselves in the first instance with doing what was most urgent, reserving the residue of our arrangements for winter; yet every day forwarded the business more than we had been aware of. On every excursion, we brought something from Falcon's Stream, that found its place in the new house, where we deposited likewise in safety the remaining provisions from the tent.

The long stay we made at Tent-House during these employments, furnished us an opportunity of perceiving several advantages we had not reckoned upon, and which we did not defer availing ourselves of. Immense turtles were very often seen on the shore, where they deposited their eggs in the sand, and they regaled us with a rich treat; but, extending our wishes, we thought of getting possession of the turtles themselves for live stock, and of feasting on them whenever we pleased. As soon as we saw one on the sands, one of my boys was dispatched to cut off its retreat; meanwhile we approached the animal, quickly and quietly without doing it any injury turned it on its back, passed a long cord through the shell and tied the end of it to a stake, which we fixed close to the edge of the water. This done, we set the prisoner on his legs again; it hastened into the sea, but could not go beyond the length of the cord: apparently it was all the happier, finding food with more facility along shore than out at sea; and we enjoyed the idea of being able to take it when wanted. I say nothing of sea-lobsters, oysters, and many other small fishes which we could catch in any number. We at length got used to and to like oysters, and occasionally had a treat of them. The large lobsters, whose flesh was tough and coarse, were given to the dogs, who preferred them to potatoes;

PLATE 13
"On every excursion, we brought something
from Falcon's Stream."

but we shortly after became possessors of another excellent winter provision which chance unexpectedly procured us.

We left Falcon's Stream very early one morning; when near Safety Bay we observed at some distance in the sea, a singular sort of spectacle which we had not before witnessed, though we had gone that way so many times. An extensive surface of the water seemed in a state of ebullition as if heated by a subterraneous fire; it swelled, subsided, foaming like boiling water: a large number of aquatic birds hovered over it, gulls, man of war birds, boobies, albatrosses, and a crowd of others we were strangers to, whose shrill cries pierced our ears; the feathered throng were in motion: sometimes they darted along the surface of the water, sometimes rose in the air, flying in a circle, pursuing each other in every direction; we were at a loss to judge whether sportiveness, pleasure or warfare produced their varied flights. The space too of seemingly boiling surface exhibited a peculiar aspect; small lights issued from it on all sides like flames disappearing and rekindling every moment. We perceived also that the motion of this part was from the main sea towards the land, and particularly Safety Bay, whither we hastened to examine this phenomenon. On our way we formed a thousand conjectures about it: my wife had accompanied us for the purpose of arranging the provisions in the new magazines; she supposed it to be merely a large sand bank, to which the tide gave the semblance of motion, and which by reflecting the beauteous tints of aurora, imparted a flame colour to the waves and caused an optical deception. This was too simple a solution for the vivid imagination of Fritz, who maintained that something extraordinary was operating at the bottom of the deep; some secret fire seeking a vent, or perhaps an earthquake, possibly the approaching irruption of a fresh volcano somewhere. Ernest strongly controverted this idea: The birds, said he, would instinctively fly from the spot, instead of collecting in heaps over it and gaily fluttering, so as to excite the surmise of there being another body in the air as large and as agitated as that in the sea: see how they plunge into it, said he; were the water hot, as Fritz thinks, they would scald their feet and beaks. The latter had little to say in reply; Well then, said he, tell us, Mr. Professor, what it is, instead of what it is not.

*Ernest.*—I am much disposed to think it is some huge sea-monster, a grampus or a whale that raises up its back sometimes like an isle, on which are a quantity of small fishes that offer an easy prey to the birds; on this account they follow the monster, striving greedily to seize all they can in darting on it: those that succeed, fly off with their prey, and the rest pursue to snatch it from them. I feel assured that this is the case, and that if we look closely we shall observe this aquatic giant stretch out its immense fins, and when sufficiently warmed by the sun and it has inhaled a fresh supply of air, it will dive into the ocean, and form a vortex capable of sinking a large ship, if near it.

*Jack.*—Yes, father, Ernest is quite right. At the very edge of the bank, and in proportion to its approach, I distinctly see something fall and rise again; one of its monstrous fins no doubt; I perceive its enormous claws too, certainly. If this great creature leaped put of the water, should we not all be in imminent danger?

*Father.*—Yes, yes, it might perhaps swallow my son Jack as people swallow a pill. But, boys, these suppositions are at best but flimsy fancies, and it is a pity that the pains you take should not produce the least semblance of truth; and I am really surprised to find you so ready to believe in the existence of a monster equal in length to this moving bank.

*Ernest.*—Upon my word, father, I have read of whales upsetting the largest ships by getting under them, and that sailors have often mistaken them for islands, got on them, sunk, and been devoured by the monster.

*Father.*—You must allow, Ernest, for a good deal of exaggeration in such accounts, if they be not altogether fabulous. It is possible a marine animal of huge dimensions may have upset a small vessel, though I presume that would be difficult; I likewise believe it possible for a whale's back to have been taken at some distance for a diminutive island; but when near, its shape and motions would soon destroy the illusion. It is certain that the whale-fishers get on the back of the animal to harpoon it; and this I believe is the foundation of these wonderful narratives. As to the moveable bank before us, I will now, on the observation I have taken, venture to inform you that it is neither more nor less than a shoal of herrings about to enter Safety Bay and fall into our hands; they will be well received by me, I assure you; and it is worth our while to get on speedily, that we may be sure of securing so valuable a booty.

*Francis.*—But, dear father, what is a herring-shoal?

*Father.*—It is an immense number of small fishes called herrings, which you ought to know, having often eaten of them in Europe. They swim so close together and occupy such a space, that they appear like a bank or island of sand several leagues in breadth, some fathoms deep, and sometimes above a hundred thousand long, at the moment of leaving the frozen sea together in a heap: they afterwards divide into bodies which cross the ocean on all sides, directing their course to the coasts and bays, where they spawn, that is, leave their eggs among the stones and sea plants, and to these spots fishermen from all parts go to catch them. The shoal is invariably followed by a legion of the largest fishes, such as bonittas, dories, sturgeons, dolphins, sea-dogs, etc. which are very fond of them. These are not their only enemies; they also draw after them, as you see, flocks of voracious birds, that rush like banditti along the surface of the water and seize all they can. The herrings appear eager to reach those parts where the tide is lowest, to escape from the voracity of the sea monsters, by getting into shallow water; but in doing this they become an easier prey to the birds and to man. Exposed to destruction in so many ways, one might wonder the species is not extinct, if nature had not provided against those accidents by their astonishing fecundity; 68,656 eggs have been found in a moderate-sized female: thus they continue undiminished notwithstanding the vast numbers which are destroyed; in some seasons and latitudes they appear in such numerous and compact bodies that the fishery is relinquished. What Jack took for arms or fins is, I imagine, the water spouted in the air by the dolphins, which keenly pursue the herrings. The whale and the grampus join in the chase, and from their size must commit enormous devastations.

*Fritz.*—It is well they have left us a few; see how the shoal enters the bay. And in reality the entrance of it was entirely filled with them: they made a loud rustling noise in the water, leaping over each other, and displaying their scales of silver hue. This accounted for the luminous sparks we had seen emitted from the sea, and which we could not previously explain. We had no time for further contemplation, but hastened to unharness our team and supply the want of nets with our hands in catching the herrings: the boys used the largest gourds in lieu of pails, which were no sooner dipped in than filled; and we should have been at a loss where to stow them, had I not thought of employing the condemned boat of tubs. No sooner thought than accomplished; I had it immediately drawn to the water's edge by the buffalo, and placed it on rollers; my wife and the two youngest lads cleaned it, whilst the other two went to the cavern for salt, and I quickly fitted up a sort of tent of sail-cloth on the strand, so as to keep off the rays of the sun while we were busied in salting. We then all engaged in the task, and I allotted to each a share adequate to his strength and skill. Fritz took his station in the water to bring us the herrings as fast as caught; Ernest and Jack cleaned them with knives; their mother pounded the salt; Francis helped all, and I placed them in the tubs as I had seen done in Europe. A joyous shout declared the general activity, though we did not get at once into a regular train with our proceedings; one of us was occasionally disengaged whilst the others were overborne with labour: this however was speedily arranged, and the business so well managed, that it was performed with speed and pleasure. I put a layer of salt at the bottom of the barrel, then of fish, the heads towards the staves, proceeding thus till my tubs were nearly full: I spread over the last layer of salt, large palm-tree leaves, on these a piece of sail cloth, and fitted in two half-rounded planks for a heading, which I pressed down with stones. This effected, I put the buffalo and the ass to the cart again, and conveyed it to our cool cellar in the rock. In a few days, when the herrings were sunk, I closed the barrels more accurately by means of a coating of clay and flax over the cloth, which kept out air and moisture completely, and secured us an excellent food for winter.

This work, in which we were engaged several days, kept us at Tent-House the whole week. Working from morning till night, we could only prepare and salt two large casks of them, and we wished to have at least eight. During this time fresh herrings were our chief aliment, and we from the novelty relished them exceedingly.

Scarcely had we finished our salting when another business arising out of it occurred; a number of sea-dogs came into the bay and river, that had followed the herrings with the utmost greediness, sporting in the water along shore, without evincing any fear of us. This fish, which is scarcely eatable, offered little attraction to our palate and table, but in a different point of view the possession of it would be very beneficial; its skin tanned and dressed, makes excellent leather. I was in great need of it for straps and harness, to make saddles for Fritz and Jack to ride the onagra and buffalo, and in short for our own use to cut up into soles, belts, and pantaloons of which articles we much wanted a fresh supply: besides, I knew the fat yielded good lamp oil, that might be substituted for tapers in the long evenings of winter; and that it would be further useful in tanning and rendering the leather pliant.

I directed my three eldest boys to kill a dozen of these large fishes with sticks and pickaxes instead of using powder, and they promptly began the attack. It is remarkable that boys in general have a disposition for the destruction of animals, which by degrees leads them to view their sufferings with indifference. I felt regret in being urged occasionally by circumstances to encourage this propensity; it therefore gave me pleasure to see them return in a few minutes and entreat me to allow them a little powder and some bullets, that they might dispatch the poor harmless creatures at once without much pain. I acquiesced of course in their entreaty and commended the humane idea, which I thought well worth the ammunition expended in the execution of it. It was in our peculiar situation impracticable for us to yield to that morbid sensibility which shudders at inflicting the smallest suffering upon an animal; nor can I help thinking such exhibitions somewhat absurd, since those very persons do not scruple to have on their table a nice chicken, a large fish, lobsters, and many other animals that have as valid a right to live as those we were necessitated to kill: however, I represented constantly to my children that cruelty and the passion of immolating without necessity, any of the brute creation, degrade man, and may lead on to the worst of crimes. On this occasion I was gratified in seeing they had surpassed me in consideration and humanity. In a very short time, after a few firings, the number of fishes was completed; we skinned them while fresh with little trouble, well rubbed them with salt on both sides, and hung them to dry in the sun, to be afterwards dressed in our grotto. Curiosity induced my wife to cook a piece of one of them, but it proved so bad that we threw it to our dogs, the eagle, and jackall, who made a hearty meal of it. The fat we preserved, carefully, of which we collected a quantity; it was first put into a copper, melted and cleansed properly, then poured into casks and kept for the tan-house and lamp. When time should allow, I purposed making soap with it, and this design excited my wife's zeal in the unpleasant though ultimately useful task we were engaged in. We also took care of the bladders, which are very large, for the purpose of holding liquids; the remaining parts that could be turned to no account were thrown into the adjoining stream, and this last act most unexpectedly procured us a regular supply of a far more palatable food—a number of fine fresh-water lobsters which came to feed on these offals. We bored through the sides of some empty chests, which we placed and kept down in the water with stones, and thus caught and preserved as in a reservoir as many lobsters as we wanted. A similar contrivance was fixed in Safety Bay, which first became filled with live herrings, and subsequently with various kinds of small fishes that were caught with ease.

At this time I likewise made some improvements in our sledge, to facilitate the carrying of our stores from Falcon's Stream to our dwelling in the rock at Tent-House. I raised it on two beams, or axle-trees, at the extremities of which I put on the four gun-carriage wheels I had taken off the cannon from the vessel; by this alteration I obtained a light and very convenient vehicle, of moderate height, on which boxes and casks could be placed with little difficulty. Pleased with the operations of the week, we set out all together with cheerful hearts for Falcon's Stream to pass our Sunday there, and once more offer our pious thanks to the Almighty for all the benefits he had bestowed upon his defenceless creatures.

# XXXIV

# NEW FISHERY;—NEW EXPERIMENTS AND CHASE;—NEW DISCOVERIES AND HOUSE

THE ARRANGEMENT OF OUR GROTTO WENT ON, SOMETIMES AS a principal, sometimes as an intermediate occupation, according to the greater or less importance of other concerns: but though we advanced thus with moderate rapidity, the progress was notwithstanding, such as to afford the hope of our being securely established within it by the time of the rainy season.

From the moment I discovered gypsum to be the basis of the crystal salt in our grotto, I foresaw the great advantages I should derive from it for our undertaking; but being unwilling to enlarge the dimensions of our dwelling by digging further, I tried to find a place in the continuation of the rock, which I might be able to blow up: I had soon the good fortune to meet with a narrow slip between the projections of the rocks which I could easily, by the means I proposed, convert into a passage that should terminate in our work-room. I found also on the ground a quantity of fragments of gypsum, and removed a great number of them to the kitchen, where we did not fail to bake a few of the pieces at a time when we made a fire for cooking, which, thus calcined, rubbed into a powder when cold: we obtained a considerable quantity of it, which I put carefully into casks for use when the time should come for finishing the interior of our dwelling. My notion was, to form the walls for separating the apartments of the squares of stone I had already provided, and to unite them together with a cement of this new ingredient, which would be the means both of sparing the timber, and increasing the beauty and solidity of the work.

It is almost incredible the immense quantity of plaster we had in a short time amassed; the boys were in a constant state of wonder as they looked at the heap, and protested they believed that I staid up at night to work. I seized the opportunity of imprinting on their minds the value of a firm and steady perseverance in an object once engaged in, the reward of which they now so agreeably experienced: When we first cast our eyes, continued I, on this rock, how little did we conceive it possible to transform it into a comfortable dwelling-place; yet we have not only in our own persons sufficed for carpenters and masons, but even plasterers too, and so effectually, that if we had it much at heart, we might adorn our walls with stucco as is the mode in Europe; we possess both the materials and intelligence, and with the addition of patience and industry, there is scarcely any thing, even what at first should seem impossible, too difficult for our performance.

The first use I made of the plaster was to complete some covers I had begun with other materials for my herring tubs, four of which I stopped down to render them impenetrable to the air; the rest of the herrings we intended to dry and smoke. For this purpose we erected a little sort of hut of reeds and branches, as is practised in Holland and America by the fishermen; we placed rows of sticks reaching from side to side across the hut, and laid the herrings upon them, and then lighted a heap composed of moss and fresh-cut branches of trees, to produce a stronger and more effective vapour for the purpose: we made the door tight, and had soon the pleasure of adding a large stock of exquisitely flavoured dried herrings to our former store for the ensuing winter.

About a month after the singular visit of the herrings, which had now entirely left our shores, we received another and not a less profitable one from a fish of a different species: we observed Safety Bay to be filled with large fishes which seemed eager to push to the shore for the purpose of depositing their eggs among the stones in fresh water. Jack was the first to discover this circumstance: he told me he had seen a great number of whales swimming about in Jackall's River, and supposed they were come in pursuit of the herrings, and that he was glad the greedy creatures would be disappointed. I replied that there must be some delusion in what he had seen, as I could not conceive of a regiment of whales arriving in our diminutive rivulet. Pray come with me, father, answered he, and look at them; some of them are as large as you, and if they are not whales, I will lay a wager that neither are they herrings. Hah, hah, master Jack, you are on the retreat then, I see; but between the whale and the herring there are many kinds and sizes, so I will e'en take side with you and wager that they are not herrings.

It however appeared to me worth while to go and convince myself on the spot, respecting these new-comers. Jack and I walked to the mouth of Jackall's River, and immediately perceived immense quantities of a large fish moving slowly towards the banks, and some of them from four to eight feet in length. By the pointed snout I supposed the largest to be sturgeons, while the smallest I pronounced to be salmon. Jack now strutted and exulted as if he had gained the command of a regiment of soldiers:—What say you, now, father? said he, this is nothing like your little paltry herrings! A single fish of this troop would fill a tub!—No doubt, answered I: and with great gravity I added—Pr'ythee, Jack, step into the river, and fling them to me one by one, that I may take them home to salt and dry.

He looked at me for a moment with a sort of vacant doubt if I could possibly be in earnest; then seizing suddenly a new idea— Wait a moment, father, cried he, and I will do so: and he sprung off like lightning towards the cavern, from whence he soon returned loaded with a bow and arrows, the bladders of the sea-dogs, and a ball of string to catch, as he assured me, every one of the fishes. I looked on with interest and curiosity to mark what was next to happen, while the animation of his countenance, the promptitude and gracefulness of his motions, and the firm determination of his manner, afforded me the highest amusement. He tied the bladders round at certain distances with a long piece of string, to the end of which he fastened an arrow and a small iron hook; he placed the large ball of string in a hole in the ground, at a sufficient distance from the water's edge, and then he shot off his arrow, which the next instant stuck in one of the largest fishes. My young sportsman uttered a shout of joy. At the same moment Fritz joined us, and witnessed this unexpected feat without the least symptom of jealousy. Well done, brother Jack, cried he, but let me too have my turn.—Saying this he ran back and fetched the harpoon and the windlass, and returned to us accompanied by Ernest, who also desired to show his prowess in a contest with our newly discovered mariners. We were well pleased with their opportune arrival, for the salmon Jack had pierced struggled so fiercely, that all our endeavours to hold the string were insufficient, and we dreaded at every throw to see it break and the animal make good its escape. By degrees, however, its strength was exhausted, and aided by Fritz and Ernest, we succeeded in drawing it to a bank, where I put an end to its existence.

This fortunate beginning of a plan for a fishery inspired us all with hope and emulation. Fritz eagerly seized his harpoon and windlass; I, for my part, like Neptune, wielded a trident; Ernest prepared the large fishing rod, and Jack his arrow with the same apparatus as before, not forgetting the bladders which were so effectual in preventing the fish from sinking when struck. We were now more than ever sensible of our loss in the destruction of the tub-boat, with which we could have pursued the creature in the water, and have been spared much pains and difficulty; but on the other hand, such numbers of fishes presented themselves at the mouth of the river, that we had only to choose among them; and accordingly we were soon loaded with them to our heart's content. Jack's arrow after missing twice, struck the third time a large sturgeon, which was so untractable that we had great difficulty in securing him. I too had caught two of the same fish, and had been obliged to go up to the middle in the water to manage my booty. Ernest, with his rod and line and a hook, had also taken two smaller ones. Fritz with his harpoon had struck a sturgeon at least eight feet in length, and the skill and strength of our whole company were found necessary to conduct him safe to shore, where we harnessed the buffalo to him with strong cords to draw him to Tent-House.

Our first concern was to clean our fish thoroughly inside to preserve them fresh the longer. I separated the eggs I found in them, and which could not be less than thirty pounds, and put them aside to make a dish called caviar, greatly relished by the Russians and the Dutch. I took care also of the bladders, thinking it might be possible to make a glue from them which would be useful for so many purposes. I advised my wife to boil some individuals of the salmon in oil, similar to the manner of preparing tunny fish in the Mediterranean: and while she was engaged in this process, I was at work upon the caviar and the glue. For the first, I washed the berries in several waters, and then pressed them closely in gourd-rinds in which a certain number of holes had been bored. When the water had run off, the berries were taken out in a substance like cheese, which was then conveyed to the hut to be dried and smoked. For the second, we cut the bladders into strips, which we fastened firmly by one end to a stake, and taking hold of the other with a pair of pincers, we turned them round and round till the strip was reduced to a kind of knot, and these were then placed in the sun to harden; this being the simple and only preparation necessary for obtaining glue from the ingredient. When thoroughly dry, a small quantity is put on a slow fire to melt. We succeeded so well, and our glue was of so transparent a quality, that I could not help feeling the desire to manufacture some pieces large enough for panes to a window frame.

When these various concerns were complete, we began to meditate a plan for constructing a small boat as a substitute for the tub raft, to come close into shore. I had a great desire to make it, as the savages do, of the rind of a tree; but the difficulty was to fix on one of sufficient bulk for my purpose; for though many were to be found in our vicinity, yet each was on some account or other of too much value to be spared. We therefore resolved to make a little excursion in pursuit of a tree of capacious dimensions, and in a situation where it was not likely to yield us fruit, to refresh us with its shade, or to adorn the landscape round our dwelling.

In this expedition we as usual aimed at more than one object: eager as we were for new discoveries, we yet allowed ourselves the time to visit our different plantations and stores at Falcon's Stream. We were also desirous to secure a new supply of the wax berry, of gourds, and of elastic gum. Our kitchen garden at Tent-House was in a flourishing condition; nothing could exceed the luxuriance of the vegetation, and almost without the trouble of cultivation we had excellent roots and plants in abundance, which came in succession, and promised a rich supply of peas, beans of all sorts, lettuces, etc.; our principal labour was to give them water freely, that they might be fresh and succulent for use. We had besides, melons and cucumbers in great plenty, which during the hottest weather we valued more than all the rest. We reaped a considerable quantity of Turkey wheat from the seed we had sown, and some of the ears were a foot in length. Our sugar-canes were also in the most prosperous condition, and one plantation of pineapples on the high ground was also in progress to reward our labour with abundance of that delicious fruit.

This state of general prosperity at Tent-House gave us the most flattering expectations from our nurseries at Falcon's Stream. Full of these hopes, we one day set out all together for our now somewhat neglected former abode.

We arrived at Falcon's Stream, where we intended to pass the night. We visited the ground my wife had so plentifully sowed with grain, which had sprung up with an almost incredible rapidity and luxuriance, and was now nearly ready for reaping. We cut down what was fairly ripe, bound it together in bundles, and conveyed it to a place where it would be secure from the attacks of more expert grain consumers than ourselves, of which thousands hovered round the booty. We reaped barley, wheat, rye, oats, peas, millet, lentils,—only a small quantity of each, it is true, but sufficient to enable us to sow again, plentifully at the proper season. The plant that had yielded the most was maize, a proof that it best loved the soil. It had already shown itself in abundance in our garden at Tent-House; but here there was a surface of land, the size of an ordinary field, entirely covered with its splendid golden ears, which still more than the other plants attracted the voracity of the feathered race. The moment we drew near, a dozen at least of large bustards sprang up with a loud rustling noise which awakened the attention of the dogs; they plunged into the thickest parts, and routed numerous flocks of birds of all kinds and sizes, who all took hastily to flight; among the fugitives were some quails who escaped by running, and lastly some kangaroos, whose prodigious leaps enabled them to elude the pursuit of the dogs.

We were so overcome by the surprise such an assemblage of living creatures occasioned, as to forget the resource we had in our guns; we stood as it were stupid with amazement during the first moments, and before we came to ourselves the prey was beyond our reach, and for the most part out of sight. Fritz was the first to perceive and to feel with indignation the silly part we had been playing, and to consider in what way we could repair the mischief. Without further loss of time, he took the bandage from his eagle's eyes (for the bird always accompanied him perched upon his-game bag,) and showed him with his hand the bustards still flying, and at no great distance. The eagle took a rapid flight. Fritz jumped like lightning on the back of his onagra and galloped over every thing that intervened in the direction the bird had taken, and we soon lost sight of him.

We now beheld a spectacle which in the highest degree excited our curiosity and interest: the eagle had soon his prey in view; he mounted above the bustard in a direct line, without losing sight of it for an instant, and then darted suddenly down; the bustards flew about in utter confusion, now seeking shelter in the bushes, then crossing each other in every direction, in the attempt to evade the common enemy; but the eagle remained steady in the pursuit of the bird he had fixed upon for his prey, and disregarded all the rest: he alighted on the unlucky bustard, fixed his claws and his beak in its back, till Fritz arriving full gallop, got down from the onagra, replaced the bandage on the eagle's eyes, seated him once more upon the gamebag, and having relieved the poor bustard from his persecutor, he shouted to us to come and witness his triumph! We ran speedily to the place. Jack alone remained in the maize plantation, meditating also the giving us a specimen of the happy effects of the education he had bestowed on the young jackall, who had slipped slily away after the birds we supposed were quails, and who on their parts were using every effort to escape; the jackall however soon overtook them, seized one of them by the wing and brought it to his master; in the same manner he had carried him at least a dozen more by the time we reached the spot: and now nothing was heard but the exclamations of Fritz and Jack, who had not words to express their self-congratulations for the good effects of their mode of training their respective animals, who, to say the truth, deserved the wonder and the praise of all. A large fat quail was immediately given to each as a token of approbation.

At the conclusion of this adventure we hastened forward to arrive the soonest possible at Falcon's Stream, and pay the earliest attention to the wounds the bustard had received from the eagle. We perceived with pleasure that it was a male, and foresaw the advantage of giving him for a companion to our solitary female of the same species, who was completely tamed. I threw a few more bundles of maize into the cart, and without further delay we arrived at our tree, one and all sinking with faintness from hunger, thirst, and fatigue. It was on such occasions that my exemplary partner evinced the superior fortitude and generosity of her temper: though more a sufferer than either of us, her first thought was what she could administer to relieve us in the shortest time, for we had consumed our little store of wine, and could not soon and easily procure milk from the cow: she contrived to bruise some of the maize between two large stones, and then put it in a linen cloth, and with all her strength squeezed out the sap; she then added some juice from the sugar-canes, and in a few minutes presented us with a draught of a cool refreshing liquid, beautifully white in appearance and agreeable to the taste, and which we received at her hands with feelings of grateful emotion.

I applied myself without loss of time to the cure of the bustard's wounds, which I washed carefully with a lotion composed of water, wine, and butter, which was our constant remedy; I then tied him by the leg close to the female in the yard. Jack had been able to preserve alive only two of the quails, which he now brought me, and I treated them in the same manner: all the others that the jackall had killed were plucked and put on the spit for supper. The rest of the day was employed in picking the grains of the different sorts of corn from the stalks: we put what we wished to keep for sowing into some gourd-shells, and the Turkey wheat was laid carefully aside in sheaves till we should have time to beat and separate it, Fritz observed that we should also want to grind it, and I reminded him of the hand-mill we had secured from our departed ally, the wrecked vessel.

*Fritz.*—But, father, the hand-mill is so small, and so subject to be put out of order:—Why should we not contrive a water-mill, as they do in Europe? We have surely rapid streams of water in abundance.

*Father.*—This is true, but such a mechanism is more difficult than you imagine; the wheel alone, I conceive, would be an undertaking far beyond our strength or our capacity. I am, however, well pleased with the activity and zeal which prompted your idea; and though I dare not bid you trust in a successful result, yet we may consider whether it may be worth while to bestow upon it further attention; we have abundance of time before us, for we shall not want a water-mill till our harvests are such as to produce plentiful crops of corn. In the mean time let us be thinking, boy, of our proposed excursion for to-morrow, for we should set out, at latest, by sun-rise.

We began our preparations accordingly: my wife chose some hens and two fine cocks, with the intention of taking them with us and leaving them at large to produce a colony of their species at a considerable distance from our dwelling-places: I with the same view visited our stable, and selected four young pigs, four sheep, two kids, and one male of each species, our numbers having so much increased that we could well afford to spare these individuals for the experiment: if we succeeded in thus accustoming them to the natural temperature and productions of our island, we should have eased ourselves of the burden of their support, and should always be able to find them at pleasure.

The next morning, after loading the cart with all things necessary, not forgetting the rope ladder and the portable tent, we quitted Falcon's Stream. The animals with their legs tied, were all stationed in the vehicle. We left abundance of food for those that remained behind; the cow, the ass, and the buffalo were harnessed to the cart; and Fritz mounted on his favourite, the onagra, pranced along before us to ascertain the best and smoothest path for the cavalcade.

We took this time a new direction, which was straight forward between the rocks and the shore, that we might make ourselves acquainted with every thing contained in the island we seemed destined for ever to inhabit. In effect, the line proceeding from Falcon's Stream to the Great Bay, might be said to be the extent of our dominions; for though Fritz and I had discovered the adjacent exquisite country of the buffalos, yet the passage to it by the end of the rocks was so dangerous, and at so great a distance, that we could not hope to domiciliate ourselves upon its soil, as we had done on our side of the rocks. We found, as usual, much difficulty in pushing through the tall tough grass and alternately through the thick prickly bushes which every where obtruded themselves. We were often obliged to turn aside while I cut a passage with my hatchet; but these accidents seldom failed to reward my toil by the discovery of different small additions to our general comfort among others, some roots of trees curved by nature to serve both for saddles and yokes for our beasts of burden. I took care to secure several, and put them in the cart.

When we had spent about an hour in getting forward, we found ourselves at the extremity of the wood, and a most singular phenomenon presented itself to our view: a small plain, or rather a grove of low bushes, to appearance almost covered with flakes of snow, lay extended before us. Little Francis was the first to call our attention to it, he being seated in the cart:— Look, father, cried he, here is a place quite full of snow; let me get down and make some snow-balls: Oh, how glad I am that we shall now have snow instead of the ugly rain which made us all so uncomfortable!

I could not resist a hearty laugh; and though sure what we saw could not in the midst of such scorching heat be snow, yet I was completely at a loss to explain the nature of what in colour and appearance bore so near a resemblance to it. Suddenly, however, a suspicion crossed my mind, and was soon confirmed by Fritz, who had darted forward on his onagra, and now returned with one hand filled with tufts of a most excellent species of cotton, so that the whole surface of low bushes was in reality a plantation of that valuable article. This most useful of almost the whole range of vegetable productions bestowed by Providence on man, which with the cost of only a little labour supplies him with apparel and commodious beds for the repose of his limbs, is found in such abundance in islands, that I had been surprised at not meeting with any before. The pods had burst from ripeness, and the winds had scattered around their flaky contents; the ground was strewed with them, they had gathered in tufts on the bushes, and they floated gently in the air.

The joy of this discovery was almost too great for utterance, and was shared by all but Francis, who was sorry to lose his pretty snow-balls; and his mother, to soothe his regret, made the cotton into balls for him to play with, and promised him some new shirts and dresses: then turning to me, she poured out her kind heart in descriptions of all the comfortable things she should make for us, could I construct a spinning-wheel, and then a loom for weaving.

We collected as much cotton as our bags would hold, and my wife filled her pockets with the seed to raise it in our garden at Tent-House.

It was now time to proceed; and we took a direction towards a point of land which skirted the wood of gourds, and being high commanded a view of the adjacent country. I conceived a wish to remove our establishment to the vicinity of the cotton plantation and the gourd wood, which furnished so many of the utensils for daily use throughout the family. I pleased myself in idea with the view of the different colonies of animals I had imagined, both winged and quadruped; and in this elevation of my fancy I even thought it might be practicable to erect a sort of farm house on the soil, which we might visit occasionally, and be welcomed by the agreeable sounds of the cackling of our feathered subjects, which would so forcibly remind us of the customs of our forsaken but ever cherished country.

We accordingly soon reached the high ground, which I found in all respects favourable to my design; behind, a thick forest gradually rose above us, which sheltered us from the north wind, and insensibly declined towards the south, ending in a plain clothed luxuriantly with grass, shrubs, and plants, and watered by a refreshing rivulet, which was an incalculable advantage for our animals of every kind as well as for ourselves.

My plan for a building was approved by all, and we lost no time in pitching our tent and forming temporary accommodations for cooking our victuals. When we had refreshed ourselves with a meal, we each took up some useful occupation; my wife and the boys went to work with the cotton, which they thoroughly cleaned and cleared from bits of the pods or other foreign substance, and which was then put into the bags and served commodiously at night for bolsters and mattresses. I, for my part, resolved to look about in all directions, that I might completely understand what we should have to depend upon in this place in point of safety, salubrity, and general accommodation. I had also to find a tree that would suit for the proposed construction of a boat; and lastly, to meet if possible with a group of trees at such fit distances from each other as would assist me in my plan of erecting my farm. I was fortunate enough in no long time to find in this last respect exactly what I wanted, and quite near to the spot we on many accounts had felt to be so enviable: but I was not equally successful for my boat, the trees in the vicinity being of too small a bulk to supply the depth necessary for keeping on the surface of the water. I returned to my companions, whom I found busily employed in preparing excellent beds of the cotton, upon which at an earlier hour than usual we all retired to rest.

# XXXV

# COMPLETION OF TWO FARM HOUSES;— A LAKE;—THE BEAST WITH A BILL

THE TREES THAT I HAD CHOSEN FOR THE CONSTRUCTION OF my farm were for the most part one foot in diameter; their growth was tolerably regular in the form of a parallelogram with its longest side to the sea, the length being twenty-four feet, and the breadth sixteen. I cut little hollow places or mortices in the trunks, at the distance of ten feet one above the other, to form two stories; the upper one I made a few inches shorter before than behind, that the roof might be in some degree shelving: I then inserted beams five inches in diameter respectively in the mortices, and thus formed the skeleton of my building. We next nailed some laths from tree to tree, at equal distances from each other, to form the roof, and placed on them, in mathematical order, a covering composed of pieces of the bark of trees cut into the shape of tiles, and in a sloping position for the rain to run off in the wet season. As we had no great provision of iron nails, we used for the purpose the strong pointed thorn of the acacia, which we had discovered the day before. This tree, which bears an elegant flower, is known by the name of *Acacia with three thorns*, and it in reality exhibits, growing all together, three strong sharp-pointed thorns, which might easily be used as weapons of defence. We cut down a quantity of them and laid them in the sun to dry, when they became as hard as iron, and were of essential service to our undertaking. We found great difficulty in peeling off a sufficient quantity of bark from trees to cover our roof. I began with cutting the bark entirely round at distances of about two feet all the length of the trunk; I next divided the intervals perpendicularly into two parts, which I separated from the tree by sliding a wedge under the corners to raise the bark by degrees; I next placed the pieces on the ground, with stones laid on them to prevent their curving, to dry in the sun; and lastly, I nailed them on the roof, where they had the appearance of the scales of fishes—an effect that was not only pleasing to the eye, but reminded us of the roofs of our native land.

On this occasion we made another agreeable discovery: my wife took up the remaining chips of the bark for lighting a fire, supposing they would burn easily; we were surprised by a delicious aromatic odour which perfumed the air. On examining the half-consumed substance, we found some of the pieces to contain turpentine, and others gum-mastich, so that we might rely on a supply of these ingredients from the trees which had furnished the bark. It was less with a view to the gratifying our sense of smelling, than with the hope of being able to secure these valuable drugs for making a sort of pitch to complete our meditated boat, that we indulged our earnestness in the pursuit. The instinct of our goats, or the acuteness of their smell, discovered for us another acquisition of a no less pleasing quality; we observed with surprise that they ran from a considerable distance to throw themselves about on some particular chips of bark which lay on the ground, and which they began to chew and eat greedily. Jack seized a piece also, to find out, as he said, what could be the reason of so marked a preference as the goats had shown. Oh, it is indeed excellent, exclaimed he; and I perceive that goats are animals of taste! Only try this little bit, brother Fritz, and tell us if it is not exactly like cinnamon? Fritz did as he was desired, and was of Jack's opinion. My wife and I then followed their example, and were convinced that it was cinnamon, though not so fine a sort as that from the isle of Ceylon.

This new commodity was certainly of no great importance to us; but we nevertheless regarded it with pleasure, as an article that would serve to distinguish some day of particular rejoicing, Ernest and Francis asked to taste it also, and agreed with us that the occasional use of it would be agreeable. The tree from which we had taken our bark was old, and the cinnamon was no doubt the coarser flavoured on this account: I remembered to have read, that young trees produce this spice in much greater perfection.

During our next meal we amused ourselves with a retrospect of the different discoveries we had made that day. I had to relate to my wife what I knew on the subject of the nature of these new productions; the turpentine, the mastich, and the cinnamon. I informed her that the two first had been discovered by the Venetians, who had gone so far as the islands of ancient Greece in search of them, and that they had afterwards become articles of commerce. And of what use is turpentine? asked Francis.

*Father.*—It is used in medicine; also for varnishes, and in the composition of resin; by putting it over the fire and mixing a little oil with it, it makes an excellent kind of pitch, and in this last form it will be of essential service to me for the outer coat of my new boat. It is also useful, applied to the wheels of any sort of carriages.

*Ernest.*—And the mastich, father?

*Father.*—This production comes from a tree of the same name; it oozes out in drops and hardens in the sun, something like amber. It is used in perfumes, and as a varnish for porcelain, being soluble in spirits of wine. As to cinnamon, I can only tell you that the best sort is a production of the island of Ceylon; it is gathered from young plants; the outside covering being first taken away, the next coat is the perfect cinnamon, and its smell is quite delicious; it is put to dry in the sun, and it rolls of itself into the shapes in which you must have seen it; they are afterwards tied in small parcels and sewed into cotton bags, which are again inclosed in reed matting; lastly, the parcels are put into buffalos' skins, which are as hard and as impenetrable as horn. By this process the cinnamon is so effectually preserved, that it may be safely transported to any distance. It is used in Europe for imparting a delicious flavour to the more delicate kinds of liqueurs and sweetmeats.

When our meal and the lecture were both ended, we resumed with ardour our undertaking of the farm, which we continued without interruption for several days.

We formed the walls of our building with matted reeds interwoven with pliant laths to the height of six feet; the remaining space to the roof was inclosed with only a simple grating, that the air and light might be admitted. A door was placed in the middle of the front. We next arranged the interior, with as much convenience as the shortness of the time and our reluctance to use all our timber would allow; we divided it half way up by a partition wall, into two unequal parts; the largest was intended for the sheep and goats, and the smallest for ourselves, when we should wish to pass a few days here. At the further end of the stable we fixed a house for the fowls, and above it a sort of hay-loft for the forage. Before the door of entrance we placed two benches, contrived as well as we could of laths and odd pieces of wood, that we might rest ourselves under the shade of the trees, and enjoy the exquisite prospect which presented itself on all sides. Our own apartment was provided with a couple of the best bedsteads we could make of twigs of trees, raised upon four legs two feet from the ground, and these were destined to receive our cotton mattresses. Our aim was to content ourselves for the present with these slight hints of a dwelling, and to consider hereafter what additions either of convenience or ornament could be made, such as plastering, etc. etc. All we were now anxious about, was to provide a shelter for our animal colonists, which should encourage and fix them in the habit of assembling every evening in one place. For several days, at first, we took care to fill their troughs with their favourite food mixed with salt, and we agreed that we would return frequently to repeat this indirect mode of invitation for their society, till they should be entirely fixed in their expectation of finding it.

I had imagined we could accomplish what we wished at the farm in three or four days; but we found in the experiment that a whole week was necessary, and our victuals fell short before our work was done. We began to consider what remedy we could apply to so embarrassing a circumstance; I could not prevail upon myself to return to Falcon's Stream before I had completed my intentions at the farm, and the other objects of my journey. I had even come to the determination of erecting another building upon the site of Cape Disappointment; I therefore decided that on this trying occasion I would invest Fritz and Jack with the important mission. They were accordingly dispatched to Falcon's Stream and to Tent-House, to fetch new supplies of cheese, ham, potatoes, dried fish, manioc bread, for our subsistence, and also to distribute fresh food to the numerous animals we had left there. I directed one to mount the onagra, and the other the buffalo. My two knight-errants, proud of their embassy, set off with a brisk trot; they at my desire took with them the old ass to bring the load of provisions. Fritz was to lead him with a bridle, while Jack smacked a whip near his ears to quicken his motions; and certainly, whether from the influence of climate or the example of his companion the onagra, he had lost much of his accustomed inactivity: and this was the more important, as I intended to make a saddle for my wife to get on his back and relieve herself occasionally from the fatigue of walking.

During the absence of our purveyors, I rambled with Ernest about the neighbouring soil, to make what new discoveries I could, and to procure if possible some cocoa-nuts or other valuable addition to our store of provisions.

We followed the winding of a river we had remarked, and which conducted towards the centre of the wall of rocks; our course was here interrupted by an extensive marsh which bordered a small lake, the aspect of which was enchantingly picturesque. I perceived with joyful surprise that the whole surface of this swampy soil was covered with a kind of wild rice, ripe on the stalk, and which attracted the voracity of large flocks of birds. As we approached, a loud rustling was heard, and we distinguished on the wing bustards, Canada heath-fowl in abundance, and great numbers of smaller birds, with the names of which we were unacquainted. We succeeded in bringing down five or six of them, and I was pleased to remark in Ernest a justness of aim that promised well for the future. The habits of his mind discovered themselves on this as on many previous occasions; he betrayed no ardour, he did every thing with a slowness that seemed to imply dislike; yet the cool deliberation and constancy he applied to every attempt he had to engage in, so effectually assisted his judgement, that he was sure to arrive at a more perfect execution than the other boys. He had practised but little in the study of how to fire a gun to the best advantage; but Ernest was a silent inquirer and observer, and accordingly his first essays were generally crowned with success. In this affair, however, of the birds, his skill would have proved fruitless, if Jack's young jackall, which had followed us in our walk, had not plunged courageously into the swamp and brought out the birds as they fell.

At a small distance was also master Knips, who had taken his post on Ponto's back. Presently we saw him jump off and smell earnestly along the ground among some thick-growing plants, then pluck off something with his two paws and eat of it voraciously. We ran to the spot to see what it could be, when, to the infinite relief of our parched palates, we found he had discovered there the largest and finest kind of strawberry, which is called in Europe the *Chili* or *pine strawberry*.

On this occasion the proud creature, man, generously condescended to be the imitator of a monkey: we threw ourselves upon the ground, as near to Knips as we could creep, and devoured as fast as we could swallow, till we felt sufficiently refreshed. Many of these strawberries were of an enormous size, and Ernest with his usual coolness, and I must needs confess there was no want of his constancy either, devoured an immense quantity: he however recollected his absent friends, and filled a small gourd-shell we had brought with us with the finest fruit, and then covered them with leaves and tied them down with a tendril from a neighbouring plant, that he might present them in perfection to his mother. I, on my part, gathered a specimen of the rice to offer, that she might inform us if it was fit for culinary purposes.

After pursuing our way a little further along the marsh, we reached the lake, which we had descried with so much pleasure from a distance, and whose banks being overgrown with thick underwood, were necessarily concealed from the momentary view we had leisure to take of surrounding objects, particularly as the lake was situated in a deep and abrupt valley. No traveller who is not a native of Switzerland can conceive the emotion which trembled at my heart, as I contemplated this limpid, azure, undulating, body of water, the faithful miniature of so many grand originals, which I had probably lost sight of for ever! My eyes swam with tears!—How glad I am to see a lake! I could almost think myself in Switzerland, father, said Ernest.

Alas, a single glance upon the surrounding pictures, the different characters of the trees, the vast ocean in the distance, destroyed the momentary illusion, and brought back our ideas to the painful reality that we were strangers in a desert island!

Another sort of object now presented itself to confirm the certainty that we were no longer inhabitants of Europe; it was the appearance of a quantity of swans which glided over the surface of the lake; but their colour, instead of white, like those of our country, was a jetty black; and their plumage had so high a gloss as to produce, reflected in the water, the most astonishing effect. The six large feathers of the wing of this bird are white, exhibiting a singular contrast to the rest of the body; in other respects these creatures were remarkable, like those of Europe, for the haughty gracefulness of their motions, and the voluptuousness of their nature. We remained a long time in silent admiration of the scene; some of the swans pursued their course magnificently on the bosom of the blue water; others stopped and seemed to hold deliberations with their companions, or to admire themselves, or caress each other; many young ones followed in the train of the parent bird, who frequently turned half round in execution of her watchful and matronly office. This was a spectacle which I could not allow to be interrupted by bloodshed, though Ernest, rendered a little vain by his success and my encomiums, would have been ready to fire upon the swans, if I had not absolutely forbidden the attempt; at the same time I consoled him with the promise that we would endeavour to obtain a pair of the interesting creatures for our establishment at Falcon's Stream.

Ponto just at this moment dragged out of the water a bird he had seized; we ran to examine it, and our surprise was extreme on remarking the singularity of its appearance. It was somewhat in shape like an otter, and, like the tribe of water-birds, web-footed: its tail was long and erect, and covered with a soft kind of hair; the head was very small, and the ears and eyes were almost invisible; to these more ordinary characters was added, a long flat bill, like that of a duck, which protruded from its snout, and produced so ludicrous an effect that we could not resist a hearty laugh. All the science of the learned Ernest, joined with my own, was insufficient to ascertain the name and nature of this animal.

We had no resource but to remain ignorant; in the mean time we christened it by the name of *Beast with a bill*, and decided that it should be carefully stuffed and preserved.

We now began to look for the shortest path for rejoining our companions at the farm, which we reached at the same time with Fritz and Jack, who had well performed the object of their journey, and were received by all with satisfaction. We, on our parts, produced our offering of strawberries and our specimen of rice, which were welcomed with shouts of pleasure and surprise.

The beast with a bill was next examined with eager curiosity, and then laid aside for the plan I had formed. My wife proceeded to pluck and salt the birds we had killed, reserving one fresh for our supper, which we partook of together upon the benches before the door of our new habitation. We filled the stable with forage, laid a large provision of grain for the fowls within their house, and began arrangements for our departure.

The following day we took a silent leave of our animals and directed our course towards Cape Disappointment. On entering Monkey Wood, innumerable animals of the species from which it derives its name began to scamper away, grinding their teeth in sign of anger at our approach. We pursued our way, and arrived shortly after at the eminence we were in pursuit of in the vicinity of Cape Disappointment; we ascended it, and found it in every respect adapted to our wishes. From this eminence we had a view over the country which surrounded Falcon's Stream in one direction, and in others of a richly diversified extent of landscape comprehending sea, land, and rocks. When we had paused for a short time upon the exhaustless beauties of the scene, we agreed with one voice that it should be on this spot we would build our second cottage. A spring of the clearest water issued from the soil near the summit, and flowed over its sloping side, forming, in its rapid course, agreeable cascades: in short, every feature of the picture contributed to form a landscape worthy the homage of a taste the most delicate and refined. I presented my children with an appropriate word.—Let us build here, exclaimed I, and call the spot—*Arcadia*; to which my wife and all agreed.

We lost no time in again setting to work upon this additional arduous undertaking; our experience at the farm enabled us to proceed in it with incredible rapidity, and our success was in every respect more complete. The building contained a dining room, two bed-chambers, two stables, and a storeroom for preserving all kinds of provisions for man and beast. We formed the roof square, with four sloping sides, and the whole had really the appearance of a European cottage, and was finished in the short space of six days.

# XXXVI

# THE BOAT;—PROGRESS IN THE ABODE OF ROCKS

UR ARCADIA BEING ENTIRELY COMPLETED, WHAT REMAINED to be done was to fix on a tree fit for my project of a boat. After much search, I at length found one of prodigious size, and in most respects suitable to my views.

It was, however, no very encouraging prospect I had before me, being nothing less than the stripping off a piece of the bark that should be eighteen feet in length and five in diameter; and now I found my rope ladder of signal service; we fastened it by one end to the nearest branches, and it enabled us to work with the saw, as might be necessary, at any height from the ground. Accordingly, we cut quite round the trunk in two places, and then took a perpendicular slip from the whole length between the circles; by this means we could introduce the proper utensils for raising the rest by degrees, till it was entirely separated. We toiled with increasing anxiety, at every moment dreading that we should not be able to preserve it from breaking, or uninjured by our tools. When we had loosened about half, we supported it by means of cords and pulleys; and when all was at length detached, we let it down gently, and with joy beheld it lying safe on the grass. Our business was next to mould it to our purpose, while the substance continued moist and flexible.

The boys observed that we had now nothing more to do, than to nail a plank at each end, and our boat would be as complete as those used by the savages; but, for my own part, I could not be contented with a mere roll of bark for a boat; and when I reminded them of the paltry figure it would make following the pinnace, I heard not another word about the further pains and trouble, and they asked eagerly for my instructions. I made them assist me to saw the bark in the middle, the length of several feet from the ends; these two parts I folded over till they ended in a point, naturally raised; I kept them in this form by the help of the strong glue I had before made from fish-bladders, and pieces of wood nailed fast over the whole: this operation tended to widen the boat in the middle, and thus render it of too flat a form; but this we counteracted by straining a cord all round, which again reduced it to the due proportion, and in this state we put it in the sun, to harden and fix. Many things were still wanting to the completion of my undertaking, but I had not with me proper utensils: I therefore dispatched the boys to Tent-House, to fetch the sledge, and convey it there for our better convenience in finishing.

Before our departure for Tent-House we collected several new plants for the kitchen-garden; and lastly, we made another trip to the narrow strait at the end of the wall of rocks, resolved, as I before mentioned, to plant there a sort of fortification of trees, which should produce the double effect of discouraging the invasion of savages, and of allowing us to keep our pigs on the other side, and thus secure our different plantations from the chance of injury. We accomplished all these intentions to our entire satisfaction, and in addition we placed a slight draw-bridge across the river beyond the narrow pass, which we could let down or take up at pleasure on our side. We now hastened our return to Arcadia, and after a night's repose we loaded the sledge with the boat and other matters, and returned to Tent-House.

As soon as we had dispatched some necessary affairs, we resumed the completion of the boat: in two days she had received the addition of a keel, a neat lining of wood, a small flat floor, benches, a small mast and triangular sail, a rudder, and a thick coat of pitch on the outside, so that the first time we saw her in the water, we were all in ecstasies at the charming appearance she made.

Our cow in the mean time had brought forth a young calf, a male; I pierced its nostril, as I had so successfully practised with the buffalo, and it gave promise of future docility and strength.

We had still two months in prospect before the rainy season, and we employed them for completing our abode in the grotto, with the exception of such ornaments as we might have time to think of during the long days of winter. We made the internal divisions of planks, and that which separated us from the stables, of stone, to protect us from the offensive smell occasioned by the animals. Our task was difficult, but from habit it became easier every day. We took care to collect or manufacture a sufficient quantity of all sorts of materials, such as beams and flanks, reeds and twigs for matting, pieces of gypsum for plaster, etc. etc. At length the time of the rainy season was near at hand, and this once we thought of it with pleasure, as the period that would put us in possession of the enjoyments we had procured by such unremitting industry and fatigue. We had an inexpressible longing to find ourselves domiciliated and at leisure to converse together on the subject of all the wondrous benefits bestowed upon us by an ever-watchful and beneficent Providence!

We plastered over the walls of the principal apartments on each side with the greatest care, finishing them by pressure with a flat smooth board, and lastly a wash of size, in the manner of the plasterers in Europe. This ornamental portion of our work amused us all so much, that we began to think we might venture a step further in the question of European luxury, and we agreed that we would attempt to make some carpets with the hair of our goats. To this effect, we smoothed the ground in the rooms we intended to distinguish, with great care; then spread over it some sail-cloth, which my wife had joined in breadths, and fitted exactly; we next strewed the goats' hair, mixed with wool obtained from the sheep, over the whole; on this surface we threw some hot water, in which a strong cement had been dissolved; the whole was then rolled up, and was beaten for a considerable time with hard sticks; the sailcloth was now unrolled, and the inside again sprinkled, rolled, and beaten as before; and this process was continued till the substance had become a sort of felt, which could be separated from the sailcloth, and was lastly put in the sun to harden. We thus produced a very tolerable substitute for that enviable article of European comfort, a carpet: of these we completed two; one for our parlour, and the other for our drawing-room, as we jocosely named them, both of which were completely fit for our reception by the time the rains had set in. All we had suffered during this season in the preceding year doubled the value of the comforts and conveniences with which we were now surrounded. We were never tired of admiring our warm and well-arranged apartments, lighted with windows, and well secured with doors from wind and rain, and our granary filled with more than a sufficient winter supply of food for ourselves and for our cattle. In the morning, our first care was to feed and give them drink; and both these were now constantly at hand, without the pains of fetching or preparing: after this we assembled in the parlour, where prayers were read, and breakfast immediately served: we then adjourned to the common room, where all sorts of industry went forward, and which contained the spinning-wheel and loom I had, though with indifferent success, constructed to gratify my wife. Here all united in the business of producing different kinds of substances, which she afterwards made into apparel. I had also contrived to construct a turning machine, having used for the purpose one of the small cannon wheels, with the help of which the boys and I managed to produce some neat utensils for general use. After dinner, our work was resumed till night, when we lighted candles; and as they cost no more than our own trouble in collecting and manufacturing the materials, we did not refuse ourselves the pleasure of using many at a time, to admire their lights splendidly reflected by the crystals every where pendent. We had formed a convenient portion of our dwelling into a small chapel, in which we left the crystals as produced by nature; and they exhibited a wondrous assemblage of colonnades, porticos, altars, which, when the place was lighted to supply the want of a window, presented a truly enchanting spectacle. Divine service was performed in it regularly every Sunday: I had raised a sort of pulpit, from which I pronounced such discourses as I had framed for the instruction of my affectionate group of auditors. The remainder of this day of rest was employed as before, in such recreations as tended to sustain cheerfulness, and fortify the bodily health of all. Jack and Francis had a natural inclination for music. I did the most I could in making a flageolet apiece for them of two reeds, on which they so frequently practised as to attain a tolerable proficiency; they accompanied their mother, who had a sweet-toned voice, the volume of which was doubled by the echoes of the grottos, and they produced together a very pleasing little concert.

Thus, as will be perceived, we had made the first steps towards a condition of civilization: separated from society, condemned perhaps to pass the remainder of life in this desert island, we yet possessed the means of happiness; we had abundance of all the necessaries, and many of the comforts desired by human beings! We had fixed habits of activity and industry; we were in ourselves serene and contented; our bodily health and strength increased from day to day; the sentiment of tender attachment was perfect in every heart: we every day acquired some new and still improving channel for the exertion of our physical and moral faculties; we everywhere beheld, and at all times acknowledged, marks of the divine wisdom and goodness; our minds were penetrated with love, gratitude, and veneration for the celestial Providence who had so miraculously rescued and preserved us, and conducted us to the true destination of man—to provide for the wants of his offspring by the labour of his hands: I trusted in the same goodness for restoring us once more to the society of our fellow-men, or for bestowing upon us the means of founding in this desert a happy and flourishing colony of human beings, and waiting in silence for the further manifestation of his holy will, we passed our days in a course of industry, innocent pleasures, and reciprocal affection. Nearly two years have elapsed without our perceiving the smallest trace of civilised or savage man; without the appearance of a single vessel or canoe upon the vast sea, by which we are surrounded. Ought we then to indulge a hope that we shall once again behold the face of a fellow-creature?—We encourage serenity and thankfulness in each other, and wait with resignation the event!